FLORICULTURE

From Greenhouse Production to Floral Design

FLORICULTURE

From Greenhouse Production to Floral Design

Ronald J. Biondo

FCAE Field Advisor in Agricultural Education
Countryside, Illinois

Dianne A. Noland

Instructor
University of Illinois

AgriScience and Technology Series

Jasper S. Lee, Ph.D.
Series Editor

Interstate Publishers, Inc.
Danville, Illinois

FLORICULTURE:

From Greenhouse Production to Floral Design

Order from

Interstate Publishers, Inc.

510 North Vermilion Street
P.O. Box 50
Danville, IL 61834-0050

Phone: (800) 843-4774
Fax: (217) 446-9706
Email: info-ipp@IPPINC.com

Preface

FLORICULTURE: From Greenhouse Production to Floral Design is a comprehensive book based on the floriculture industry. It takes the reader beyond the most basic levels of horticulture. It includes in one volume all phases of floriculture and eliminates the need for two separate books.

The first 13 chapters are devoted to the greenhouse industry and the production of floriculture crops. Greenhouse structures, equipment, and management techniques are covered, as well as specific growing instructions for the different floriculture crops. The final 12 chapters shifts from production to the use of floriculture crops in the floral design industry. Floral design basics, as well as specific design techniques are covered. Business aspects of pricing design work and retail floral shop operation are also included.

This book represents a new approach in horticulture education. It is intended to be exactly what is needed in today's horticulture programs for greenhouse production and floral design. A student- and teacher-friendly approach is used. Many color photographs and line drawings enrich the book and give it added meaning. Activities are provided that go beyond the classroom.

Acknowledgments

The authors of *Floriculture: From Greenhouse Production to Floral Design* would like to acknowledge numerous people for their contributions to this book.

Special recognition goes to Dr. Marvin Carbonneau, Professor Emeritus University of Illinois for his instruction, Dr. John Culbert, Professor Emeritus University of Illinois, our floral design instructor, and to Mike Schaefer of Schaefer Greenhouses Inc. for his open door policy and the time spent discussing greenhouse crop production.

Floral design students deserving special recognition include Amanda Frederiksen, Kathryn Dieter, Jill Van Dyne, and Jennifer Hall.

Many others deserve thanks for their contributions including:

- Tom Cosgrove, *Greenhouse Product News*
- Talmadge McLaurin and Frances Dudley, *Florists' Review*
- Lim-King Brady, Crystal Company
- Louis D'Amours, Berger Peat Moss
- David H. Johnson, United Greenhouse Systems
- Roy Klehm, Klehm Nursery
- Jennifer Sparks, Society of American Florists
- Brian Corr and Ginny Kovach, Ball Horticultural Company
- Arthur Clesen Inc.
- Steven E. Newman, Extension Greenhouse Specialist, Colorado State University
- Art Floral
- Dave Thill, Mid-American Growers
- Andre Rutte, DeVroomen Holland Garden Products

- Kuhn Flowers
- Carl Reed, Barrington High School
- Alice White-Klinkhamer, International Flower Bulb Centre
- Christine Kelleher, Yoder Brothers, Inc.
- Doug Abbott, Abbott"s Florist
- CO-EX Corporation
- Tim Landers, Benchmark Foliage
- Randy Strode, Agristarts, Inc.
- Mike Soucek, Natural Beauty of Florida
- Marty Knox, Knox Nursery, Inc.
- Greg Stack, Fredric Miller, and James E. Schuster, University of Illinois Extension
- Joe Steffen teacher, Newark High School
- Jim Frost, Urban Floral, Inc.
- Ludvig Svensson, Inc.
- Hank Maday, Maday Greenhouses
- Mike Cherim, The Green Spot, Ltd.
- The Geiger Companies
- USDA Agricultural Research Service

Special appreciation is due to Ester V. Biondo for her sharp proofreading, and to my wife, Wendy J. Biondo, for her patience and support. Special thanks to my husband and son, Dave Negargard and Drew. Of course much credit goes to Dan Pentony, Jane Weller, Kim Romine, and Vernie Thomas of the Interstate Publishers, Inc. staff for their support and an incredible amount of work required to put the final product in print.

Ronald J. Biondo
Dianne A. Noland

Contents

ix

1

The Floriculture Industry

Quick! Mother's Day is approaching and you need to show your mother that you care. You could buy some candy, but somehow candy doesn't express your feelings. You could buy a card, but that doesn't appear to be enough. If you are like many people, a floral product seems to be most appropriate. Now, you must choose a bouquet, a houseplant, a corsage, a potted azalea, or one of many other floral products that are available. In fact, the number of items from which to choose can make the decision difficult. The good news is you have a wide selection of choices.

Have you ever given thought to where all these floral products come from? Have you considered how these products are grown so they are available at specific times of the year? Have you ever marveled at the ability some people have in designing floral arrangements? Most people don't give these things much thought. They simply appreciate the availability of the floral products. However, people who do pose these questions touch upon the exciting industry of floriculture.

1-1. There are many floral products. (Courtesy, Society of American Florists)

OBJECTIVES

1 Describe the scope of the floriculture industry

2 Explain the importance of the greenhouse industry

3 Describe the extent and value of the floral design industry

4 Identify careers found in the floriculture industry

TERMS

bedding plants
buyer
conditioning
cut flowers
cut foliage
floral arranger
floral designer
floral production
floriculture
foliage plants
greenhouse

grower
ornamental horticulture
plant propagation
potted flowering plants
retail floral manager
retail florist
salesperson
wholesale floral manager
wholesale florist
vase life

WHAT IS FLORICULTURE?

The literal definition of *floriculture* is the "culture of flowers." Floriculture is based on flowering and foliage (leafy) plants. It is an international, multibillion dollar industry. Floriculture businesses include the production of the floral crops, the distribution of the crops from the grower to the consumer, and the processing of crops before sale. Some common floriculture businesses are florist shops, floral supply companies, and production greenhouses. Floriculture is a major part of a larger industry called ornamental horticulture. *Ornamental horticulture* is the practice of growing and using plants for decorative purposes. Another major part of the ornamental horticulture includes the nursery/landscape industry.

1-2. Floriculture is the "culture of flowers."

*F*LORAL PRODUCTION

Floral production involves the growing of flowering or foliage crops to sale size or maturity. The value of floriculture crop production in the United States has shown steady growth. The total wholesale value of floriculture crops in the United States is nearly $4 billion. The states of California (22 percent) and Florida (19 percent) lead the way in floriculture production. Amazingly, 54 percent of all floriculture production in 1997 involved just five states—California, Florida, Michigan, Texas, and Ohio. Bedding plant production represented 47 percent of the wholesale value of all floriculture crops in 1997.

1-3. Growers are in charge of crop production. (Courtesy, *Greenhouse Product News*)

Floriculture production involves people with an understanding of plants and plant growth. The person in charge of the crop production is called a **grower**. Large greenhouse operations will employ a number of growers, each of whom may focus on one or more specific crops. Other job titles associated with floriculture production include production supervisor, marketing manager, and greenhouse worker.

Production begins with some form of plant reproduction, whether by seed or by a portion of a plant. Plant reproduction is commonly known as **plant propagation**. The new or young plants are grown to a size or an age at which they may be sold for further production purposes. Some might be sold directly to the consumers.

Most floriculture crops are produced in some type of greenhouse structure. A **greenhouse** is a structure enclosed by glass or plastic that allows light

1-4. Greenhouse structures allow light transmission for plant growth. Pictured is the conservatory at Kew Gardens, England.

transmission for plant growth. Greenhouses give growers the ability to control environmental conditions affecting a crop. Greenhouses allow a high level of light to reach the plants. They can be heated or cooled depending on the needs of the plants. Watering and fertilizer applications are also carefully controlled by the grower. In addition to providing control of specific growing conditions, greenhouses allow plants to be grown throughout the year.

Greenhouse growers often specialize in growing certain crops. The decision to grow certain crops is based on a number of factors. The most important factor determining which crops are produced is profit. Can the crop be sold for a profit? The climate is another very important factor. The greatest concern with climate is the amount of sunlight and the average temperature. One reason the major producers of cut carnations and roses are located in Columbia, South America is because the climate is perfect for growing these crops. Greenhouses are not needed to produce these crops in Columbia.

Nearness to the market influences decisions as to what crops are grown. Cut flowers can be grown far from the marketplace. They are relatively light weight. As a result, the cost of shipping cut flowers by air, even across oceans, is affordable. Potted plants are most often grown locally because of the cost of shipping. Laws also restrict the movement of soil across borders.

Short descriptions of the major types of floriculture crops follow:

Cut flowers—Some floral production operations focus on supplying cut flowers to wholesale florists. That is, they grow flowers, cut them when they reach a certain maturity, and sell them to a wholesaler. Roses, carnations, chrysanthemums, and orchids are a few common cut flowers. *Cut foliage* or leaves grown for floral design work are also grown and harvested. Leatherleaf,

1-5. Florists work with cut flowers and foliage. (Courtesy, Society of American Florists)

I-6. The poinsettia is a popular potted flowering plant. (Courtesy, Paul Ecke Poinsettias)

lemonleaf, and huckleberry are common foliage materials used in floral work. Those in the industry often refer to cut foliage as "greens."

Potted flowering plants—A large segment of the floriculture industry is the production of flowering plants in pots. The plants may be propagated by seed or through asexual means, such as cuttings of plants. The young plants are grown to the flowering stage in a greenhouse structure. The entire plant and the pot are then shipped to market. Some popular potted flowering plants are poinsettias, chrysanthemums, Easter lilies, and African violets.

Foliage plants—Some growers produce potted plants to be sold as foliage plants. Foliage plants are grown for their leaves rather than for their flowers. They are also called houseplants. Florida is a large producer of foliage plants, which are shipped throughout the United States. Philodendrons, dieffenbachias, figs, scheffleras, and dracaenas are common foliage plants produced for use in homes and offices.

I-7. Florida is the largest producer of foliage plants. (Courtesy, *Greenhouse Product News*)

1-8. This person checks bedding plant orders for a large commercial greenhouse operation.

Bedding plants—Many greenhouse growers produce bedding plants in the spring for outdoor planting. Bedding plants are herbaceous, annual flowers and vegetables. They lack the ability to survive freezing temperatures and therefore, must be planted outdoors after the risk of spring frost. They are usually started by seed and grown in a greenhouse during the late winter and spring. Gardeners transplant the fairly mature plants in the landscape. By producing the plants well before a safe planting date, gardeners are given a longer period during which they can enjoy the plants. Bedding plants include impatiens, petunias, marigolds, tomatoes, and many other plants.

1-9. Bedding plants outsell all other floriculture crops.

FLORAL DISTRIBUTION

There are several channels in which floral crops can be distributed. The shortest route is from the local grower to the local consumer. The consumer may make a purchase at the production site or the grower may transport the plants to a nearby retail outlet. The longest distribution channel involves the international market. In the international market, crops move from the producer to an exporter, to a wholesaler, to a retailer, and finally to the consumer.

Although the distance involved in the international market is great, the distance itself seems less important than the time it takes to get the products to buyers. It is critical that floral products are delivered to market as soon as possible. Regular air traffic linking the world today makes the international market possible.

At one time, nearly all cut flowers sold in the United States were grown in the United States. Today, imports account for most of the major cut flowers sold in the United States. Ninety percent of the carnations, 71 percent of the roses, and 89 percent of the cut chrysanthemums sold in the United States are produced in other countries.

The international wholesale market for cut flowers and foliage is located in Holland. Holland is recognized as the leader of the floriculture industry. Other countries that are major exporters or importers of floral crops include Columbia, Israel, Italy, Kenya, and the United States. Carnations grown in Columbia, roses grown in Israel, and exotic flowers grown in Hawaii are flown to the flower auctions in Holland. Buyers from around the world inspect and buy the flowers in the auctions. Once purchased, the flowers are shipped by air or road to wholesale businesses. The wholesaler repackages the flowers and takes orders from retail florists. Because flowers are perish-

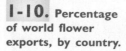

1-10. Percentage of world flower exports, by country.

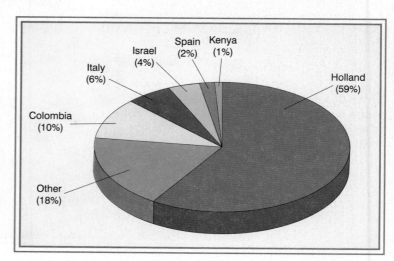

1-11. Holland is recognized as the leader in the floriculture industry. Shown is an international flower auction in Aalsmeer. (Courtesy, Floyd Giles)

able, they must be bought and shipped very quickly. The following example illustrates how amazingly the market works. A rose could be harvested in Israel one day, sold to a wholesaler in Holland the same day, and displayed in a retail floral shop in Seattle, Washington, the next day.

Wholesale Florists

The *wholesale florist* purchases cut flowers, cut foliage, and hard goods from a number of suppliers. An important job in the wholesale florist business is that of the buyer. The *buyer* locates sources of products and places bids or offers for purchase. The buyer must be very knowledgeable because the variety of available cut flowers and foliage numbers in the thousands.

1-12. Wholesale florists buy and sell flowers. (Courtesy, Society of American Florists)

Also, the floral materials are often only available during certain seasons of the year. The hard goods purchased include ribbon, vases, hand tools, tape, and numerous other products used by florists. The wholesale florists resell and distribute the goods to retail businesses or to other wholesalers.

A *wholesale floral manager* oversees the operations of the business. He or she supervises the staff, estimates retail demands for products, and prepares long-range plans. Another position of importance is the salesperson. The *salesperson* has direct and usually frequent contact with the retail florist. The salesperson takes orders and arranges delivery of the products. Wholesale florists generally do not sell directly to the public.

Retail Florists

Floriculture crops are sold to consumers through retail outlets. Traditionally, the *retail florist* provides floral design services, cut flowers, and other floriculture crops. Retail florists have typically been small independent businesses. Along with the retail florists, greenhouses and garden centers are recognized sources of cut flowers, foliage, and potted flowering plants. However, sales have expanded greatly to other retail outlets including supermarkets, gas stations, and large retail stores, such as Wal-Mart and Kmart. These new outlets have made the purchase of floriculture crops more convenient for many people.

The *retail floral manager* has the responsibility of coordinating the operations of the business. Tasks associated with this position include managing personnel, working with budgets, and maintaining the store's inventory.

1-13. Retail florists display their products in attractive ways.

1-14. Floral designers create designs. (Courtesy, Kuhn Flowers, Jacksonville, FL)

Highly skilled positions in the florist trade involve floral arrangers and designers. These people are artists that use flowers and other materials in their art work. *Floral arrangers* have the training required to make and copy floral designs. *Floral designers* are considered to be more skilled than arrangers in that they have the ability to create and design unique floral art.

Given a customer order, arrangers and designers choose flowers and the necessary floral supplies to construct floral arrangements. Floral work may involve fresh cut flowers, cut foliage, everlasting flowers (both dried and silk), and other materials. Flowers are selected and used to express feelings of love and sorrow, as well as to decorate homes and offices. Experienced florists of-

1-15. Flowers are given to celebrate special occasions, such as the birth of a child, or two.

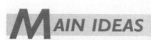 **Flowers are conditioned to extend their lives.**

fer helpful advice to customers on flower selection, care, colors, and costs. Special occasions, such as anniversaries, weddings, parties, holidays, and funerals, make up the bulk of floral sales.

FLORAL PROCESSING

Floral processing involves the handling and preparation of floral products for sale. Processing occurs primarily with the cut flower industry. Growers process floral crops for shipping. Usually, the wholesaler conditions cut flowers and foliage upon receipt of the materials. *Conditioning* involves treatments that extend the life of the flowers. Further processing of cut flowers and foliage is done by retail florists before sale to the public.

It is important for cut flowers to be moved from the grower to the consumer as quickly as possible. That is because flowers begin to die once they are cut from the plant. Handling the flowers involves keeping them cool. Lower temperatures slow the life processes of the flowers. Flowers are also placed in clean water with a floral preservative. The preservative provides the flower with food and reduces the growth of bacteria that can clog conductive tissues. The proper handling of flowers serves to extend their vase life. *Vase life* is the length of time cut flowers and foliage live after they have been cut.

REVIEWING

MAIN IDEAS

Floriculture is part of the ornamental horticulture industry. It includes those areas pertaining to the production and use of flowering and foliage (leafy) plants. Major business components of the floriculture industry are the production of the floral crops, the distribution of the crops from the grower to the consumer, and the processing of crops before sale.

Floral production involves the growing of flowering or foliage crops for sale. The value of floriculture crop production in the United States has shown steady growth. California accounts for 22 percent and Florida accounts for 19 percent of floriculture production in the United States. Production begins with plant propagation. Growers grow the plants and most often use greenhouse structures. Greenhouses allow the control of environmental factors. Profitability, climate, and distance to market influence which crops are grown in a particular operation. The major types of plants produced are cut flowers and foliage, potted flowering plants, foliage plants, and bedding plants.

Distribution of floriculture products is an important part of the industry. Consumers often purchase potted flowering plants, foliage plants, and bedding plants at the production site or at a retail outlet near the production site. The international market is important in terms of cut flowers and foliage. In the international market, crops move from the producer to an exporter, to a wholesaler, to a retailer, and finally to the consumer. Today, imports account for 90 percent of the carnations, 71 percent of the roses, and 89 percent of the cut chrysanthemums sold in the United States.

Floral processing involves the handling and preparation of floral products for sale. Proper handling of flowers serves to extend their vase life or the length of time cut flowers and foliage live after they have been cut. Cut flowers and foliage are processed by florists—people who sell cut flowers and floriculture crops. Floral arrangers and designers choose flowers and the necessary floral supplies to construct floral arrangements. Floral arrangers have the training required to make and copy floral designs. Floral designers are considered to be more skilled than arrangers in that they have the ability to create and design unique floral art.

QUESTIONS

Answer the following questions. Use correct spelling and complete sentences.

1. What is floriculture?
2. What is floral production?
3. What is the role of a grower?
4. Why are greenhouses beneficial in producing crops?
5. What factors influence the decision to produce certain crops?
6. What are the major floriculture crops? Define each.
7. How has air travel changed the floriculture industry?
8. What is vase life?
9. How do floral arrangers and floral designers differ?
10. What skills do florists call upon besides making arrangements?

EVALUATING

Match the term with the correct definition. Write the letter by the term in the blank provided.

a. greenhouse
b. bedding plants
c. floral designer
d. potted flowering plants
e. plant propagation
f. foliage plant
g. floriculture
h. retail florist
i. grower
j. ornamental horticulture
k. floral production
l. vase life

_____ 1. Considered to be more skilled than a floral arranger in that he or she has the ability to create and design unique floral art.

_____ 2. The growing of flowering or foliage crops to sale size or maturity.

_____ 3. A potted plant, sometimes called a houseplant, grown for its leaves rather than for its flowers.

_____ 4. The length of time cut flowers and foliage live after they have been cut.

_____ 5. Poinsettia, chrysanthemum, Easter lily, and African violet plants grown, shipped to market, and sold in a pot.

_____ 6. The "culture of flowers."

_____ 7. A business that provides floral design services, cut flowers, and other floriculture crops.

_____ 8. The practice of growing and using plants for decorative purposes.

_____ 9. Plant reproduction.

_____ 10. A structure enclosed by glass or plastic, which allows light transmission for plant growth.

_____ 11. The person in charge of the crop production.

_____ 12. Herbaceous, annual flowers and vegetables for outdoor planting.

EXPLORING

1. Make an appointment with a local greenhouse grower or florist for a 10 minute interview. Prior to the interview compose a list of questions that interest you about their work. Dress appropriately and conduct the interview in a professional manner. Who knows, your effort may open doors for future employment.

2. Visit a retail floral outlet. Record all the different types of plants for sale. Investigate further to determine where they were produced. Look into how they were produced and how they ended up at the retail outlet.

3. Ask your school administration and instructor to allow you to job shadow for a day. Then, identify a wholesale florist, a greenhouse grower, a floral designer, or similar person who you can observe for a day.

2

Greenhouse Structures, Climate Control, and Automation

Have you ever had the opportunity to visit a greenhouse on a cold January day? It could be below freezing outside with a foot of snow on the ground, but the interior is full of life. Green growing plants, some in flower, are a welcome sight. The air feels warm and humid, as it might feel on a spring day. The atmosphere lifts the spirit, and thoughts of winter are left behind. It is no wonder people love visiting or working in greenhouses.

While greenhouse structures and the ability to control the climate within them create a pleasant atmosphere, they also contribute to a large industry. The facilities make the growing of plants possible throughout the year. Across the United States in 1997, greenhouse space for the production of floriculture crops total 466 million square feet. One usually does not have to travel far to see a greenhouse operation. The total of 9,666 greenhouse operations in 1997 also provided many employment opportunities.

2-1. There are nearly 10,000 commercial greenhouse operations in the United States.

15

OBJECTIVES

1 Identify greenhouse designs

2 Identify and describe greenhouse glazing materials

3 Explain environmental controls

4 Describe methods of heating and cooling greenhouses

5 Describe plant bench materials and spacing

6 Describe automated systems

7 Identify safety hazards in the greenhouse

TERMS

acclimatization
acrylic structured sheets
analog controls
automated seeders
automated transplanters
bench
computer controls
computerized environmental
   management
conservatory
energy curtain
environmental controls
even-span greenhouse
fan and pad cooling system
fiberglass
fog system
glass
glazing
headhouse

hoop house
hot water system
infrared heat system
lean-to greenhouse
polycarbonate structured sheets
polyethylene
pot fillers
retractable-roof greenhouse
ridge-and-furrow greenhouse
rolling bench
short-day curtains
spaghetti tubes
steam heat
structured sheets
thermostats
tray mechanization
uneven-span greenhouse
unit heaters
vent

GREENHOUSE STRUCTURES

The production of most floriculture crops greatly differs from other agricultural horticultural production. One factor that makes it so is the greenhouse. A greenhouse is a structure enclosed by a translucent material in which plants are grown. Translucent materials allow light, necessary for photosynthesis, to reach the plants inside. The material also serves as a barrier between the outside and inside environments. Greenhouse structures give the grower control of environmental factors within the structure. Growers can regulate the temperature, water, humidity, and to some extent, light.

2-2. Greenhouses give growers control of the growing environment. (Courtesy, *Greenhouse Product News*)

TYPES OF GREENHOUSE STRUCTURES

Styles of greenhouses vary greatly. The material used, the shape of the greenhouse, and the load capacity contribute to the differences. However, there are four basic styles of greenhouse structures. They are lean-to, even span, uneven span, and ridge-and-furrow.

The *lean-to greenhouse* structure is attached to a building. The building provides support for the roof. If a lean-to structure is used for growing crops, it should be placed on the south side of the building.

Even-span greenhouse structures have roofs with an even pitch and an even width. These are single houses. *Hoop houses*, so called because of the arching pipes used in the framework, are a type of low-cost, even-span greenhouse.

2-3. A lean-to greenhouse.

2-4. An even-span greenhouse.

Uneven-span greenhouses have roofs with an unequal pitch and width. Use of the uneven span structure is limited to hillsides. Because the trend toward automated operations favors flat ground, few of these greenhouse structures are built today.

Ridge-and-furrow greenhouse structures consist of a number of greenhouses connected together along the length of the houses. Shared side walls are eliminated, creating a large interior space. Fewer outside walls also result in lower heating costs. Gutters are installed where the individual houses

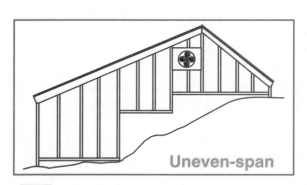

Uneven-span

2-5. An example of an uneven-span greenhouse.

2-6. A ridge-and-furrow greenhouse.

connect to remove water. In cold climates snow loads are a concern because the snow cannot slide off of the roofs. One solution is to run heating pipes under the gutters to melt the snow.

Ridge-and-furrow greenhouse ranges are best oriented in a north-south fashion. This eliminates permanent shadows that would be cast by the gutters. Ridge-and-furrow houses are widely used in automated operations.

Modern greenhouse structures are being designed and built with higher gutters. That means the entire roof supported by the framework is higher. The higher structures provide better air circulation and more even temperatures. Higher structures also mean cooler summer temperatures at bench

2-7. This modern greenhouse has high gutters allowing the use of automated systems.

2-8. This headhouse includes material storage, restrooms, offices, a potting area, and plenty of room to package plants for shipping.

level. Another advantage made possible in modern structures is the use of automated systems, such as energy curtains.

While crop production occurs in the greenhouse, many other tasks are performed in a ***headhouse***. A headhouse is a structure attached to the greenhouse. It serves as a storage area for growing media, containers, fertilizers, and other materials. It is a work area. The potting and packaging of plants take place in the headhouse. In cold climates, headhouses often have overhead doors to allow trucks to enter. The trucks can then be loaded indoors without the risk of damaging the plants. Chemicals are stored in the headhouse in locked storage cabinets vented to the outside. Also, office space is often included in the headhouse so staff can conduct business.

THE GREENHOUSE FRAMEWORK

The greenhouse structure consists of a framework that provides support for the covering material. Ideally, a framework should be strong, while creating the least amount of shade possible. Narrow, light frameworks allow the maximum amount of light to reach the plants. The framework must be strong. It must be able to withstand snow loads in areas where it snows and hold the coverings under high wind conditions. Another important consideration is the amount of maintenance the framing material requires. There is a great advantage to using framework materials that are maintenance free.

Aluminum and aluminum/steel combination frameworks are commonly used in modern greenhouses. Though somewhat costly, they are long lasting and maintenance free. Wood, angle iron, and galvanized steel are used as

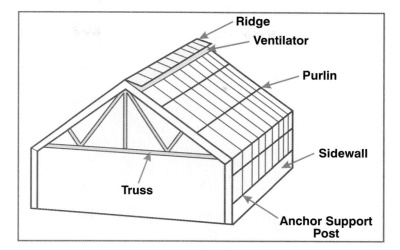

2-9. Structural components of the greenhouse framework.

Ridge

Ventilator

Purlin

Sidewall

Truss

Anchor Support Post

2-10. The frame must be strong enough to withstand snow loads.

well. The disadvantages of these materials are wood and iron need to be painted, while galvanize treatments wear off.

COVERING (GLAZING) MATERIALS

The covering of a greenhouse is often referred to as the *glazing*. There are several considerations in choosing a glazing material. Durability or the life of the material before it needs to be replaced is an important factor. Light transmission is important. The cost of the material needs to be considered. A fourth consideration is that of heat loss, which affects heating bills.

2-11. Polyethylene is used to cover these greenhouses.

Polyethylene, structured sheets, and glass are available glazing materials. Each material has advantages and disadvantages.

Polyethylene (poly) is the most widely used glazing material. Its flexible sheets, usually 6-mil in thickness, are stretched over the greenhouse framework. It is generally used in double layers with air blown between the layers to produce a 3- to 9-inch bubble-like covering. The air bubble effectively insulates the house. Heating costs of a double poly house are roughly one-third less than that of a glass-covered greenhouse. Polyethylene sheets are also inexpensive.

Poly is not very durable, however. That is because ultraviolet light breaks down the plastic. Improved poly sheets with ultraviolet light inhibitors last three to four years before they need to be replaced. One layer of poly cuts

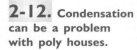 

2-12. Condensation can be a problem with poly houses.

light transmission to 85 to 90 percent, and two layers of poly reduce light transmission to 70 to 75 percent. The lower light transmission limits the type of crop that can be produced, particularly in the North. Poly houses have a tight growing environment that doesn't "breath." As a result, humidity levels can become quite high. Under humid conditions, a fungus disease of floriculture crops, *Botrytis*, can become a problem.

Structured sheets have grown quickly in popularity. Structured sheets are made from three materials. They are polycarbonates, acrylic, and fiberglass.

Polycarbonate structured sheets are the most widely used structured sheets. They are commonly manufactured with a "twin wall" held together by ribs. The resulting appearance is hollow tubes, side by side, running the length of the sheet. The tubing effect provides insulation and cuts heating costs. Polycarbonate sheets are treated with ultraviolet light inhibitors and are typically guaranteed for 10 years.

Polycarbonates have a good light transmission—80 percent. They resist hail damage. For that reason, polycarbonates are the product of choice in the hail belt stretching from Colorado to Texas. Polycarbonate sheets are also easy to work with and flexible. They can be bent around hoop greenhouses. Polycarbonates are fire resistant. A drawback is polycarbonate sheets are expensive.

Acrylic structured sheets are manufactured with twin walls in the same fashion as polycarbonate sheets. Therefore, they provide good insulation. They have a high light transmission, 86 percent, second only to glass. Acrylics last 8 to 10 years. Acrylics cost a bit more than polycarbonates. They are less flexible than polycarbonates and they are more prone to hail damage.

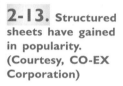 **2-13.** Structured sheets have gained in popularity. (Courtesy, CO-EX Corporation)

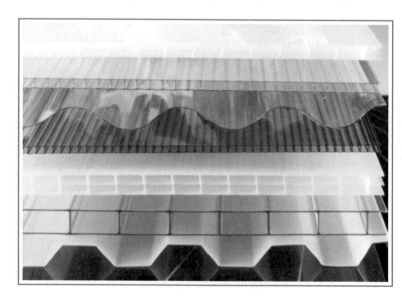

2-14. Glass is the best material for crop production.

Fiberglass was widely used in the 1960s and 1970s. Its use has dropped significantly since the introduction of polycarbonates and acrylics. Light transmission on new sheets is good, but it discolors after 7 to 10 years. Hail can cause some damage. Fiberglass is highly flammable, and it has poor insulating ability.

Glass is considered the best material for plant production. It provides the highest light transmission of any glazing material at 88 to 89 percent. The panes of glass overlap producing openings that allow air exchange. The initial cost of glass is expensive. It is very long lasting, provided it doesn't break. In fact, over the long term it can be less costly than other coverings.

Unfortunately, glass is breakable. Greenhouse owners find the purchase of hail insurance and crop insurance necessary. Tempered glass, which is about double the strength of regular glass, is available. It withstands hail better, but it is more expensive. The increased strength allows for the use of larger panes. Supports for the glass are placed farther apart increasing light transmission. Also, heat loss is reduced with the larger panes. Still, glass has very poor insulation qualities.

RETRACTABLE-ROOF GREENHOUSES

Technological advances provide another option for growers in terms of greenhouse structures. *Retractable-roof greenhouse* structures have roofs that can be opened and closed. They allow the grower to open the house to the elements when weather is favorable for plant growth and close the roof when the crops need protection. When open, crops are exposed to 90 percent sunshine and fresh air. Retractable-roof greenhouses are becoming more popular because they are a low-cost way to provide extra growing space.

Three main styles of retractable-roof greenhouses are on the market today. Flat roof houses are used for the purposes of shade and frost protection. Peaked roofs are designed for snow loads and keeping out rain. Sawtooth roof designs allow venting when other parts of the roof are closed. Polyethylene is used to cover the retractable-roof structure. When desired, sections of the poly are withdrawn and folded up by electric motors. The entire roof can be opened or closed in minutes.

Retractable-roof greenhouses are excellent for crops that prefer the outdoors, such as bedding plants, perennials, and field-grown cut flowers. Retractable-roof greenhouses also help plants become acclimated to the outdoors through exposure to the natural elements. **Acclimatization** is the

2-15. Retractable-roof greenhouse structures have roofs that can be opened and closed.

process in which plants adjust to a different growing environment. Other advantages are fewer disease problems due to better ventilation, reduced irrigation because of rainfall, and more effective temperature control for DIF.

Depending on the location of the greenhouse operation, a retractable-roof greenhouse may or may not be used year-round. Some growers use retractable-roof greenhouses for poinsettia production in the fall. Northern growers leave the greenhouse idle in the winter months. In warmer areas of the South, however, the structure may be in use throughout the year.

Greenhouse Benches

The level at which crops are grown in a greenhouse depends on the crop itself. The intended use of the greenhouse is another factor that is considered. A **conservatory** is a greenhouse designed for the display of plants. Conservatory plants are grown in beds on the floor to give a natural appearance.

2-16. Conservatory plants are often grown in ground beds for a natural appearance. (Courtesy, *Greenhouse Product News*)

Since conservatories house tropical plants, including trees, they are the largest greenhouses built.

In production operations, plants might be grown on benches, on the floor, or in beds. Bedding plants and potted plants in most production greenhouses are grown on benches two to three feet off the ground. However, some production does occur on the floor of the greenhouses. Cut flowers, such as roses and carnations, are usually grown in beds within the greenhouse. This is because cut flowers are not moved during production. Care and harvesting of the cut flowers is also easier when the plants are grown lower.

A *bench* is a structure that holds crops off the ground. The advantages of benches are numerous. To begin with, the plants are at a level that is com-

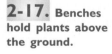

2-17. Benches hold plants above the ground.

2-18. Rolling benches maximize growing space in this greenhouse.

fortable for greenhouse employees. The raised benches allow water to drain from the containers. Also, it is easier to provide heat from below the plants.

Benches are manufactured from materials that can withstand the wet conditions in a greenhouse. They must also be strong enough to carry a lot of weight. Modern greenhouses use benches made from 13-gauge expanded galvanized steel, aluminum, and plastic. An alternative material for benches is rot-resistant wood, such as redwood or cedar. The recommended widths of benches are 3 feet, when working from one aisle, and 6 feet, when working from both sides.

Benches are arranged depending on the use of the greenhouse. In conservatories and educational greenhouses, aisles are wide to allow the movement of groups of people. The benches are usually stationary, too. In production greenhouses, the goal is to use as much space as possible for the growth of crops. Therefore, aisles are kept narrow, often the minimum of 18 inches. *Rolling benches* maximize growing space in the greenhouse. Rolling benches rest on pipes. This allows each bench to be rolled from side to side. With this system, only enough space needs to be kept for one aisle. One person can easily roll a large bench to create an aisle.

CLIMATE CONTROL

When one thinks of a climate, the temperature, humidity, precipitation, and the amount of sunshine often come to mind. Florida is considered to have a warm climate, while Alaska is considered to have a cold climate. People have no control of these large climates. However, greenhouse structures

2-19. Growers monitor growing conditions.

2-20. Thermostats are low cost and easy to install.

and climate control systems provide growers with the power to control temperature, water, humidity, and light within the greenhouse.

The greenhouse structure itself creates an enclosed environment. Yet, without the ability to manage the greenhouse climate, production of quality plants would not be possible. For example, quality of a crop is often determined by the ability to maintain temperatures within a few degrees. *Environmental controls* are devices used to automatically turn greenhouse systems on or off. Four types of environmental controls are associated with greenhouse use.

Thermostats are low cost and easy to install. There are two types, on-off and proportioning thermostats. On-off thermostats control fans, heaters, and vents with a change of temperature. Proportioning thermostats provide continuous control of systems with changes in temperature.

Analog controls use proportioning thermostats or electronic sensors to run amplifiers and electronic circuitry. They integrate the operations of heating and cooling equipment. The result is better performance than thermostats alone.

Computer controls utilize microprocessors. The microprocessors make complex judgements based on information from a number of sensors. Those sensors might gather information on temperature, relative humidity, and sunlight.

Computerized environmental management systems are expensive, but they are accurate and offer the greatest range of uses. All pieces of automated equipment can be controlled together. For instance, vents may be opened or closed at the same time curtains are opened or closed. Computerized environmental management systems also can be programmed to provide different zones in the greenhouse with different climate conditions.

In recent years, computerized environmental management systems have made controlling the climate easier. The computers are sophisticated and they have become very affordable. Most growers are using computerized systems or are looking into adding computers to their operations.

2-21. Computer controls utilize microprocessors to make complex judgements based on information from a number of sensors. (Courtesy, Ed Pryor Photographers Ltd.)

Heating and Cooling

Advanced growing schedules for floriculture crops involve pinpoint temperature control. Temperatures must vary between night and day as well as during different stages of the crop. Full control of temperature involves efficient cooling and heating systems. This is particularly true in the North.

During the day, cooling is a main concern. Radiant energy from the sun can quickly raise greenhouse temperatures. The heat can throw plant production off schedule. For example, potted chrysanthemum crops can be lost from heat stall. It can cause undesirable growth, such as Easter lilies

2-22. A plant damaged by exposure to cold temperatures.

stretching. In severe heat, plant tissues can be damaged. Excessive heat inside a greenhouse can be a problem even when it is cold outside.

The ability to heat a greenhouse is equally important. Greenhouses need additional heat on cold, cloudy days and at night. It is at those times when levels of radiant energy are low. On cold, partly sunny days it is common for the heating and ventilation system to work alternately. When sunny, the house may need to be cooled. When a cloud blocks the sun's rays, temperatures drop, and heat is required.

Heating Systems

Greenhouses are heated by several different methods. The trend is to use **hot water**. Modern boilers are small and efficient. The water is heated in the boilers and pumped through pipes in the greenhouse. The pipes are most often placed under the benches or in the floor. Hot water systems have relatively low maintenance. The heat is delivered evenly. The temperature of the water can be adjusted as needed. Hot water heat systems can also be designed to provide separate temperatures to different houses.

Steam heat is used in greenhouses. Steam has been the standard method for heating cut flower operations. Large boilers bring water to a boil to produce steam. The steam then flows through pipes in the greenhouse. Steam heat is not as uniform as hot water heat. Nor is it as easy to adjust the temperature. One advantage to steam heat is the steam can be used to sterilize growing medium.

Small greenhouses and double-poly hoop houses are generally heated with **unit heaters** or hot air heaters. Air is heated within the unit then,

2-23. Heating pipes placed under benches deliver heat under the crop.

2-24. Water is heated in boilers to produce steam heat.

blown by fans throughout the greenhouse. Unit heaters are less expensive to install than hot water systems. However, the long-term fuel costs for unit heaters are higher. Some growers prefer the heat to be delivered under the bench. Unit heaters deliver the heat above the crops. A common practice is to install unit heaters in large ranges as backup heaters for hot water or steam systems.

Many growers choose to use polyethylene tubes to evenly distribute warm air. They generally run the length of the greenhouse, and they have holes along the side of the tube. The tubes are attached to fans associated with unit heaters. When the fans are operating, the tubes inflate. Air is

2-25. These unit heaters provide the necessary heat in this retractable-roof greenhouse.

2-26. Polyethylene tubes help circulate air for uniform heat and to reduce foliar diseases

blown through the holes in the tube. Polyethylene tubes promote an even circulation of air in the greenhouse. The result is uniform temperatures and fewer problems with foliar diseases.

Infrared heat systems produce heat energy that is absorbed by the plants, media, and benches. The heat then transfers to the air space around them. Therefore, infrared heat does not heat the air directly. The whole system is very similar to the way the Sun heats Earth. High fuel efficiency of infrared heat results in low operating costs. Also, foliar diseases, such as *Botrytis*, appear to be less of a problem. Infrared heat systems are placed at the peak of a

2-27. This photo shows propane-fired infrared heaters at the peak of the greenhouse.

greenhouse so the energy can radiate throughout the house. For that reason, they function best in higher structures. On the down side, the required placement of the system eliminates the use of energy curtains.

Energy Curtains

Modern greenhouses are equipped with energy curtains. *Energy curtains* are automated systems utilizing fabrics that insulate the greenhouse at night and shade the crops during the day. The curtains are installed from gutter to gutter. With today's higher greenhouse structures, the curtains are 8 to 12 feet above the ground. Computerized environmental management systems open and close the curtains based on preset light levels or temperatures.

Research has shown that energy curtains have a significant effect on greenhouse temperatures. The shade produced by curtains results in temperatures 8 to 10 degrees cooler than in full sun. The cooler temperatures reduce stress on the plants. Also, less water and fertilizer are required in the production of the crop. The curtains have an opposite effect when closed at night. Heat energy is contained within the greenhouse. The energy saved in terms of fuel costs ranges between 25 and 35 percent. For this reason, the use of energy curtains in colder regions has increased.

The same technology applies to the use of *short-day curtains*. These curtains block light from reaching the crops. When closed for 12 to 13 hours a night, they produce a short-day (actually a long-night) effect. This ability to control light duration is critical in the timing of poinsettia, chrysanthemum, and kalanchoe crops. Two materials used for the curtains are a black poly-

2-28. Energy curtains can be opened to allow maximum light or closed to shade the crops during the day.

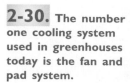 **Short-day curtains can be closed to darken a greenhouse for short-day crops, like these poinsettias.**

propylene or an aluminum and polyethylene combination. The environmental control system opens and closes the curtain at prescribed times each day.

Cooling and Ventilation Systems

The number one cooling system used in greenhouses today is the *fan and pad cooling system*. Fan and pad cooling systems are based on the evaporation of water. These systems involve a wall of cellulose or aspen pads on one end of the greenhouse. The pads are kept wet by a system of pumps and gutters that recirculate the water. On the other end of the greenhouse, there is a series of fans. The fans pull air through the pads and across the greenhouse. As the air passes through the pads, the water evaporates. The air is cooled as the water evaporates. This process can be compared to the cooling effect perspiration has on the skin.

2-30. The number one cooling system used in greenhouses today is the fan and pad system.

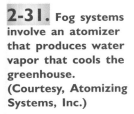 **2-31.** Fog systems involve an atomizer that produces water vapor that cools the greenhouse. (Courtesy, Atomizing Systems, Inc.)

Fan and pad systems provide lower temperatures in the areas closest to the pads. The air warms as it crosses the greenhouse.

Another method of cooling involves a *fog system*, sometimes referred to as a mist system. Fog systems involve an atomizer that produces water vapor. The water vapor cools the house by flash evaporation. Fog systems increase the humidity within the house while they cool. One advantage of fog systems is that they effectively lower the temperature throughout the entire house. Fog systems are most often found in the southern states.

Natural cooling through ventilation is used where possible. *Vents* consist of panels that open and allow air exchange with the outside. Roof vents are

2-32. The roof of this modern greenhouse opens to provide ventilation and to increase light levels.

effective. Hot air rises. As it does so, it escapes through the vent located at the peak of the house. Operating roof vents is much less expensive than fan and pad systems. Some greenhouse designs use both systems of cooling. Initial cooling is achieved by roof vents. However, if temperatures rise, the roof vents shut and the fan and pad system turns on.

OTHER AUTOMATED SYSTEMS

Many automated systems being used today involve handling of plants. Handling of plants is labor intensive. Growers typically handle millions of plants in a year. The labor required to propagate, pot, move, care for, harvest, and package the plants is costly. Cut flower production is the most labor intensive. Labor alone can account for 35 percent of the production costs. Bedding plant production also requires a great deal of labor. Fortunately, technological developments have assisted growers in performing some tasks.

Some of the technological developments are discussed briefly:

One of the first automated greenhouse systems helped workers fill pots or flats with growing medium. The *pot fillers* fill pots with the medium. Workers feed empty pots to be filled into the mechanism. Pot filler machines fill the pots and lightly pack the medium. Another worker receives the pots for stacking or the pots move down a conveyor for planting.

2-33. Even with technological advances floriculture production can be labor intensive.

2-34. These workers use a pot filling machine to fill pots with growing medium.

Automated seeders permit the sowing of hundreds of flats of bedding plant seeds. The seeders require few workers for operation. Larger producers of bedding plants rely on automated seeders.

Automated transplanters have become standard equipment in middle- and large-sized greenhouse operations. Small plants are removed from seed flats and planted into pots for finishing.

One of the most labor-intensive activities in the greenhouse is the moving of plants to and from the growing area. Carts have been used for years. Conveyor belts are one of the most efficient ways to move plants in the

2-35. This person uses an automated seeder to sow thousands of flats of bedding plant seeds in a season.

2-36. These people are receiving pots that an automated transplanter has planted with small plants from flats.

2-37. Tray mechanization is a transport method gaining popularity.

greenhouse. Another transport method gaining popularity is ***tray mechanization***. Also known as Dutch trays or palletized benches, this system consists of benches that hold 100 or more pots. The trays are rolled on a series of rails from one area of the greenhouse operation to another. In more advanced operations, robots have replaced the rail system and move the trays to growing areas using bar codes.

Automated irrigation systems save labor. Some automated watering systems are ebb and flood, capillary mats, spaghetti tubes, and irrigation booms. With an ebb and flood system, water is pumped into a watertight bench at regular intervals. The medium absorbs the water through the drain holes of the pots. Ebb and flow benches conserve water, provide accurate nutrient levels, and allow for optimum spacing of plants. Capillary mats consist of porous mats laid on a bench and wetted. The medium in the pots absorbs the water by capillary action. ***Spaghetti tubes*** involve tubing that provides water to individual pots. Irrigation booms water large areas of bench space quickly making them useful for bedding plant production. Computers control the booms.

2-38. Bar codes were automatically placed on these pots at planting.

2-39. This ebb and flood system involves pumping nutrient solutions into the watertight benches at regular intervals.

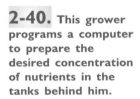

2-40. This grower programs a computer to prepare the desired concentration of nutrients in the tanks behind him.

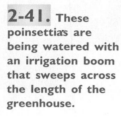

2-41. These poinsettias are being watered with an irrigation boom that sweeps across the length of the greenhouse.

GREENHOUSE SAFETY

2-42. Wet floors or aisles can promote algae growth and result in slippery conditions.

The nature of the work in a greenhouse can lead to injury. It is important for workers to be aware of common hazards they may encounter. Depending on the hazard, measures should be taken either to proceed with caution or to correct the problem. Some of the most common greenhouse hazards and safety procedures follow.

Wet areas—Wet and humid conditions in greenhouses create water puddles and algae buildup on walkways. The result is often slippery conditions that can lead to falls.

Recommended safety practices:

■ Post warning signs indicating slick areas.

■ Treat the slick surfaces to reduce algae growth.

■ Periodically inspect the walkways.

Cluttered aisles—Hoses, plants, carts and other items that clutter the aisles create tripping hazards.

Recommended safety practices:

- Check the aisles regularly to see that they are free of obstacles.

- Make sure hanging plants are secure and provide safe passage.

Faulty electrical wiring—Poor electrical wiring is a major cause of fires. Temporary wiring, improper splicing, and the excessive use of extension cords are the most common electrical problems in greenhouses.

Recommended safety practices:

- Have the fire department or a professional electrician inspect the greenhouse wiring.

- Use standard twist connectors to join wires.

- Only use extension cords with adequate capacity to carry the current.

2-43. Hoses lying in aisles can become tripping hazards.

2-44. Electrical outlets in the greenhouse should be well-grounded.

2-45. Chemicals must be stored safely.

- Never place extension cords under carpets where they can be damaged from traffic. Undetected damage can lead to smoldering.
- See that all joints are secured within a junction or receptacle box.
- Locate breakers and service boxes away from areas that will be wet.

Use of chemicals—Care must be taken when mixing and applying chemicals. Poisoning can occur through contact with skin and by inhaling fumes. Recommended safety practices:

- Schedule the application of chemicals when temperatures are cool.
- Always read and follow instructions on the chemical label.
- Only allow employees trained in the use of chemicals to handle them.
- Wear safety gear when mixing and applying chemicals.

REVIEWING

MAIN IDEAS

Greenhouse structures are enclosed by translucent materials. They give growers of floriculture crops control of environmental conditions important to plant growth. There are four basic styles of greenhouse structures: lean-to, even span, uneven span, and ridge-and-furrow. Ridge-and-furrow houses are widely used in automated operations. A headhouse is a structure attached to the greenhouse. It serves as a work area and as a storage area.

The covering of a greenhouse is often referred to as the glazing. Polyethylene is the most widely used greenhouse covering. It is flexible and stretches over the greenhouse framework. Structured sheets have grown quickly in popularity. Structured sheets are made polycarbonates, acrylic, and fiberglass. They offer good light transmission and some products have excellent insulation properties. Glass is the best glazing material for the production of floriculture crops. However, it is expensive and breakable. Technological advances have provided retractable-roof greenhouse structures. Their roofs open and close allowing plants to be exposed to the elements when weather is favorable. Benches hold crops off the ground. Rolling benches maximize the growing space in a greenhouse.

Environmental controls are devices used to automatically turn greenhouse systems on or off. Four types available include thermostats, analog controls, computer controls, and computerized environmental management systems. Greenhouses are heated by several different methods. The trend is to use hot water. Steam heat, unit heaters, and infrared heat systems are other methods. Energy curtains are automated systems used to insulate the greenhouse at night and shade the crops during the day. Fan and pad systems, fogging systems, and vents cool greenhouses.

Automation has reduced the labor involved in the greenhouse industry. Major automated systems include pot fillers, automated seeders, automated transplanters, plant transport systems, and automated irrigation systems.

Safety is also a concern in the greenhouse industry. Wet floors, cluttered aisles, poor electrical wiring, and storage of chemicals are common hazards in the greenhouse industry.

QUESTIONS

Answer the following questions. Use correct spelling and complete sentences.

1. Why are greenhouses so valuable to greenhouse growers?
2. How do the styles of greenhouses differ?
3. What are important considerations when selecting the greenhouse framing?
4. What are the advantages and disadvantages of the different glazing materials?
5. Why are retractable-roof greenhouses gaining in popularity?
6. What is used to control the greenhouse environment?
7. How are greenhouses heated?
8. What systems are used to cool greenhouses?
9. What are some technological advances in automation that have reduced labor?
10. What are some of the potential hazards for employee safety in the greenhouse?

EVALUATING

Match the term with the correct definition. Write the letter by the term in the blank provided.

a. automated seeders
b. fan and pad
c. environmental controls
d. polyethylene (poly)
e. acclimatization
f. glass

g. headhouse
h. ridge-and-furrow greenhouse
i. unit heaters
j. retractable-roof greenhouse
k. rolling benches
l. ebb and flood

_____ 1. The process in which plants adjust to a different growing environment.

_____ 2. Method of heating that involves the heating of air, which is blown by fans throughout the greenhouse.

_____ 3. Considered the best material for plant production as it provides the highest light transmission of any glazing material at 88 to 89 percent.

_____ 4. Structures have roofs that can be opened and closed.

_____ 5. Permit the sowing of hundreds of flats of bedding plant seeds.

_____ 6. Benches that rest on pipes for movement, thus maximizing the growing space in the greenhouse.

_____ 7. Structure attached to the greenhouse that serves as a storage area and a work area.

_____ 8. Number one cooling system used in greenhouses today. Cooling is based on the evaporation of water.

_____ 9. Automated system in which water is pumped into a watertight bench at regular intervals.

_____ 10. Structure consisting of a number of greenhouses connected together along the length of the houses.

_____ 11. Devices used to automatically turn greenhouse systems on or off.

_____ 12. The most widely used glazing material consisting of flexible sheets, usually 6-mil in thickness.

EXPLORING

1. Contact a greenhouse operation to arrange a visit. During the visit, note the construction materials used for the structure(s). Record the types of automated equipment used in production of the crops. Ask the grower to explain how the structure and equipment operate. Another objective might be to keep a list of conditions that could be hazards to the greenhouse workers.

2. Familiarize yourself with the high school greenhouse. Ask your instructor how it is designed to operate. What are some of the differences between the high school greenhouse and the larger commercial operations?

3

Growing Media and Plant Nutrition

Have you ever noticed a new born baby? It is dependent on its parents for everything it needs. When the baby is hungry, it cries to be fed. When the baby is thirsty, it cries for something to drink. The baby lets it be known if it is experiencing other discomforts as well. Since the baby's sole means of communication is crying, parents often have to guess what the baby needs.

Plants are similar to babies in some ways. They have needs, which if not addressed, could result in death. Plants are dependent on the growing medium in which their roots grow. They draw moisture and nutrients from the growing medium. Plants do not communicate, although they do show symptoms of distress. The grower must be able to detect the needs of the plants. Mostly, the grower learns to anticipate the proper growing medium and the nutritional needs of the greenhouse crops.

3-1. The health of a plant is often determined by the growing medium.

OBJECTIVES

1 Describe the qualities of a good growing medium

2 Identify materials used as growing media

3 Explain the differences between soil and a soilless medium

4 Identify nutrients for plant growth and fertilizers that provide nutrients

5 Describe recommended fertilization practices

6 Describe the importance of pH on greenhouse crop production

TERMS

aeration
available water
bark
bulk density
calcined clay
cation exchange capacity
coir
fertilizer
fertilizer injector system
growing medium
macronutrient
micronutrient
mineral soil
nutrient deficiency
organic matter
parts per million (ppm)

peat moss
perlite
pH
plant nutrition
plastic foam
porosity
rock wool
sand
slow release fertilizers
soilless mix
soil pH
soluble salts
unavailable water
vermiculite
water-soluble fertilizers

GROWING MEDIUM

The health and quality of floriculture crops rest largely with the growing medium. The **growing medium** is the material in which plants are grown. In field production and the home garden, soil is the growing medium. In greenhouse production, a variety of materials are used as growing media. The medium used has a direct impact on the quality of the crop grown. Why is the growing medium so important? What function does the growing medium play in plant growth that makes it so important? The importance of the growing medium rests with four basic functions.

3-2. The growing medium provides plant support, water, nutrients, and gases. (Courtesy, *Greenhouse Product News*)

- Growing medium holds water for plant use.
- Growing medium provides nutrients for the plant.
- Growing medium permits the exchange of gases to and from the plant roots.
- Growing medium provides support for the plant.

GREENHOUSE GROWING MEDIA ARE DIFFERENT

Have you ever taken soil from outside to use for growing plants in pots? If so, you might have noticed that the soil became hard, that it did not soak water up very quickly, or the plants grew poorly. When used in containers, even good soils lose characteristics important for quality plant growth. Since most greenhouse crops are grown in containers, the growing medium for greenhouse purposes must be different from soils found outside.

Production of greenhouse crops has some specific demands that are often different from the production of outside plants. Rapid growth is required of greenhouse crops. Growers produce a crop quickly, ship it, and bring in a new crop. Therefore, the growing medium must provide conditions that encourage plant growth. Another requirement of greenhouse crops is that they be uniform. A crop in which all the plants have the same rate of growth and development is highly valued by customers. To ensure that the plants grow at the same rate, the growing medium used must be uniform.

DESIRABLE PROPERTIES OF MEDIA

Research has improved greenhouse growing medium. Through research, desirable properties of high quality medium have been identified. In addition, growers have been given a greater understanding of medium and its properties. Discussion of desirable medium properties follows:

Organic Matter

The organic matter in the medium must be stable and must function throughout the life of the crop. *Organic matter* is decayed or partially decayed remains of plants and animals found in the medium. It should remain stable and not break down before the crop is finished. Peat moss and bark are the most common sources of organic matter in growing medium.

3-3. The medium shown consists of mostly organic matter.

Bulk Density

Bulk density is the ratio of the mass of dry solids in a medium to the volume of the medium. Light bulk density eases handling and shipping of the

3-4. Easter lilies need a medium with a heavy bulk density.

potted plants. High or heavy bulk density is needed to provide support for plants. Easter lilies need a medium with a heavy bulk density. The growing medium's bulk density should be light enough to ease handling and heavy enough to support the plant.

*P*orosity

The spaces between the solid particles of a growing medium are pores. A higher percentage of pores or ***porosity*** in a medium results in better water drainage and aeration or the exchange of gases. Good mineral or garden soils have about 50 percent pore space. Organic media used in greenhouses have between 75 and 85 percent pore spaces.

*A*eration

Aeration is the exchange of gases in the medium. Pore spaces that allow air pockets within the medium are vital for healthy root growth. Root cells use oxygen from the

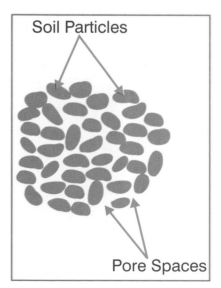

3-5. A higher percentage of pores or *porosity* in a medium results in better water drainage and aeration or the exchange of gases.

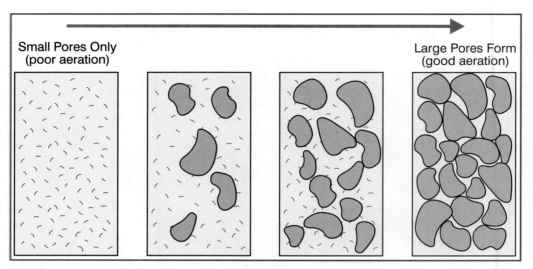

Small Pores Only
(poor aeration)

Large Pores Form
(good aeration)

3-6. Pore spaces that allow air pockets within the medium are vital for healthy plant growth.

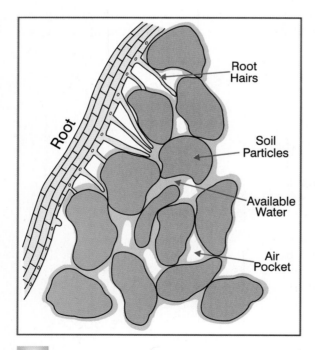

Root Hairs

Root

Soil Particles

Available Water

Air Pocket

3-7. Available water is water that can be absorbed by the plant roots.

pore spaces to convert sugars to energy. This chemical process is known as respiration. A byproduct of this respiration is carbon dioxide. It is important that a medium has sufficient pore spaces to allow an exchange of carbon dioxide and oxygen.

Water-holding Ability

A growing medium must store water that is available for plant use. *Available water* is water that can be absorbed by the plant roots. Available water is found in the pore spaces of the medium. Some water in the growing medium is considered unavailable for plant use. *Unavailable water* is a thin film of water that binds so tightly on media particles that it cannot be used by plants.

pH

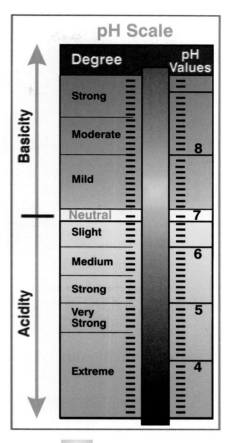

3-8. The pH scale.

The acidity or alkalinity of the medium is measured as **pH**. A 14-point scale is used to measure pH. A neutral pH is 7.0. Any reading between zero and 7.0 is acid, and a solution between 7.0 and 14.0 is said to be alkaline or basic. The pH is determined by the concentration of hydrogen (H^+) ions and hydroxyl ions (OH^-) in the soil solution. A sample of pure water has an equal number of H^+ and OH^- ions and is therefore neutral.

Medium pH plays a large role in the availability of nutrients in the medium. Most essential elements for plant growth are available to most plants when the soil pH is between 5.5 and 7.0. If the pH is too low or too high, the availability of nutrients is restricted. Most plants grow best when the soil pH is between 6.0 and 7.0. Azaleas do best when the pH is 5.5 to 6.0.

Cation Exchange Capacity

Cation exchange capacity is the measure of a medium's capacity to hold nutrients. Many nutrients are positively charged cations, such as potassium (K^+), Calcium (Ca^{+2}), Magnesium (Mg^+), Copper (Cu^+), Iron (Fe^{+2} or Fe^{+3}), Manganese (Mn^{+2}), and Zinc (Zn^{+2}). Particles in the medium have negative charged sites. The cations are attracted to these negatively charged sites on medium particles. This is the same principle of attraction that applies to magnets.

The cations can leave the medium particle and be replaced by a cation held in the medium solution. For instance, a potassium atom may leave the particle and be replaced by a copper atom dissolved in the soil water. This replacement of one cation for another is called cation exchange. The fertility of a medium is directly related to the number of cations a medium can attract

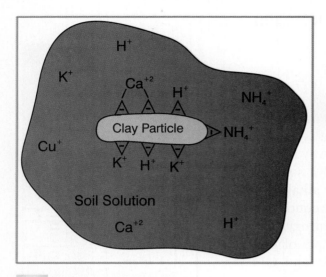

3-9. Negatively charged particles in the growing medium attract and hold positively charged cations.

and hold. The greater the cation exchange capacity, the greater the fertility of the medium.

GROWING MEDIUM COMPONENTS

Most medium used today consists of a mixture of two or more components. More than one component is needed to produce a medium that has desirable properties for plant growth. The medium may or may not include soil. In fact, soil is used less frequently now than ever before. Field or mineral soils are seldom uniform, and finding quality soil, free of herbicide residues, has become more difficult. Those media that lack any mineral soil are often referred to as **soilless mixes**.

Soilless mixes are the standards in the floriculture industry today. One advantage to using soilless media is they are uniform or always the same. Soilless mixes consist largely of peat moss or bark with perlite and/or vermiculite. The basic components are sterilized to eliminate disease and insect and weed problems. After sterilizing the materials, nutrients are added and the pH is adjusted for optimal plant growth. Soilless media tend to lack reserves of nutrients for plant use. Typically, treble phosphate and slow release micronutrients are added to media. Also, PNO_3 is often added as a starter fertilizer. For some crops, peat-based soilless media have too low a pH for optimum growth. The pH is raised to acceptable levels by adding limestone or gypsum.

Growers either purchase prepared growing medium in bulk or mix their own medium. Materials commonly used in growing medium mixes include mineral soil, sand, sphagnum peat moss, coir, vermiculite, pine bark, perlite, plastic foam beads, calcined clay, and rock wool. Combined in the right proportions these materials deliver the desired properties needed for plant growth. The decision of which materials to use is determined by the availability of the material, the cost of the material, shipping costs, and the

3-10. This photo shows peat moss being dug in Canada. (Courtesy, Berger Peat Moss)

grower's preference. Materials used have certain characteristics that contribute to a quality medium.

Peat Moss

One of the most widely used components of medium is ***peat moss***. It is an organic material dug from peat bogs. Canada, and to a lesser extent, Michigan and Florida are sources of peat for growers in the United States. Cana-

3-11. One of the most widely used components of medium is peat moss.

3-12. Coir, made from the husks of coconuts, has similar properties to peat moss. (Courtesy, Crystal Company)

3-13. Vermiculite is lightweight and has good water holding ability and aeration.

dian peat is very uniform and of high quality. Peat moss has light bulk density, good moisture-holding ability, good air space qualities for the exchange of gases, adequate cation exchange capacity, and a stable pH that is usually between 3.5 and 4.5.

Coir

Coir is made from waste products of the coconut industry and is therefore considered a renewable resource. Its characteristics are similar to those of peat moss. It has high water-holding ability and excellent drainage. Another advantage to coir is that it encourages faster rooting of plants. A disadvantage is it has high salt content, as coconuts grow near the sea. Coir is being used mostly in England and Holland, but is gaining popularity in the United States.

Vermiculite

Vermiculite is a common ingredient in growing medium. The origin of vermiculite is a mineral called mica. Mica is heated to 1800° F, which causes it to expand like an accordion. Spaces made by the expansion result in good water-holding ability and aeration. It is a lightweight material and can be easily compressed. Vermiculite is available in different grades, ranging from a fine grade for use with seeds to a coarse grade measuring more than 1/4 inch in diameter. Vermiculite has a good cation exchange capacity and a neutral to slightly alkaline pH (6.3 to 7.8). It also provides small amounts of calcium, magnesium, and potassium for plant use. African vermiculite has a high potassium content.

Perlite

Perlite originates from volcanic rock. The rock is crushed, then quickly heated to temperatures of 1800° F. The heat causes it to pop like popcorn to form a lightweight, white aggregate. Perlite is a good lightweight substitute for sand. It is stable, sterile, has little cation exchange capacity, has a pH of 7.5, and provides good water drainage and aeration. Perlite contains fluorides that cause leaf damage to some monocotyledon plants including freesias, dracaenas, and spider plants.

3-14. Perlite is a good lightweight substitute for sand.

Bark

Bark from trees is obtained as a byproduct through the timber industry. It is relatively inexpensive, and thus, lowers the cost of the growing medium. The most widely used bark in the greenhouse industry is pine bark. Bark that is ground into fine pieces is the most useful because of its uniform qualities. Bark improves the moisture-holding ability and aeration of a mix. After peat moss, bark is the second best organic-matter medium component.

3-15. Pieces of bark can be seen in the medium shown.

Sand

   Sand is found naturally and is a result of the wearing of rock. Sand is heavy and has a high bulk density that provides solid support for larger plants. It improves water drainage and aeration when used with soil. The sand particles can actually reduce aeration in peat or bark mixes by filling pore spaces created by the peat or bark. The pH of sand is between 7.5 and 8.5. If used, sand must be sterilized to destroy pythium and rhizoctonia disease organisms.

3-16. Sand is heavy and has a high bulk density.

Table 3-1. Characteristics of Medium Components

Material	Bulk Density	Aeration Qualities	Water-Holding Qualities	pH	Cation Exchange Capacity
Bark	Low	High	High	Slightly acid	Low
Calcined Clay	Moderate	High	Low	Varies	Good
Coir	Low	High	High	Slightly acid	Low
Mineral Soil	High	Low	Varies	Varies	Good
Peat Moss	Low	High	High	Acid	Low
Perlite	Low	High	Low	Slightly alkaline	None
Rock Wool	Low	High	High	Slightly alkaline	Low
Sand	High	High	Low	Alkaline	Low
Plastic Foam	Low	High	Low	Neutral	None
Vermiculite	Low	High	High	Slightly alkaline	High

Plastic Foam

Plastic foam flakes or beads (the most common is Styrofoam) are a synthetic polystyrene material. Plastic foam is very lightweight and stable. While it provides good drainage and aeration, it lacks cation exchange capacity, water-holding abilities, and has a neutral pH. It also tends to float to the surface of growing media.

Calcined Clay

Calcined clay is clay aggregate heated to form a hard, stable particle. It has a high bulk density. Calcined clay improves water drainage and aeration in a medium. It also has some cation exchange capacity.

Rock Wool

Rock wool is a human-made material from an igneous rock, basalt. The rock is heated to temperatures of 2700°F, and once liquefied, it is spun into fibers similar in appearance to cotton candy. Rock wool is used extensively in hydroponic operations. Rock wool cubes are used in plant propagation. Granular forms of rock wool are used as a medium component. Rock wool has good water-holding capacity and good aeration. It is slightly alkaline and has a low cation exchange capacity.

*M*ineral Soil

Mineral soil is obtained from nature and is the result of weathered rock. It has become more difficult for growers to find uniform mineral soil with a favorable pH and good structure and texture. Mineral soil must be free of agricultural herbicides and sterilized before use.

3-17. Mineral soil must be free of agricultural herbicides and sterilized before use.

PLANT NUTRITION

One aspect of plant production over which growers can have great control is plant nutrition. *Plant nutrition* involves the absorption of nutrients for plant growth. The nutritional needs of greenhouse plants require close attention because the plants are wholly dependent on what is available in the growing medium. Current fertilizer practices allow growers to adjust and deliver nutrients to maintain desired plant growth.

Plant growth is dependent on 17 essential elements, often referred to as nutrients. Three of the elements, oxygen, hydrogen, and carbon make up 89 percent of a plant's tissue by dry weight. The plant through natural processes acquires these three elements. They are considered to be nonfertilizer nutrients. There is one exception to this. In some operations, carbon is provided to plants through the release of carbon dioxide gas into the greenhouse atmosphere.

Six of the 17 essential elements are required in greater quantity than the others. They are called *macronutrients.* The macronutrients are nitrogen (N), phosphorus (P), potassium (K), calcium (Ca), magnesium (Mg), and sulfur (S). Nitrogen, phosphorus, and potassium are considered to be primary nutrients because

3-18. CO_2 burners release carbon dioxide gas into the greenhouse atmosphere.

Table 3-2. Essential Elements			
	Element	Chemical Symbol	Percent of Plant's Dry Weight
Nonfertilizer	Carbon	C	
	Hydrogen	H	89
	Oxygen	O	
Macronutrients	Nitrogen	N	4.0
	Phosphorus	P	0.5
	Potassium	K	4.0
	Calcium	Ca	1.0
	Magnesium	Mg	0.5
	Sulfur	S	0.5
Micronutrients	Iron	Fe	0.02
	Manganese	Mn	0.02
	Chlorine	Cl	0.01
	Boron	B	0.006
	Zinc	Zn	0.003
	Copper	Cu	0.001
	Nickel	Ni	0.0005
	Molybdenum	Mo	0.0002

they are used in complete fertilizers. Calcium, magnesium, and sulfur are said to be secondary macronutrients because plants need moderate amounts. These secondary macronutrients may or may not be used in complete fertilizers.

The other eight essential elements are needed in small quantities. They are called **micronutrients**. Sometimes they are called trace elements. They are boron (B), copper (Cu), chlorine (Cl), iron (Fe), manganese (Mn), molybdenum (Mo), sodium (Na), nickel (Ni), and zinc (Zn). Six of these, boron, copper, iron, manganese, molybdenum, sodium, and zinc, are supplied to plants as fertilizers. Nickel and chlorine need not be added as a fertilizer. Plants obtain sufficient quantities of them through the medium or water.

*F*ERTILIZERS

A **fertilizer** is any material added to growing medium that provides nutrients for plants. Adding nutrients in the form of fertilizers is necessary to improve plant growth and development. Fertilizers are particularly important with the use of soilless mixes. Because soilless mixes lack reserves of nutrients, the nutrients must be supplied regularly to the plants. Also, quick production of quality crops is achieved when all the nutrients required of plant growth are provided at the optimum rates.

Different plants have different nutrient level requirements. Also, plants have different nutrient requirements based on their stage of growth. For potted flowering plants, there are five stages of growth. In the first or juvenile

3-19. Water soluble fertilizers used in the greenhouse often come with a blue indicator dye. (Courtesy, University of Illinois Extension)

Table 3-3. Common Fertilizers Used in Greenhouse Crop Production

	Percent Nitrogen	Percent Phosphorus	Percent Potassium	Other Characteristics
Water-Soluble Fertilizer Compounds				
Ammonium nitrate	33	0	0	Acid
Ammonium sulfate	21	0	0	Acid
Calcium nitrate	15	0	0	Basic Provides Calcium
Diammonium sulfate	21	53	0	Acid
Magnesium nitrate	11	0	0	Neutral
Monoammonium phosphate	12	62	0	Acid
Monopotassium phosphate	0	53	35	Basic
Potassium chloride	0	0	60	Neutral
Potassium nitrate (saltpeter)	13	0	44	Basic
Potassium sulfate	0	0	51	Neutral
Sodium nitrate	16	0	0	Basic
Urea	45	0	0	Acid
Slow Release Fertilizers				
Osmocote (coated)	14	14	14	3-4 month release
Sierra (coated)	17	6	10	Plus micronutrients 8-9 month release
Nutricote (coated)	18	6	8	Plus micronutrients 100 day release
ProKote	20	3	10	Plus micronutrients 7-9 month release
MagAmp	7	40	6	3-5 month release

stage, the plant is a young seedling or cutting. In the second stage, vegetative or leafy growth is encouraged. The vegetative stage is followed by the flower bud initiation stage, the flower bud development stage, and the flowering stages. Each stage calls for different rates of fertilizers. When in the vegetative stage, plants use more nitrogen, and when in the flowering stage, they require less nitrogen and more phosphorus.

There are two widely used methods to deliver fertilizers to greenhouse plants. One involves the use of water-soluble fertilizers with an injector system, whereby the plants are fertilized as they are watered. The other involves the use of slow release fertilizers.

Fertilizer Injector Systems

Fertilizer injector systems are standard equipment in today's greenhouses. There are many types of injectors on the market. Basically, they work the same. A concentrate of water-soluble fertilizer is mixed in a tank. *Water-soluble fertilizers* dissolve completely in water and stay in solution. The concentrations of the water-soluble fertilizers are also easily adjusted. The fertilizer concentrate is then mixed with the water in exact proportions before irrigating plants. With fertilizer injectors growers can provide exact levels of nutrients.

There are a number of advantages to using fertilizer injectors. The greenhouse plants are provided with constant liquid feeding. This is especially important with soilless media that have a low cation exchange capacity. The plants are fertilized when they are watered thus reducing labor. All the plants of a particular crop receive the same levels of nutrients. This assists in producing a uniform crop. In addition, adjustments to the level of nutrients in solution can be made easily.

3-20. Fertilizer injectors deliver exact amounts of nutrients to plants.

Calculating ppm

Nutrients in solution are measured in ***parts per million*** or ppm. Growers can refer to tables in reference books or to instructions with their injector system to determine the amount of fertilizer needed to reach a desired ppm. However, growers must also understand how to calculate parts per million (ppm) of fertilizer nutrients.

An example problem might call for 200 ppm nitrogen. The chosen fertilizer is calcium nitrate with an analysis of 15-0-0. A rule of thumb in calculating ppm is that *1 oz of anything in 100 gallons H_2O equals 75 ppm.*

Problem: Wanted, 200 ppm N
             15-0-0 Calcium Nitrate

Multiply the percent of the nutrient in the given fertilizer by 75.

.15 N × 75 = 11.63 ppm N (if 1 oz added to 100 gallons)

200 ÷ 11.63 = 17.2 oz of fertilizer needed in 100 gallons to get 200 ppm

---

If the injector system delivers 1:100 (one gallon concentrate mixed with 99 gallons water for a total of 100 gallons), 17.2 ounces of fertilizer is needed for each gallon of concentrate. If the tank holds 30 gallons of concentrate, 516 ounces (32.25 pounds) of fertilizer is needed to deliver 200 ppm.

Slow Release Fertilizers

Slow release fertilizers are self-defined by their name. These products continually discharge a small amount of nutrients over a period of time. They are available in two forms. One form consists of a water-soluble fertilizer held within a plastic resin or sulfur coating. The coating is designed to allow a small

3-21. Slow release fertilizers can be mixed with the growing medium prior to planting or applied to the medium surface after potting.

amount of fertilizer to be slowly released. They have the appearance of little round beads and are sometimes mistaken as insect eggs by the uninformed. The other type of slow release fertilizer comes in a granular form. This type releases no more than 1 percent of the fertilizer in a 24-hour period.

The use of slow release fertilizers has declined with the increased use of water-soluble fertilizers through injector systems. Growers have a much greater control with the fertilizer injector systems. However, there are some advantages to the slow release fertilizers. Slow release fertilizers can be safely mixed with the growing medium prior to planting. Slow release fertilizers provide a more constant supply of nutrients than water-soluble fertilizers. This is particularly true when watering is less frequent. Slow release fertilizers work well when capillary mats are used to water plants. Also, slow release fertilizers can be used to extend the shelf life of plants once they leave the greenhouse.

NUTRIENT DEFICIENCY

Plant quality and thus, profits, are lost if the plants cannot obtain the essential nutrients from the medium. Even if only one necessary nutrient is missing, the plant can develop deficiency symptoms. For example, nitrogen promotes the growth of green, leafy tissue. If the available nitrogen is low, the plant may take on a yellow appearance. The growth rate slows and the plant

3-22. Discoloration of leaves is often a result of nutrient deficiency.

often is stunted. This happens even when all the other essential nutrients are available.

If a plant fails to receive the needed nutrients, it will show signs of ***nutrient deficiency***. Nutrient deficiencies most often surface as an unhealthy plant appearance. Symptoms vary with the nutrient that is in short supply. Common symptoms of deficiencies include discoloration of the leaves, death of leaf tissue, and stunted growth. Because of the complex interactions of nutrients in plant processes, deficiency symptoms for different nutrients are often very similar. Laboratory tests, including the analysis of plant tissues, can be used to determine which nutrient is lacking.

SOLUBLE SALTS

A problem that arises with the use of water-soluble fertilizers is the build-up of soluble salts. The nutrients that are in solution along with mineral salts from the water and medium contribute to the soluble salt content in the growing medium. ***Soluble salts*** consist of these dissolved mineral salts. High levels of soluble salts are harmful to plants. Young plants are especially sensitive.

The damage caused by soluble salts is through a process known as reverse osmosis. As the salt concentration builds up in the growing medium, it prevents water molecules from being absorbed by the roots. In severe cases, water is drawn from the root cells into the growing medium. The resulting damage caused by soluble salts is the burning of the roots. Wilting or the death of leaf tissues follows the injury or death of the roots.

Damage from soluble salts can be avoided by preventing a buildup of soluble salts in the growing me-

3-23. Watering heavily so that water drains through the bottom of the pot reduces soluble salt build up.

dium. A good practice is to water the plants until water drains from the container. As the water flows through the growing medium, it carries soluble salts with it. This is known as leaching.

REVIEWING

**AIN IDEAS**

Growing medium serves four major functions for plants. It holds water for plant use and provides nutrients for the plant. Growing medium permits the exchange of gases to and from the plant roots. Also, growing medium provides support for the plant. Some characteristics of growing medium are desirable. Properties to consider include organic matter, bulk density, porosity, aeration, water holding ability, pH, and cation exchange capacity.

Greenhouse growing media consist of different components. Materials commonly used in growing media mixes include mineral soil, sand, sphagnum peat moss, coir, vermiculite, pine bark, perlite, plastic foam beads, calcined clay, and rock wool. Combined in the right proportions these materials deliver the desired properties needed for plant growth.

Plant nutrition involves the absorption of nutrients for plant growth. Greenhouse plants are wholly dependent on what is available in the growing medium for their nutritional needs. Plant growth is dependent on 17 essential elements, referred to as nutrients. Three of the elements, oxygen, hydrogen, and carbon make up 89 percent of a plant's tissue by dry weight. Six of the 17 essential elements are called macronutrients because they are used in greater quantity. The macronutrients are nitrogen (N), phosphorus (P), potassium (K), calcium (Ca), magnesium (Mg), and sulfur (S). The other eight essential elements are needed in small quantities and are called micronutrients. They are boron (B), copper (Cu), chlorine (Cl), iron (Fe), manganese (Mn), molybdenum (Mo), sodium (Na), nickel (Ni), and zinc (Zn).

Fertilizers are materials added to growing medium that provide nutrients for plants. Water-soluble fertilizers dissolve completely in water and stay in solution. Fertilizer injector systems are standard equipment in today's greenhouses for providing exact levels of water-soluble nutrients. Nutrients in solution are measured in parts per million or ppm. Slow release fertilizers continually discharge a small amount of nutrients over a period of time. Nutrient deficiencies and soluble salts are two problems associated with fertilization programs.

QUESTIONS

Answer the following questions. Use correct spelling and complete sentences.

1. What are the functions of a growing medium?
2. What are the desirable properties of a growing medium?
3. Why is aeration in a growing medium important?
4. Why is pH of a growing medium important?
5. Why are soilless mixes a standard in the greenhouse industry today?
6. How do macronutrients and micronutrients differ?
7. What advantage is there to using water-soluble fertilizers?
8. How do slow release fertilizers work?
9. What are symptoms of nutrient deficiency?
10. Why are high concentrations of soluble salts considered to be bad?

EVALUATING

Match the term with the correct definition. Write the letter by the term in the blank provided.

a. aeration
b. cation exchange capacity
c. coir
d. micronutrients

e. growing medium
f. vermiculite
g. soluble salts
h. fertilizer

i. bulk density
j. organic matter
k. parts per million
l. slow release fertilizers

_____ 1. Made from waste products of the coconut industry and is similar in properties to peat moss.

_____ 2. A common ingredient in growing media that originates as a mineral called mica.

_____ 3. Any material added to growing media that provides nutrients for plants.

_____ 4. The measure of a medium's capacity to hold nutrients.

_____ 5. Eight essential elements, sometimes they are called trace elements, needed in small quantities.

_____ 6. The ratio of the mass of dry solids in a medium to the volume of the medium.

_____ 7. The material in which plants are grown.

_____ 8. The measure of nutrients in solution.

_____ 9. Consist of dissolved mineral salts.

_____ 10. Fertilizers that continually discharge a small amount of nutrients over a period of time.

_____ 11. The exchange of gases in the medium.

_____ 12. Decayed or partially decayed remains of plants and animals found in the medium.

EXPLORING

1. Obtain samples of different growing medium components by contacting manufacturers or buying materials at a retail store. Touch and look at the materials. Weigh the materials. Soak the materials with water. Note your observations based on the desirable properties of a growing medium discussed in this chapter. You might also try growing plants in the different components.

2. Set up an experiment in the classroom or at home whereby four plants of the same species are given different fertilizer rates. Start with plants of the same size, in the same type of medium, and in identical containers. Calculate the ppm of four different fertilizer solutions (gallon milk jugs work well). For example, the plants might be given no fertilizer, 200 ppm nitrogen, 400 ppm nitrogen, and 800 ppm nitrogen. Grow the plants in the same location and water with the nutrient solution as needed. Observe the plants closely and record your findings.

4

Plant Anatomy

Are you interested in floriculture? If you are, you will need to know some of the basic information known by those in the industry. People in the industry deal with plants. They know the parts of a plant. They understand the functions of the parts. This knowledge allows them to do two things. They can communicate clearly with other people in the floriculture industry. It also improves their ability to grow, handle, and work with floriculture crops.

The study of plant anatomy also helps to satisfy a curiosity to know what makes plants tick. The knowledge helps to answer questions. Why does a plant have roots? How does a plant move materials from its leaves to its roots? Why are leaves green? How are flowers involved in seed production? The answers to these and many other questions are more easily understood with the study of plant anatomy.

4-1. People in the floriculture industry understand the functions of plant parts. (Courtesy, Cargill)

OBJECTIVES

1 Identify the major plant organs and their components

2 Describe the functions of the root system

3 Discuss the functions of the stem

4 Describe the functions of the leaves

5 Identify different types of leaves

6 Describe the functions of the flower

7 Identify different types of flowers

8 Relate plant functions to floriculture practices

TERMS

adventitious roots
anther
anthocyanin
apical dominance
apical meristem
auxin
basal rooters
bract
bud
bud scale
bulbs
calyx
cambium
carotene
catkin
chlorophyll
complete flowers
compound leaves
corms
corolla
corymb
cuticle

cyme
determinate
dicot
epidermis
filament
flavonol
flowers
guard cells
head
imperfect flower
incomplete
   flower
indeterminate
inflorescence
lateral bud
leaf blade
leaves
margin
mesophyll
monocot
ovary
ovule

palisade layer
palmately
   compound
panicle
pedicel
peduncle
perianth
perfect flowers
petals
petiole
pinnately compound
pistil
pollen
primary root
raceme
receptacle
rhizome
root cap
root hairs
root system
root tuber
secondary root

sepals
simple leaves
solitary flower
spadix
spathe
spike
spongy layer
stamens
stem tubers
stigma
stolon
stomata
style
tepal
terminal bud
umbel
variegation
xanthophyll
xylem

PLANT ORGANS AND THEIR FUNCTIONS

Like people, plants are complex organisms. Plants are made of organs consisting of tissues and cells. People have organs consisting of tissues and cells, too. Our heart, liver, kidneys, and other organs carry out important functions enabling us to live. If one organ fails, our life is at risk. Plant organs, including roots, stems, leaves, and flowers, are equally important to the plant's survival.

Understanding plant growth and the function of plant organs is very important to the floriculture industry. Growers strive to promote rapid growth and high quality crops. To achieve this goal, they manipulate greenhouse conditions. They also apply their knowledge of plants and the functions of the different plant organs.

*R*OOTS

Very often, the health of a plant can be linked to its root system. The roots can be considered the foundation for plant growth. When discussed collectively, the roots are referred to as a ***root system***. The root system performs important functions for the plant. Water and minerals are absorbed into the plant root system from the growing medium. The root system anchors the plant so it can grow upright. The root system also stores food manufactured in the leaves.

If you were to take a close look at a root, you would notice certain features. The first thing you might notice is that most healthy roots are white or cream in color. Another feature is the abundance of tiny ***root hairs*** found near the growing tip of the root. Root hairs greatly increase the surface area of the root allowing more water and minerals to be absorbed into the

4-2. The root system supports above ground growth of a plant. Shown is a Zebra Plant, *Aphelandra squarrosa.*

4-3. This photo shows root hairs along a young root. (Courtesy, Agricultural Research Service, USDA)

plant. Actually, the majority of water and nutrient absorption occurs through the root hairs.

When a seed begins to grow, it sends out a single, main root, called the *primary root*. The primary root absorbs water and nutrients and anchors the seedling. As the primary root grows, it produces many smaller root branches called *secondary roots*. It is on the young, developing roots of a plant that root hairs can be seen. As roots grow, their tips are protected from coarse soil. This is accomplished by a mass of cells called the *root cap*. As the plant grows and the root system develops the roots grow in all directions forming a tangled mass.

Not all roots begin growth from root tissue. Some roots begin growth from the stem or a leaf. These roots are called *adventitious roots*. Many greenhouse crops are started or propagated by cuttings. In these cases, a stem or leaf is removed from a mother plant and placed in a growing me-

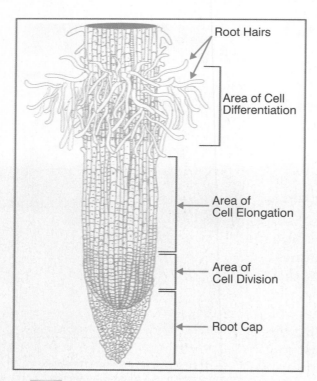

Root Hairs

Area of Cell Differentiation

Area of Cell Elongation

Area of Cell Division

Root Cap

4-4. A diagram of the growing point of a root.

dium or a specially designed rooting cube. Given the right conditions, adventitious roots grow from the stem or leaf. Cuttings from some plants, such as poinsettias, chrysanthemums, and zonal geraniums, produce adventitious roots at the base of the stem cutting. These plants are called **basal rooters**. Other plants, particularly tropical foliage plants, produce adventitious roots along the stem.

Growers recognize the importance of a healthy root system. As a result, they use practices that contribute to healthy root growth. They select growing media and containers best suited for the plant. They plant the plants at appropriate depths. They are also careful to provide the right amounts of water when needed. The importance of the medium and watering practices must not be overlooked. Growing medium kept too wet limits oxygen available to the roots. Without oxygen, the root cells die. Wet conditions are also ideal for plants to become infected

4-5. Shown are adventitious roots sprouting from the nodes of this philodendron.

4-6. Basal rooting is characteristic of chrysanthemum cuttings.

4-7. The brown roots on this rooted zonal geranium cutting indicate the presence of disease possibly caused by cold, wet conditions.

with soil-borne diseases, such as *Rhizoctonia* and *Pythium*. Medium that dries excessively often results in wilting and death to cell tissues from loss of moisture.

Care is taken to avoid a buildup of soluble salts in the growing medium. Soluble salts are dissolved minerals and fertilizers in the water. Over time soluble salts can build up in the medium. High concentrations of salts have a burning effect on roots. To prevent the buildup of soluble salts, it is recommended to leach or wash the soluble salts from the growing medium by watering thoroughly.

Roots can become large food-storage organs. A structure called a ***root tuber*** is an enlarged food-storage root with adventitious shoots. As the adventitious shoots develop, they produce adventitious roots that expand to become tubers. Root tubers are used in propagation. Examples of plants with root tubers include dahlia, tuberous begonia, and sweet potato.

STEMS

As with roots, stems serve important functions for the plant. Stems hold the leaves in a position to take the best advantage of sunlight. Stems conduct water and minerals absorbed by the roots to the leaves. Stems conduct food made in the leaves to the rest of the plant. Stems store food and water in their tissues. Stems produce new living tissues.

Conductive Tissues

The life flow of a plant is found in its stems. Just as we need to continually pump blood through our bodies, a plant needs to conduct water, minerals, and food to all of its parts. The plant can accomplish this with special conductive tissues called xylem and phloem. Xylem and phloem tissues in the root are continuous with the xylem and phloem tissues of the stem, which are continuous with the xylem and phloem in the leaves and flowers.

The conductive tissue in the stem that transports water and minerals from the roots to the leaves is called the *xylem*. Xylem cells also have stiff walls that provide structural support for the plant. Xylem is located in the roots, stem, leaves, and flowers. Cut flowers in a vase continue to flower because of the flow of water up through the xylem tissues.

4-8. Stems hold the leaves and flowers in an upright position.

4-9. Conductive tissues in stems keep leaves and flowers supplied with water and minerals.

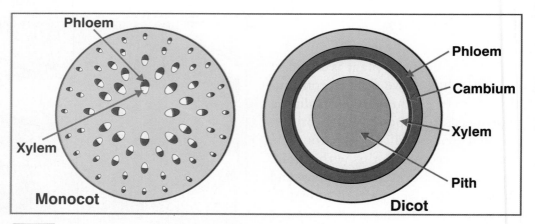

4-10. The location of xylem and phloem within a stem differs between monocots and dicots.

Food made in the leaves is transported to the rest of the plant through the *phloem* tissue. Phloem, like the xylem, is found throughout the plant. The roots would die if the plant lacked the ability to move food to the root system.

The location of xylem and phloem within a stem differs with the type of plant. Monocotyledons or monocot plants have xylem and phloem scattered throughout the stem. *Monocot* plants include narrow leaf plants. Easter lilies, iris, spider plants, and dracaenas are examples of monocotyledons. Dicotyledon plants or *dicot* plants have xylem and phloem in a ring within the stem. Dicots also have a layer of cells called the *cambium* where cell division takes place. These dividing cells become either xylem or phloem cells depending on which side of the cambium they are located. Examples of dicots are hydrangea, florist azalea, African violet, and chrysanthemum.

Buds

Stems have structures called *buds*. Buds contain undeveloped leaves, stem, or flowers. *Bud scales* cover and protect these undeveloped parts during dormancy. On some plants, the buds can be difficult to see. Buds tend to produce either vegetative or flowering parts of the plant. Vegetative buds contain immature leaves. Flower buds hold immature flowers. Usually, flower buds are visibly larger than vegetative buds. This is the case with the florist azalea and hydrangea.

The large bud at the tip of a stem is referred to as the *terminal bud*. The terminal bud is important because it contains the *apical meristem* or the primary growing point of the stem. Hormones, called *auxins*, are produced in the apical meristem. The auxins migrate down the stem and influence the growth of the stem.

Buds located along the sides of a stem are **lateral buds**. Lateral buds can be found where the leaf petiole is attached to the stem. Lateral buds closest to the apical meristem are inhibited from developing by the concentration of auxins. The apical bud exerts its dominance over the lateral buds. The term to describe this is **apical dominance**. Further down the stem, lateral buds develop as the influence of the auxins becomes weaker. The lateral buds also will develop if the terminal bud is removed, as is the case when plants are pinched.

4-11. Buds protect undeveloped flowers.

Specialized Stems

Stems can become specialized as in the case of bulbs, corms, rhizomes, and stem tubers. These structures serve as underground food and water storage organs. **Bulbs** are short, flattened stems that bear fleshy food storage leaves. At the base of each fleshy leaf there is a bud. Examples of bulbs include the tulip and Narcissus. Corms, although they look like bulbs, differ in structure. A **corm** is a short, swollen, underground stem. Crocuses and gladioli are corms. A **rhizome** is an underground horizontal stem. Iris,

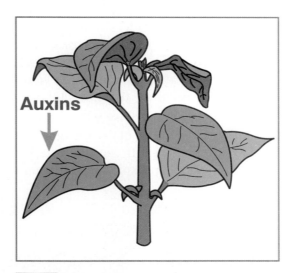

4-12. Auxins, produced in the apical meristem, inhibit the development of lateral buds.

alstroemeria, and calla lilies are rhizomes. **Stem tubers** are swollen tips of a rhizome. The Irish potato is a stem tuber.

A stem structure similar to a rhizome is the stolon or runner. The difference is the **stolon** is a stem that grows horizontal above the ground and may produce roots at its tip or at nodes. Airplane, or spider, plants and strawberry begonia are two foliage plants that produce stolons.

LEAVES

Leaves are plant organs responsible for the production of food (sugars) for the plant. All life on Earth is dependent on this food-producing reaction that takes place in the leaves. It is called *photosynthesis*. Growth and development of greenhouse crops is determined by the rate of photosynthesis.

Leaves are thin organs containing specialized cells. There is an upper and lower *epidermis* or a protective layer of cells. The epidermis cells have an exterior coating that is waxy. The waxy coating, called the *cuticle*, serves to prevent excessive water loss from the leaf tissues. Cacti, jade plants, and kalanchoes have thick cuticles. Other plants have hairy leaves, in addition to the cuticle, that help to reduce water loss. Examples of hairy leaf plants are African violets, gloxinia, zonal geranium, and purple passion plant.

Leaves have the capability to "breath" too. There are pores or openings in the epidermis called *stomata* (singular: stoma). These openings allow the exchange of oxygen, carbon dioxide, and water vapor. Most stomata can be found on the underside of leaves. The movement of water vapor through stomata is referred to as *transpiration*. The stomata are opened and closed by a pair of *guard cells*. When water is plentiful and light is shining, the guard cells are pumped full of water. This causes the cells to push apart, creating an opening to allow an exchange of gases.

The stomata close when water leaves the guard cells, causing the cells to collapse. Stomata close at night. They also close when the plant is experiencing water stress. If the medium dries out or if the roots cannot replace the water lost by transpiration, the plant tries to conserve water. The plant might

4-13. The purple hairs are easy to see on the leaves of this Purple Passion Plant, *Gynura purantiaca.*

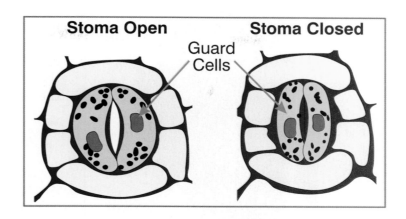

4-14. The stomata are opened and closed by a pair of guard cells.

even wilt or become limp. When the stomata close, CO_2 is no longer available, so photosynthesis stops. Wilting can be a serious problem with some greenhouse crops. For instance, if potted chrysanthemums wilt, they cannot reach their full potential.

Sandwiched between the epidermal layers is the photosynthetic tissue of the leaf known as the *mesophyll.* Mesophyll is a Greek word meaning "the middle of the leaf." The bulk of photosynthetic activity for a plant takes place in the mesophyll cells. Just below the upper epidermis is a stacked layer of mesophyll cells called the *palisade layer.* Underneath the palisade layer is a loosely arranged layer of mesophyll cells called the *spongy layer.* Throughout the mesophyll, there is a network of veins. Each vein contains xylem and phloem tissues. The veins are numerous enough so every cell is reached for exchange of materials. The xylem keeps the mesophyll cells supplied with

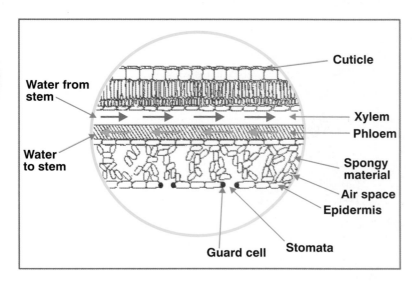

4-15. The bulk of photosynthetic activity for a plant takes place in the mesophyll cells.

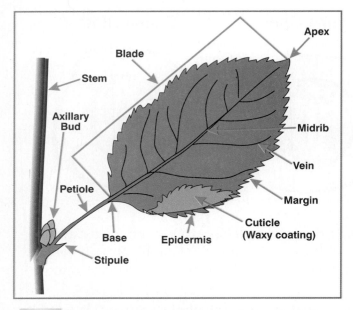

4-16. The simple leaf consists of a leaf blade and petiole.

water and minerals for the production of food. The food is then transported to the rest of the plant through the phloem.

Types of Leaves

Leaves come in a great variety of shapes, sizes, and colors. Leaves are also useful when trying to identify plants. There are different parts to a leaf. The large broad part of a leaf is called the *leaf blade*. The leaf blade provides a large surface area that increases the amount of solar energy absorbed for photosynthesis. The edge of the leaf blade is referred to as the *margin*. The margins can be one of many forms including wavy, toothed, lobed, and entire or smooth. The leaf blade is connected to the stem by the *petiole* or leaf stalk. Water and minerals flow through the xylem in the petiole to the cells in the leaf blade.

Leaves may be simple or compound. *Simple leaves* consist of a single leaf blade and a petiole. *Compound leaves* are made of a petiole and two or more leaf blades called leaflets. Compound leaves may be *pinnately compound* or *palmately compound*.

Even when a plant is grown and used for its flowers, the foliage is important. A desirable plant will have leaves with an overall healthy appearance. They should have a good color and be free of disease and physical damage.

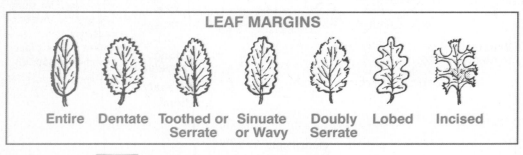

4-17. Margins or the edges of leaves differ with the species.

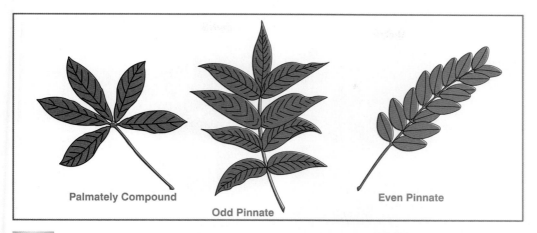

Palmately Compound

Odd Pinnate

Even Pinnate

4-18. Compound leaves have two or more leaflets and may be pinnately compound or palmately compound.

Many floriculture crops are produced because of the ornamental value of the leaves. Most tropical houseplants are valued for their leaves.

Leaf Color and Texture

Pigments determine the color of leaves. Pigments are coloring materials found in the cells. Most plants have a green color due to the pigment chlorophyll. One would expect this since **chlorophyll** absorbs light and is a key component of the photosynthetic process.

Other pigments in the plant produce a wide variation of yellows, blues, and reds. The pigment **carotene** produces orange-yellow colors. It plays a much smaller role in photosynthesis than chlorophyll. Carrots have a high carotene content. **Xanthophyll** is a pigment with colors that range from yellow to nearly no color at all. **Anthocyanins** are responsible for many of the blue, purple, and red colors. **Flavonols** produce yellow and cream colors. Both anthocyanins and flavonols

4-19. Healthy leaves have good color and are free of disease.

4-21. This Hosta exhibits variegated leaf patterns. (Courtesy, *Greenhouse Product News*)

4-20. Anthocyanins are responsible for blue flower colors. (Courtesy, Ball Horticulture Co.)

have a greater influence on flower colors than leaf coloration.

The abundance of the green chlorophyll in leaves and stems usually masks the colors of other pigments. Other pigments are not seen unless the chlorophyll dies or is present in lower concentrations. A good example is the fall coloring of trees. Cold temperatures kill the chlorophyll allowing the other pigments to be seen. Plants with leaf colors other than green generally have a lower concentration of chlorophyll.

Many floriculture plants are valued for the different color patterns of their leaves. These patterns are referred to as *variegation*. Examples of variegated plants include coleus, prayer plant, caladium, and Croton.

Modified leaves sometimes take on a petal-like appearance. They are referred to as *bracts*. The best example of a flowering plant with showy bracts is the poinsettia. The red, pink, or white structures are techni-

4-22. Poinsettias have showy bracts.

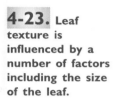

4-23. Leaf texture is influenced by a number of factors including the size of the leaf.

cally bracts, not petals. The small yellow structures to the center of the bracts are the actual flowers.

The texture of a leaf, which is so important to the aesthetic appeal, varies from species to species. Texture is influenced by many factors. The size of the leaf has a major impact on texture. Other factors are the margin of the leaf (entire leaves lack serrations or sinuses), the surface of the leaf (glossy verses rough), the venation of the leaf, and whether the leaf is simple or compound.

*F*LOWERS

The floriculture industry is based on the beauty of flowers. At times, it is easy to forget that flowers are plant organs with a specific function. *Flowers*

4-24. Plant breeders develop new varieties of flowers. (Courtesy, Ball Horticultural Co.)

are the reproductive organs of plants. A flower's function is to produce seeds through sexual reproduction. The seeds become the next generation of plants. Plant breeders work with flowers to produce new varieties of flowers for the industry.

Parts of a Flower

The flower typically consists of four different parts. They are the sepals, the petals, the stamens, and the pistil. The flower stem is known as the *pedicel*. The tip of the stem that holds the flower parts is the *receptacle*.

The exterior of the flower consists of green, leaf-like structures called *sepals*. The sepals fold back as the flower opens. Collectively, the sepals of a flower are called the *calyx*. Hibiscus and the standard carnation are good examples of flowers with a calyx that surrounds the flower petals. The florist hydrangea is an unusual plant in that the sepals take on the colorful role that petals usually play.

Petals are located just inside the sepals. They are usually thought of first when discussing flowers. *Petals* appear leaf-like and are often very colorful. The function of brightly colored petals is to attract pollinators, such as insects and birds. Bees tend to be attracted to blue and violet flowers; hummingbirds tend to be attracted to red flowers. The collection of petals on a flower is referred to as the *corolla*.

Together, the sepals and petals are called the *perianth*. The perianth surrounds the reproductive parts of the flower. The functions of the perianth are to protect the reproductive parts of the flower and to attract pollinators. The perianth is not essential to the reproductive functions of the flower. With some plants, a clear distinction between petals and sepals cannot be made. In

4-25. Parts of a flower.

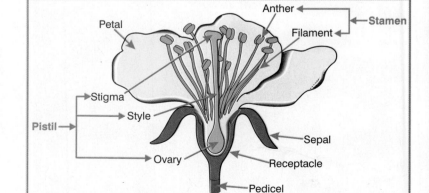

hello.

4-26. Tulips have tepals.

hell

these cases, the parts of the perianth are called *tepals*. Tulip flowers and many monocots have tepals.

The reproductive parts are found at the center of a flower. The *stamens* or male reproductive parts of a flower are arranged around the female parts of the flower. The stamen consists of a stalk called the *filament* and an anther. The *anther* produces and holds the pollen. The *pollen* grains contain the male sex cells. Lilies have pronounced stamens and produce an abundance of pollen.

The female part of the flower is the *pistil*. The pistil has three main parts, the stigma, the style, and the ovary. The *stigma* is found at the end of

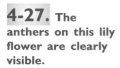

4-27. The anthers on this lily flower are clearly visible.

the pistil and it has a sticky surface on which pollen can be caught. The neck of the pistil is referred to as the *style*. The third part is the *ovary*, which contains one or more ovules. The eggs are produced and seeds develop within the *ovule*. As the seeds form, the ovary becomes a fruit. Ornamental pepper and Christmas cherry are potted plants grown for their attractive fruit.

Flowers that have sepals, petals, stamens, and a pistil are *complete flowers*. A flower that lacks any one of these parts is called an *incomplete flower*. Flowers that have both the male and female parts are said to be *perfect flowers*. Those that lack one of the two sex structures are *imperfect flowers*.

Numerical Plan of Flowers

Most flowers have a definite number of parts. Monocot flowers usually come in threes. They have three sepals, three petals, and usually three or a multiple of three stamens. This pattern can be seen in lilies, gladioli, iris, freesia, and orchids. Dicots are usually constructed in forms of four or five. These numbers are easiest to see in the sepals and petals.

4-28. The flower parts of gladioli and other monocots are in multiples of three. (Courtesy, Ball Horticultural Co.)

Forms of Flowers

Flowers are borne on plant stems in one of two ways. Some plants have *solitary flowers*, such as the tulip, narcissus, and rose. Other plants have flower clusters, known as an *inflorescence*. An inflorescence is actually the branching system of the stem. The main stem of an inflorescence is known as the *peduncle*. Pedicels that branch from the peduncle support individual flowers.

One way in which types of inflorescence are classified is by the sequence of flowering within the flower cluster. If the first flower to open is at the apex of the stem and the progression of flowering is downward or outward, the inflorescence is said to be *determinate*. Some examples of determinate flowers

4-29. A rose is a solitary flower.

include liatris, kalanchoe, and African violet. If the last flower to open is terminal on the main axis and the progression of flowering is inward or upward, the inflorescence is ***indeterminate***. Freesia, cineraria, snapdragon, and stock have indeterminate inflorescence.

4-30. An inflorescence consists of clusters of flowers on a stem.

4-31. When the first flower of an inflorescence to open is at the apex of the stem and the progression of flowering is downward, the inflorescence is said to be determinate.

4-32. This snapdragon is indeterminate because the last flower to open is terminal on the main axis. (Courtesy, *Greenhouse Product News*)

Inflorescence Types

Cyme—A cyme takes on several forms, although they are usually a flat-topped inflorescence. A dichasium cyme bears a terminal flower on a peduncle with a pair of branches that produce lateral flowers. It may be simple or compound. A monochasium cyme has a terminal flower, and below it, one branch that produces a single lateral flower. The terminal flower is the oldest. Alstroemeria is a cyme. Baby's breath is a compound dichasium cyme.

Spike—A spike is an elongated inflorescence with a central axis along which are sessile flowers. Gladioli and liatris are spike inflorescences.

Raceme—A raceme is an elongated inflorescence with a central axis along which are simple pedicels of more or less equal length. Examples of racemes include snapdragon, delphinium, Scotch broom, and stock.

Panicle—A panicle is an elongated inflorescence with a central axis along which there are branches that are themselves branched. Astilbe and begonia have a panicle inflorescence.

4-33. Liatris (spike) has flowers attached to the main stem without stalks.

4-34. Delphinium (raceme) has flowers attached to the main stem by short stalks. (Courtesy, Ball Horticultural Co.)

4-35. Astilbe (panicle) has a highly branched inflorescence. (Courtesy, Ball Horticultural Co.)

Corymb—A corymb is a flat-topped inflorescence having a main vertical axis and pedicels or branches of unequal length. Yarrow is an example of a corymb.

Umbel—An umbel is an inflorescence having several branches arising from a common point. A simple umbel consists of flowers with single pedicels. Compound umbels have secondary branching in the form of pedicels at the end of a ray. Queen Anne's lace and amaryllis have umbels.

4-36. Amaryllis (umbel) has flower stalks that arise from a common point at the tip of the stem.

4-37. Anthurium (spadix) has a spike with a thickened, fleshy axis, enveloped by a showy bract.

4-38. Sunflower (head) has an inflorescence made up of a cluster of sessile flowers.

Spadix—A spadix is a spike with a thickened, fleshy axis, usually enveloped by a showy bract called a *spathe*. Floriculture crops with a spadix include calla lily and anthurium.

Catkin—A catkin is a spike, raceme, or cyme composed of unisexual flowers without petals and falling as a unit. Catkins are found on willows, alders, and birch.

Head—A head is a rounded or flat-topped cluster of sessile flowers. Head inflorescences of the aster family resemble single flowers. These consist of centrally grouped flowers called disc flowers encircled by ray flowers. Plants with head inflorescence are very important to the floriculture industry. Some common plants that have a head inflorescence are gerbera daisy, chrysanthemum, sunflower, marigold, dahlia, strawflowers, and cineraria.

REVIEWING

MAIN IDEAS

Plants have four main structures including the roots, stem, leaves, and flowers. Each structure performs specific functions for the plant.

Roots support the above ground growth of a plant. They absorb water and minerals, and they anchor the plant. Root hairs increase the surface area for water absorption. Adventitious roots grow from the stem. Roots also store food for the plant. Growers understand the importance of maintaining a healthy root system.

Stems hold the leaves and flowers upright. Materials within the plant are transported up through the xylem and down through the phloem. Buds along the stem protect undeveloped leaves, stems, and flowers. The terminal bud at the apical meristem produces auxins that inhibit the growth of lateral buds. Underground stem structures that store food and water include bulbs, corms, rhizomes, and stem tubers.

Leaves are organs with the responsibility of making food. Most photosynthetic activity occurs in the mesophyll layer of cells. The stomata are openings in the leaf controlled by guard cells. They allow the exchange of gases. Leaves may be simple or compound. Pigments in the cells give the leaves color. Chlorophyll, a green pigment, is in abundance and converts light into stored energy.

A flower is the reproductive organ of a plant. The flower typically consists of four different parts. They are the sepals, the petals, the stamens, and the pistil. A single flower on a flower stem or peduncle is called a solitary flower. An inflorescence is a flower cluster. The structure of an inflorescence allows it to be classified.

QUESTIONS

Answer the following questions. Use correct spelling and complete sentences.

1. What are the major parts of a plant?
2. What are the functions of a root?
3. What are the functions of a stem?
4. What does the xylem do for a plant?
5. What is the function of the leaf?
6. What role does pigment play in a plant?
7. What is the function of the flower?
8. What parts make up a complete flower?
9. What is the difference between a determinate and indeterminate flower inflorescence?
10. How do inflorescence types differ?

EVALUATING

Match the term with the correct definition. Write the letter by the term in the blank provided.

a. phloem
b. root hairs
c. stoma
d. stamen

e. corolla
f. determinate
g. stomata
h. lateral bud

i. adventitious root
j. calyx
k. bract
l. petiole

_____ 1. All of the sepals of a flower.

_____ 2. An inflorescence whose first flower to open is at the apex of the stem and the progression of flowering is downward or outward.

_____ 3. All of the flower petals.

_____ 4. Male part of a flower.

_____ 5. Thin roots that absorb water and minerals.

_____ 6. The stem of a leaf.

_____ 7. Pore or opening in the leaf.

_____ 8. Conductive tissue through which food moves.

_____ 9. Contain undeveloped leaves, flowers, or stem and are located along the stem.

_____ 10. Sticky surface at the end of the pistil.

_____ 11. Modified leaves that take on a petal-like appearance.

_____ 12. Roots that begin growth from the stem or a leaf.

EXPLORING

1. Collect leaves from different types of plants. Placed them under a microscope. Examine the stomata. Tear the leaves and look at the interior cells. Are there differences between the plants?

2. Sow some radish seeds on a moist paper towel. Put the towel in a plastic bag. Remove the plastic bag in three days and look at the roots. Identify the primary root and the root hairs. Examine the root hairs under magnification.

3. Look at a flower in the garden. See if you can identify the major parts of the flower. Remove the sepals and petals to get a better view of the pistil.

5

Life Processes and Growth Regulators

Does plant life fascinate you? Do you find it interesting that small seeds can produce beautiful bedding plants? Do you enjoy the great variety of floral products available to you, in all their colors? It has been said that people with an interest in gardening and horticulture love life. They love the life processes involved in plant growth. However, the greatest appreciation for plants is usually associated with their aesthetic qualities.

The challenge for those in the floriculture industry is to deliver floral products people find attractive. After determining what is considered attractive, growers must be able to produce the floral products when people want them. To do so, growers must first understand the life processes of plants. Then, growers need to manipulate growing conditions for optimum growth and development. They may also need to use materials that regulate growth to produce high quality crops.

5-1. Beautiful plants are a result of complex life processes.

93

OBJECTIVES

1 Explain photosynthesis in simple terms

2 Describe cellular respiration and its importance in plant growth

3 Identify plant growth regulators (PGR)

4 Recognize the functions of plant hormones

5 Relate the application of synthetic growth regulators to the floriculture industry

TERMS

abscisic acid
cellular respiration
cellulose
chloroplasts
cytokinin
enzymes
ethylene
etiolation
gibberellins
gravitropism
growth retardants

hormones
indoleacetic acid (IAA)
indolebutyric acid (IBA)
metabolism
naphthaleneacetic acid
  (NAA)
phototropism
plant growth regulators
  (PGR)
starch
synthetic growth regulators

LIFE PROCESSES OF PLANTS

Plants are living organisms. As such, they have complex chemical processes that direct growth and development. Photosynthesis and respiration are two major processes. These and other life processes are regulated by hormones and conducted by enzymes.

5-2. Photosynthesis takes place in green plants.

PHOTOSYNTHESIS

Green plants have the unique ability to produce their own food. The process is known as photosynthesis. During photosynthesis, simple molecules are converted into more complex molecules. The complex molecules store energy in the form of chemical energy for later use. The photosynthetic process can be broken down into two stages, the light reaction and CO_2 fixation.

The process of producing food begins with the light reaction phase. Light energy is trapped and used to fuel the photosynthetic process. The harnessing of light energy is made possible by pigments found in chloroplasts. **Chloroplasts** are specialized organelles within the individual plant

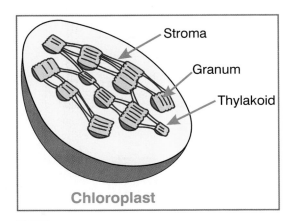

5-3. Chloroplasts are specialized organelles that contain chlorophyll.

cells. As light enters the chloroplast, chlorophyll, carotene, and xanthophyll pigments absorb the energy.

Chlorophyll, the primary pigment involved in the manufacture of food, uses the light energy to make the high-energy compounds, ATP and NADPH, that power reactions in the cells. Chlorophyll uses the energy to split water molecules, H_2O, during the first phase of the photosynthetic reaction. Oxygen atoms from the water molecules bond to form O_2. The O_2 escapes through the stomata into the atmosphere. Hydrogen atoms from the water molecule are incorporated into sugar molecules as the process continues in CO_2 fixation.

During the CO_2 fixation phase of the photosynthetic reaction, energy in the ATP and NADPH is used to form sugars. Carbon dioxide enters through the stomata and is available to the chlorophyll in the cells. The CO_2 combines with hydrogen from the water molecule. Glucose and fructose $(C_6H_{12}O_6)$ are assembled. Although they both have the same formula, their molecular structures differ.

Glucose and fructose fuel plant growth. They are the source of energy for the plant's life processes. All live cells in the plant benefit as the sugars are transported through the phloem to the rest of the plant. The simple sugars can also be combined to form a more complex sugar, sucrose $(C_{12}H_{22}O_{11})$.

The sugar molecules may be processed further to form starch and cellulose. These are huge molecules resulting from the bonding of thousands of

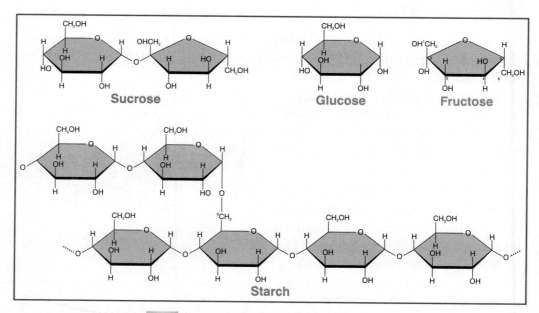

5-4. Sugars are produced in photosynthesis.

5-5. Supplemental lighting is being used with these chrysanthemum cuttings in December.

glucose molecules. **Starch** serves as the principle way in which food is stored for plants. When needed, it is easily broken down into glucose or converted into other plant products by plant enzymes. The **cellulose** is applied to cell walls for strength and rigidity. Once sugars are converted to cellulose, they are not reclaimed for other purposes.

A simple chemical equation for photosynthesis follows:

$$6\,CO_2 + 12\,H_2O \xrightarrow[\text{chlorophyll}]{\text{light}} C_6H_{12}O6 + 6\,O_2 + 6\,H_2O$$

It is to the advantage of greenhouse growers to maximize the photosynthetic activity in their crops. High rates of photosynthesis contribute to healthier plants. Also, crops develop more rapidly when photosynthetic rates are high. Therefore, growers strive to maintain optimum levels of limiting factors, such as water and light. They carefully monitor watering. Supplemental lighting may be used. Also, some greenhouse operations are equipped with CO_2 burners to raise CO_2 levels, and thus, speed plant growth.

CELLULAR RESPIRATION

The chemical process known as **cellular respiration** is the reverse of photosynthesis. In cellular respiration, sugars made in photosynthesis are broken down into simpler molecules. In the process of breaking the chemical

5-6. Growth and development are results of cellular respiration.

bonds, energy is released. The energy is applied towards growth and development of the plant.

Cellular respiration is extremely important in the growth and development of plants. All living plant cells respire or use energy to live and function, including humans. To germinate, a seed needs to break down the food that has been stored in the cotyledons or endosperm. For root cells to function, they need to convert sugars to energy.

Cellular respiration involves sugars produced in the photosynthetic process along with oxygen and water. In fact, oxygen is a critical ingredient to the reaction. This explains why plant roots need a medium that is well aerated. In the reaction, chemical energy is released when the molecular bonds of the sugar molecules are broken. The extracted energy, ATP, drives a variety of chemical reactions in the cell. By-products of the reaction include carbon dioxide and water.

A simple equation for cellular respiration follows:

$$C_6H_{12}O_6 + 6O_2 + 6H_2O \longrightarrow 12H_2O + 6CO_2 + Energy$$

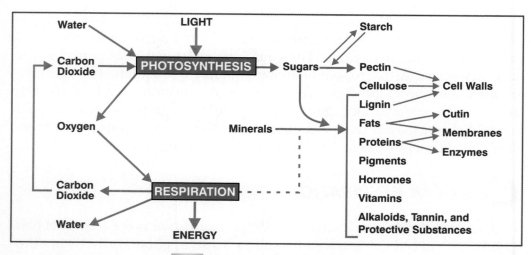

5-7. Plant metabolism flow chart.

Actual plant growth, fueled by cellular respiration, takes place primarily at night when photosynthesis is shut down. With signals from hormones, **enzymes** or chemical activators are produced. Each enzyme has a specific job. With split-second timing, they break down sugars and recombine them with nitrogen and other minerals. Many complex molecules are produced. They include starches, pectin (to bind cells), lignin (a tough, durable substance), cellulose, lipids (fats), proteins, pigments, hormones, vitamins, and alkaloids and tannins (materials that protect plants from pests and diseases).

All of the chemical reactions in a plant fall under a term, **metabolism**. The speed at which chemical reactions occur is influenced by temperature. Plant metabolism is slowed in cool or cold temperatures and is more rapid in warmer temperatures. Growers adjust greenhouse temperatures to control the quality and timing of floriculture crops. Florists keep cut flowers in coolers to slow metabolism. Some greenhouse crops can be placed in coolers to slow their development.

5-8. Soil temperatures can be monitored with a soil thermometer.

5-9. These florist azaleas are being moved to a cooler to slow their metabolism.

GROWTH REGULATORS

Naturally occurring or synthetic chemicals regulate all growth and development of plants. These chemicals are known as *plant growth regulators (PGR)*. They may promote growth, inhibit growth, or modify plant growth and development. Natural chemicals produced by plants to regulate growth are called *hormones*. Other chemical compounds that regulate growth, but are not produced by plants, have been discovered by plant physiologists. These compounds are called *synthetic growth regulators*.

PLANT HORMONES

There are five different hormones produced in plants: auxins, gibberellins, cytokinins, ethylene, and abscisic acid. Each hormone promotes many different plant responses, and each is effective in very low concentrations. Each interacts with the other hormones in complex ways to produce plant responses. Ultimately, several different hormones may affect a particular plant response.

Auxins

Auxins are a group of compounds that stimulate certain plant responses. The major plant response influenced by auxins is cell elongation. Auxins are produced in the apical meristem of a plant's stem and migrate down the stem. They move from one cell to the next, rather than through the xylem or phloem. The primary auxin is *indoleacetic acid (IAA)*.

Auxins are responsible for *phototropism*, or the ability of a plant to bend towards a light source. The way this works is the auxins move down the

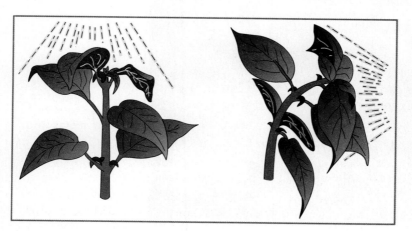

5-10. Auxins are responsible for phototropism, the ability of a plant to bend towards light.

shaded side of a stem causing those cells to elongate more than the cells on the bright side of the stem. The effect is a stem bending towards the light.

Auxins cause a plant's response to the force of gravity. When a stem is placed on its side, auxins move to the lower side of the stem. Cells on the lower side elongate and the stem curves upwards. This response to gravity is known as *gravitropism* or geotropism. It is easy to see in plants that have tipped over in a greenhouse.

Auxins play a role in apical dominance. As they move down the stem from the apical meristem, they inhibit growth of side shoots.

5-11. A plant's response to gravity that results in a stem growing upward is known as gravitropism.

Lateral buds farthest away from the apical meristem are influenced the least by the auxins. As a result, they develop sooner than buds closest to the tip. Pinching off the apical meristem stops the flow of auxins down the stem, allowing side shoots to develop. Pinching is a common practice used to produce bushy, well-branched crops. A few greenhouse crops that are pinched include poinsettias, zonal geraniums, and chrysanthemums,

Root development on the cuttings of some plants is promoted naturally by auxins. Many foliage plants produce plenty of auxin to make rooting easy. Other plants need to be treated with a synthetic auxin to produce roots.

Gibberellins

Gibberellins are produced in stem and root apical meristems, in seed embryos, and in young leaves. They induce stem cell elongation and cell division. Gibberellins play a key role in stimulating the development of flowers. They also have an important role in the production of enzymes during seed germination.

Gibberellins cause internodes to stretch. This action is related to the intensity of light. Under high light intensity, the hormone's effect is inhibited. However, if light levels are low, gibberellins cause the internodes to lengthen. By this action, leaves are raised to a position whereby they can be in position to capture light. A common problem in the greenhouse occurs when plants

5-12. Gibberellins cause internodes to stretch.

5-13. Foliar application of gibberellic acid is sometimes used to induce flowering of azaleas and hydrangeas in place of a cold treatment.

are spaced too closely to one another. The plants shade one another. Stretching takes place that results in less compact plants, weaker stems, and ultimately a crop of lesser value. Plants grown in low light or darkness develop a severe case of stretching known as *etiolation*.

Gibberellic acid is sometimes used as a growth regulator. One use is as a substitute for cold treatment for azaleas and hydrangeas. The treated azaleas and hydrangeas produce flowers without actually having gone through a cold period. Gibberellic acid is also used to increase the peduncle (flower stem) length on the pompon chrysanthemum and the stem elongation on the standard chrysanthemum, fuchsia, and geranium.

Cytokinins

Cytokinins are responsible for cell division and differentiation. They are produced in the roots and transported throughout the plant through the xylem. Cytokinins play a role in apical dominance of intact plants. While auxins inhibit the growth of lateral shoots, cytokinins promote lateral shoots. In roots, the situation is reversed. Auxins promote the branching of roots, and cytokinins inhibit branching.

Cytokinins are important in plant propagation. In tissue culture or micropropagation, cytokinins must be added to the medium for cell division to occur. Also in tissue culture, cytokinins work with auxins causing cells to form plant organs. Medium with a high level of cytokinins in relation to auxins induces shoot formation. A low level of cytokinins in relation to auxins promotes root formation.

Cytokinins, and to a lesser extent auxins and gibberellins, delay aging or senescence of plants. Cells of plants age as they do in other organisms. Once the aging process in a plant begins, it is irreversible. Senescence is accelerated in portions of a plant removed from the main plant. Cut flowers are a good example. Their source of cytokinins, produced in the roots, is lost, and their lives are shortened. Cut flowers are sometimes sprayed with cytokinins to delay senescence and to extend their vase life.

Ethylene

Ethylene is a colorless gas produced in the nodes of stems, ripening fruits, and dying leaves. It causes the thickening of stems. It also speeds the aging of plant parts, particularly fruit. As cells age, chlorophyll breaks down, cell membranes weaken, and cell walls soften. Ripening fruit produces ethylene, which triggers the production of more ethylene, speeding the ripening process.

5-14. When the source of auxins is removed by pinching, cytokinins promote the growth of lateral shoots.

5-15. Cytokinins are added to tissue culture medium to promote cell division.

Ethylene gas is used and avoided depending on the floriculture operation. Growers for years placed ripened fruit with florist hydrangeas as part of the production schedule. The ethylene caused hydrangeas to drop their leaves before the plants were placed in a cooler. If cut flowers could cringe, they would in the presence of ethylene. Ethylene shortens the life of the flowers. Therefore, they should never be stored with ripe fruit or decaying leaves that might give off ethylene.

5-16. Abscisic acid causes stomata to close during times of drought.

Abscisic Acid

Abscisic acid is a growth-inhibiting hormone. It is largely responsible for seed dormancy. The influence of abscisic acid over seed dormancy decreases during winter, while levels of gibberellins and cytokinins increase. The re-proportioning of the hormones leads to germination in the spring. Abscisic acid also contributes to senescence along with ethylene.

Another role abscisic acid plays becomes most apparent when a plant is under stress. It is abscisic acid that causes stomata to close during times of drought. By doing so, the amount of water lost from plant tissues is reduced.

SYNTHETIC GROWTH REGULATORS

A number of synthetic compounds are utilized in the floriculture industry. They range from materials that promote growth to those that inhibit growth. With some plants, some synthetic growth regulators are more effective than others.

Rooting Compounds

Synthetic auxins are also used in the horticulture industry to promote rooting of cuttings. Cuttings are treated with synthetic growth regulators to increase the number of cuttings that form roots, to speed rooting, to increase the number and quality of roots, and to increase the uniformity of the roots.

The two synthetic root-promoting materials most widely used are **naphthaleneacetic acid (NAA)** and **indolebutyric acid (IBA)**. Of these, IBA is the best material for general use. It can be used with a wide variety of plants and it is nontoxic over a wide range of concentrations. These materials are available in a liquid formulation or mixed with talc.

Growth Retardants

Growth retardants are widely used in the greenhouse industry. These chemicals inhibit the action of gibberellins on stem elongation. As a result, plants are more compact. Compact plants are more attractive, often greener, and easier to transport. Although growth is slowed, flowers tend not to be affected. The major growth retardants and some of their uses follow:

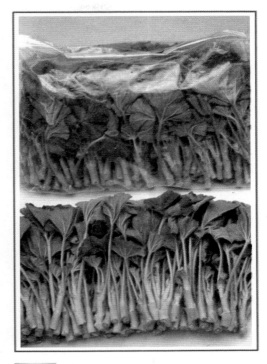

5-17. These zonal geranium cuttings will be treated with rooting hormones before sticking. (Courtesy, Ball Horticultural Co.)

- Ancymidol (A-Rest) is used to control the height of bedding plants, zonal geraniums, foliage plants, eustoma, and monocot plants, including lilies.

- Paclobutrazol (Bonzi) is used control the height of tulips, gloxinia, gerbera daisies, and freesias.

- Chlormequat (Cycocel) is an effective retardant on poinsettias, zonal geraniums, seed geraniums, and hibiscus.

- Ethephon (Florel or Pistil) is used with geraniums grown from cuttings to encourage branching (mostly stock plants), and with hyacinths, daffodils, and foliage plants to control height.

- SADH (Alar or B-Nine) is the most important growth retardant. It is used to control the height of many crops including bedding plants, zonal geraniums, perennials, chrysanthemums, gloxinia, hydrangeas, gerbera daisies, exacum, eustoma, and kalanchoe.

- Uniconizole (Sumagic) is used to control the height of perennials and lilies.

5-18. Growth retardants are used to produce compact plants. (Courtesy, Ball Horticultural Co.)

As with any chemical, certain precautions need to be followed when working with growth regulators. Suggestions for applying growth regulators follow:

■ Read the label and follow instructions as to the use of the material.

■ Wear appropriate safety gear when mixing and during application.

■ Apply the proper growth regulator to the proper plant at the proper time and at the proper application rate.

■ Be sure the plant is well established with a good root system before applying any growth regulator.

■ Apply the material uniformly either as a foliar spray or by thoroughly soaking the soil mass when drenching.

■ Although more difficult to apply, a single drench of Cycocel or A-Rest will generally be more effective than spray treatments.

■ If possible, split a full-strength application into two half-strength applications

5-19. Growth regulators produce different results when used in different concentrations. (Courtesy, *Greenhouse Product News*)

REVIEWING

MAIN IDEAS

One of the two major life processes in plants is photosynthesis. This chemical reaction has two phases. The first phase involves the trapping of light energy by pigments in the chloroplasts. One of those pigments, chlorophyll, converts the light energy to high energy ATP and NADPH and breaks water molecules. In the second phase sugars are manufactured. Glucose and fructose are stored energy for the plant. They can be processed further to be sucrose, starch, and cellulose.

The other important chemical process in plants is cellular respiration. Cellular respiration is the opposite of photosynthesis in that energy is released as the stored sugars are broken down. Cellular respiration takes place primarily at night when photosynthesis is shut down. Enzymes, produced with signals from hormones, make complex molecules including starches, pectin, lignin, cellulose, lipids, proteins, pigments, hormones, vitamins, and alkaloids and tannins. All of the chemical processes are a plant's metabolism.

Plant growth regulators (PGR) regulate all growth and development of plants. They may promote growth, inhibit growth, or modify plant growth and development. Natural chemicals produced by plants to regulate growth are called hormones. Plants produce five hormones, auxins, gibberellins, cytokinins, ethylene, and abscisic acid. Each hormone promotes many different plant responses, and interacts with the other hormones in complex ways to produce plant responses.

Other chemical compounds that regulate growth but are not produced by plants are called synthetic growth regulators. Synthetic root-promoting materials are used to increase the number of cuttings that form roots, to speed rooting, to increase the number and quality of roots, and to increase the uniformity of the roots. Growth retardant chemicals result in compact plants.

QUESTIONS

Answer the following questions. Use correct spelling and complete sentences.

1. How is chlorophyll involved in the photosynthetic reaction?
2. How are sugars formed in CO_2 fixation?
3. How does cellular respiration differ from photosynthesis?
4. What are products resulting from enzyme activity?
5. How do hormones and synthetic growth regulators differ?
6. What are the major functions of auxins?
7. What are the major functions of gibberellins?
8. What are the major functions of cytokinins?

9. What are the major functions of ethylene?

10. What are the major functions of abscisic acid?

11. What are some uses of synthetic growth regulators?

EVALUATING

Match the term with the correct definition. Write the letter by the term in the blank provided.

a. chloroplasts
b. gibberellins
c. hormones
d. starch
e. growth retardants

f. enzymes
g. plant growth regulators (PGR)
h. senescence
i. metabolism
j. phototropism

_____ 1. Serves as the principle way in which food is stored for plants.

_____ 2. Chemical activators.

_____ 3. Produced in stem and root apical meristems, they induce stem cell elongation and cell division.

_____ 4. Aging of plants.

_____ 5. All of the chemical reactions in a plant.

_____ 6. Natural chemicals produced by plants to regulate growth.

_____ 7. The ability of a plant to bend towards a light source.

_____ 8. Widely used in the greenhouse industry to inhibit the action of gibberellins on stem elongation.

_____ 9. Natural occurring or synthetic chemicals that regulate all growth and development of plants.

_____ 10. Specialized organelles within the individual plant cells.

EXPLORING

1. Run an experiment using synthetic rooting hormones. Take stem cuttings. Treat some of the cuttings with different concentrations of rooting hormone. Leave other cuttings untreated. Place the cuttings under conditions that induce rooting. Monitor the rooting and determine what effect the treatments might have had on the outcome.

2. Visit a local greenhouse and investigate their practices. What do they do to maintain high levels of photosynthetic activity? Ask what advantage it is for them to produce a crop quickly. Do they use growth regulators? If so, how do they use them and on which crops?

6

Plant Propagation

Take a cutting of a *Philodendron*, and put it in water. Throw some marigold seeds in the garden, and watch them grow. Starting new plants is fun. In fact, few aspects of the floriculture industry are as enjoyable as plant propagation. Producing new plants through propagation is constructive. It gives one a feeling of achievement. In a sense, propagating plants is creative. Maybe you have witnessed an older family member start plants in the home. People through the years have gained satisfaction from propagating plants in their own homes.

More importantly, plant propagation is a major component of greenhouse production. All cut flowers, potted flowering plants, and foliage plants begin as seeds or are propagated by some part of the plant. In effect, millions of plants are propagated annually throughout the industry. Some people even specialize in the propagation of plants.

6-1. Millions of plants are propagated annually in the floriculture industry. (Courtesy, University of Illinois Extension)

OBJECTIVES

1 Describe the importance of hybridizing plants for the greenhouse industry

2 Describe the importance of propagating plants for the industry

3 Explain methods of sexual propagation

4 Explain methods of asexual propagation

5 Describe the role of tissue culture and biotechnology in the greenhouse industry

TERMS

air layering
asexual propagation
budding
bulbils
bulblets
callous
chromosomes
clone
cormel
cotyledon
cross-pollination
cutting
deoxyribonucleic acid (DNA)
diploid
division
double fertilization
embryo
endosperm

explant
fertilization
genes
genetic engineering
germination
grafting
haploid
hybrid
hybridization
layering
leaf-bud cutting
leaf cutting
leaf-petiole cutting
plantlet
pollination
polyploid
rootstock
scarification
scion

scooping
scoring
seed
seed coat
self-pollination
separation
sexual propagation
stem cutting
sticking cutting
stock plant
stratification
tetraploid
tissue culture
triploid
viability
vigor
zygote

PLANT PROPAGATION

Plant propagation is simply increasing the number of plants. It is accomplished in one of two general ways. The plants can be produced from seed, which is referred to as sexual reproduction, or they can be produced from parts of a plant by means of asexual reproduction. The methods of propagation and techniques used vary with the plant and the preference of the grower.

SEXUAL PROPAGATION

Sexual propagation involves flowers and seeds. In sexual propagation, flowers are pollinated and eggs fertilized. It involves the fusion of sex cells, sperm and egg. Since both cells contribute genetic material, the resulting offspring is genetically different from the parent plants.

6-2. Sexual reproduction involves seeds. (Courtesy, Ball Horticultural Co.)

Pollination

The transfer of pollen to the female part of a flower is called *pollination*. In nature, flowering plants accomplish pollination a number of ways. Colorful, scented flowers attract birds, insects, bats, and other animals. These

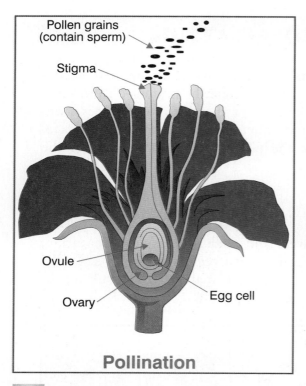

Pollen grains
(contain sperm)

Stigma

Ovule

Ovary

Egg cell

Pollination

6-3. The transfer of pollen to the stigma is called pollination.

creatures unknowingly pick up pollen from the anthers and, when they visit another flower, deposit the pollen on the stigma. The plant rewards pollinators with sugary nectar. Other plants rely on the wind to transfer pollen to the stigma. The force of the wind physically moves pollen from one flower to another. Since there is no need to attract pollinators, these plants do not produce colorful flowers with large petals, scents, or nectar.

When the pollen of a plant pollinates a flower on the same plant, it is called *self-pollination*. Some plants have this ability; others do not. When the pollen of a plant pollinates the flower of another plant, it is said to be *cross-pollination*.

Most of the flower and plant varieties used in the floriculture industry today are the result of cross-pollination by plant breeders. The

6-4. Cross-pollination involves flowers of two different plants.

6-5. Most floriculture crops are hybrids.

plant breeders select plants for outstanding characteristics, such as flower color and disease resistance. Then, they collect pollen from one plant and transfer it to the flower of another. Their hope is to have the outstanding characteristics expressed in the offspring. This process is called *hybridization*. The offspring of two plants of the same or related species that differ genetically is said to be a *hybrid*. The advantage of hybridizing is desired traits of different parent plants can be combined in the offspring.

Plant Genetics

An understanding of genetics is necessary when hybridizing plants. Genetic information is stored in every cell of a plant in long molecular chains made of *deoxyribonucleic acid (DNA)*. Segments of the DNA, called *genes*, code for life processes and the appearance of a plant. For instance, genes in a petunia plant may code for a red flower. Genes in that petunia plant also tell it when to flower and how many petals to make. An individual plant may have 100,000 genes informing it what to do and how to look.

Genes are arranged in a set of *chromosomes*. The nuclei of normal cells contain a double set of chromosomes and are said to be *diploid* (2n). Reproductive cells, sperm and egg, have a single set of chromosomes and are said to be *haploid* (1n). When fertilization occurs, both the sperm and the egg contribute a single set of chromosomes. The resulting zygote ends up with a normal double set. In this way, traits from each of the parent plants may be passed on to the offspring.

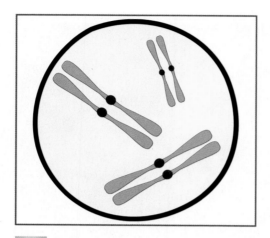

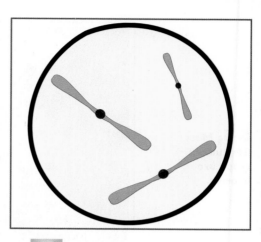

6-6. A normal cell with a double set of chromosomes is diploid.

6-7. Reproductive cells are haploid.

In the floriculture industry, many plants have more than the normal double set of chromosomes. They are said to be ***polyploid***. Plants that have three sets of chromosomes are *triploid* (3n). Those with four sets of chromosomes are ***tetraploid*** (4n). Polyploids, endowed with extra sets of chromosomes, produce vigorous growth. They also have larger flowers, leaves, and fruit than their diploid counterparts. Consequently, they are popular choices for the garden. Many daylily, dahlia, and gladiola varieties are polyploid. Polyploid plants frequently are sterile and cannot be propagated sexually. Therefore, they must be propagated through asexual means.

6-8. The two larger flowers on the left in this photograph are tetraploid Stella de Oro daylilies. The ones on the right are diploid Stella de Oro daylilies. (Courtesy, Klehm Nursery)

Fertilization

Once the pollen lands on the stigma, it grows a thin pollen tube down the style to the ovary. The cell within the grain of pollen divides to form two sperm nuclei. These travel down the pollen tube to an ovule that holds the egg. The ovule of the flower eventually becomes the seed. *Fertilization* is accomplished when a sperm fuses with an egg.

Fertilization in flowering plants is unlike fertilization in any other living organism. This is because both sperm nuclei in the pollen grain are involved in fertilization. This process, unique to flowering plants, is actually a *double fertilization*.

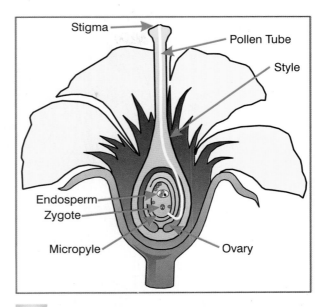

6-9. Fertilization occurs when the sperm fuses with the egg to form a zygote.

The first fertilization occurs when a sperm fuses with the egg. The fertilized egg is called a *zygote*. In this process, the sperm carries genetic material from the male part of the flower. The egg contains genetic material from the female part of the flower. The resulting zygote contains genetic material from both the male and female parts of a flower. Through cellular division the zygote becomes the *embryo* or immature plant.

In the second fertilization, a sperm nucleus fuses with two nuclei in the ovule. It develops into the endosperm. The *endosperm* is tissue in which food is stored for the embryo.

Seeds

Seeds are truly a wonder of nature. They contain everything necessary for the growth and development of a new plant under the right conditions. *Seeds* have an embryo and a source of stored food contained within a seed coat. The *seed coat* is a protective shell that protects the embryo and the endosperm from drying and from physical injury. The seed coat also plays an important

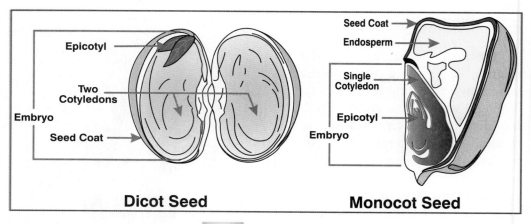

Dicot Seed   Monocot Seed

6-10. Parts of a seed.

6-11. The cotyledons of dicots provide food for the developing seedling.

role in determining when outside conditions are right for **germination**, the beginning of growth.

The **embryo** is held in a dormant or resting phase inside the seed. It has a stem, root, and one or two seed leaves called **cotyledons**. Embryos of monocotyledon (monocot) plants have one cotyledon, while those of dicotyledon (dicot) plants have two cotyledons. Monocot plants store the bulk of their energy in the endosperm. Dicots store their food in the two cotyledons. When germination begins, the embryo draws energy from the stored food to emerge from the soil and to develop leaves. Once the leaves have developed, the seedling can manufacture its own food.

Seed Germination

Seeds are designed to wait for favorable conditions to begin growth. The wait for the favorable conditions may take many years. It is fascinating to think about how seeds can lay dormant for many years and suddenly spring to life when given the right conditions for survival.

One mechanism some seeds have to help ensure survival is called stratification. *Stratification* is the process whereby a seed must go through a period of cold temperatures before it will germinate. This mechanism makes sense. Without this waiting period, a seed could germinate during a warm spell in December and die with the arrival of freezing temperatures. Lilies, roses, and pansies are three examples of plants that require a stratification period to germinate.

Another dormancy mechanism is *scarification*, or the breaking down of the seed coat. Some seeds have very hard, thick seed coats that provide excellent protection for the seed. However, the seed coat prevents the absorption of water and germination under normal conditions. In nature, these seeds must pass through the acid stomach of an animal to wear down the seed coat or lay in the soil where microorganisms can eat away the seed coat before the seeds can germinate. Some examples of plant seeds that require scarification are geranium, lupine, and canna.

CONDITIONS FOR SEED GERMINATION. What are the right conditions for seed germination? Water is necessary for seeds to germinate. At the same time, seeds need oxygen to germinate. Seeds need optimum temperatures. They may also have a light requirement. The exact need regarding each of these factors varies with the plant species. Also, it should be noted that if any one of these environmental factors is not favorable, the seed may not germinate.

The first step in the germination process is the absorption of water, which triggers a number of activities within the seed. The seed swells with moisture. The embryo changes from a dormant state to an actively growing plant. Respiration occurs. Proteins are

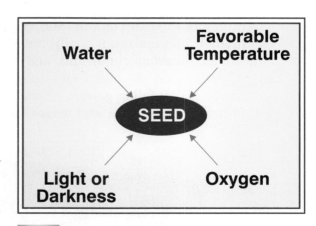

6-12. Seeds germinate when given the right conditions.

synthesized. Gibberellins stimulate the production of enzymes. The enzymes, in turn, convert starches stored in the endosperm or the cotyledons to sugar. The embryo breaks through the seed coat and develops a primary root. Then, the stem of the embryo sprouts upward. After germination, the seedling needs light, water, and minerals to begin producing its own food.

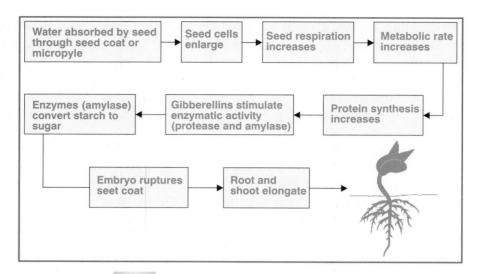

6-13. Steps of the seed germination process.

Seed Quality and Storage

The quality of seed used is very important to greenhouse growers. Seed quality refers to both viability and vigor. *Viability* is the ability of seeds to germinate under optimum conditions. *Vigor* is the ability of seeds to germinate under different conditions and still produce healthy seedlings. High quality seeds that produce usable seedlings are important to growers. Low quality seeds that fail to germinate are financial losses. In addition, they take space in the greenhouse and waste labor.

6-14. Proper storage maintains seed viability and vigor. At Pan American Seed, seeds are stored under cool, dry conditions. (Courtesy, Ball Horticultural Co.)

Store seeds in a cool dry location to maintain seed vigor and viability. Storage with a temperature of 40° F and a relative humidity between 20 and 40 percent is acceptable. Small growers often place their seed in sealed containers in a frost-free refrigerator. Growers for large greenhouse operations store their seed in coolers that deliver the optimum storage conditions. No matter how they are stored, the quality of the seed will decrease over time.

A high percentage of seeds capable of producing usable seedlings is desired. Seed companies run tests to determine what percentage of the seeds will germinate. That information must be printed on the seed packet. The date for which the seed is packaged also appears on the package.

Seeds may be altered or enhanced to improve performance or handling. They may be de-winged, de-fuzzed, or de-tailed for ease of handling. They might also be pelleted, coated, scarified, or primed. However, enhancing the seeds in these ways shortens the period of time the seed can be stored.

6-15. The germination rate and the year for which the seed is packaged are printed on the packet. (Courtesy, Ball Horticultural Co.)

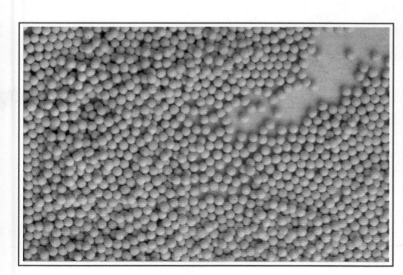

6-16. Seed is often pelleted to ease handling. (Courtesy, Ball Horticultural Co.)

Sowing Techniques

Use of proper techniques in sowing seed improves germination results. To get good results, the grower first needs to recognize optimum germination conditions for the particular seed being planted. Does the seed need to be stratified or scarified? Does the seed need to be exposed to light or covered? How moist should the medium be and at what temperature should the medium be maintained? These are some questions that should be addressed.

The seed treatment for most floriculture crops is similar. In general, the growing medium temperature for seed germination is around 75°F. Large operations have germination rooms that provide the optimum temperatures. On a smaller scale, the seed flats can be kept warm with the use of germinating pads or systems that pump warm water through tubing under the seed flats.

6-17. Warm water is pumped through tubing under flats to keep the medium warm for improved germination.

Most seeds germinate in darkness and are planted at a depth three times the depth of the seed. Planting seeds too deep can make it difficult for the embryo to emerge. If planted too shallow, the moisture level may not be optimum or the seed may be exposed to light when it needs darkness.

Maintaining a uniform moisture level in the medium is very important. If the medium dries during the germination process, the seeds will likely die. Moisture levels can be maintained by covering the seed flats with plastic or glass.

Automation has changed seeding practices in many greenhouse operations. Machines costing thousands of dollars place seed directly in flats.

6-18. Automated seeders sow seeds directly into plug trays. (Courtesy, *Greenhouse Product News*)

However, hand seeding is performed in smaller operations. Some practices for successful seed germination follow:

- Start with clean containers with drainage holes.

- Use a clean, fine-textured medium prepared for seed germination.

- Level the medium in the seed flat, while firming it slightly. Moisten the medium prior to sowing the seed.

- Use fresh, viable seed. Do not open the seed packet until it is time to sow.

- Sow the seed in rows to reduce the spread of disease, if it is introduced.

- Sow the seeds at a proper depth. If recommended, cover the seed with medium.

- Label the flat with the seed variety planted and the date sown.

- Mist the flat to insure thorough wetting of the medium and to improve contact between the seed and medium. Avoid watering practices that create a heavy flow, as it can wash medium and seeds out of position.

- Maintain proper medium temperature. Monitor the medium temperature, not the air temperature.

- Cover seed flats with poly or glass to maintain the moisture level and humidity. Black poly might be used to insure darkness, but must be removed once the seeds start to germinate.

- Transplant the seedlings when they have developed their first set of true leaves. Do this by carefully lifting the seedlings from the medium. Avoid tearing the roots. Also, handle the seedlings by their leaves or cotyledons so as not to damage the easily bruised stems.

6-19. Techniques for hand seeding include: add medium and level, moisten medium, make trenches for seed, sow seed, cover seed as required, and label flat.

A SEXUAL PROPAGATION

Asexual propagation is plant reproduction using the vegetative parts of a plant. Leaves, stems, or roots might be used. Unlike sexual propagation, asexual propagation results in offspring that are the genetic duplicates, or *clones* of the parent plant.

There are certain advantages associated with asexual reproduction:

Recombination of genes that would occur in sexual reproduction does not occur. Therefore, plants with outstanding characteristics can be produced without the risk of losing the desired characteristics, such as flower color or leaf variegation. Some plants are difficult to reproduce sexually. They may

6-20. The yellow chrysanthemums in this photograph were propagated asexually and are therefore genetically identical.

produce few seeds or the seeds they produce may result in low germination rates. Huge numbers of genetically identical plants (clones) can be produced. Plants can be grown that are free of diseases. Mature plants are obtained more rapidly as compared to seed.

Methods

There are many methods of propagating plants asexually. Some plants are easily propagated in a number of ways. Other plants respond best to a particular method. Cuttings, grafting, layering, separation, division, and tissue culture are types of asexual propagation methods.

6-21. These rooted chrysanthemum cuttings are newly potted.

Many plant varieties and cultivars are patented, much like an invention is patented. If they are propagated, a royalty is paid to the owner of the patent. Failure to do so is against the law. Some companies specialize in providing rooted cuttings and stock plants to growers. Chrysanthemums are a good example of a floriculture crop propagated by specialists. Most greenhouse growers buy rooted chrysanthemum cuttings and pot them up. The royalties are factored into the cost of the cuttings.

Herbaceous Cuttings

One of the most common and simplest methods of asexual propagation is that of **cuttings**. Cuttings may be made from portions of stems, leaves, or roots. Most greenhouse crops are propagated by herbaceous or soft stem cuttings. Growers often keep **stock plants** or buy new stock plants each year from which stem cuttings are removed. The apical meristems of stock plants are pinched to encourage branching. Other types of herbaceous cuttings include leaf cuttings, leaf-petiole cuttings, and leaf-bud cuttings.

Once taken, cuttings are given optimal environmental conditions to promote the regeneration of the missing plant organ or organs. Environmental conditions critical for successful rooting include proper temperature, high humidity, and sufficient light. The rooting media must be free of disease organisms. It should also have good water-holding ability and good aeration.

Rooting is a complex physiological process. The time it takes for the cuttings to root depends on many factors. The plant species or variety, the age of the plant, the type and location of the cutting, the absence or presence of leaves, and the nutritional status of the plant influence rooting.

6-22. Cuttings are taken from stock plants.

6-24. These poinsettia stem cuttings were stuck in rock wool rooting cubes.

Stem Cuttings

6-23. The most widely used asexual propagation method for floriculture crops is stem cuttings.

Propagation by **stem cuttings** is the preferred method for poinsettias, chrysanthemums, zonal geraniums, kalanchoe, carnations, and many foliage plants. The cuttings, 2 to 5 inches in length, are taken in the morning when the tissues are turgid or full of water. A sharp knife or razor is used

6-25. Sticking cuttings directly into finish pots.

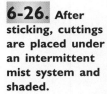

6-26. After sticking, cuttings are placed under an intermittent mist system and shaded.

6-27. In the home, plastic bags are placed over the container to maintain high humidity around the cuttings.

for the cuts. It is also advisable to disinfect the knife between stock plants to avoid spreading disease. Any flowers on the stem should be removed.

The distal end of the cutting, or the end closest to the root system, is usually dipped in a rooting hormone to hasten the formation of adventitious roots. The cuttings are then placed in rooting cubes or directly into a medium. This practice of placing the cuttings is known as **sticking cuttings**.

After the cuttings are stuck, they are placed under an intermittent mist system. The mist is applied between dawn and sunset to reduce water loss from transpiration. They are misted regularly until the roots form and can absorb moisture for the plant. The propagation area is often shaded to reduce stress from the sun. Bottom heat is also provided to maintain a medium temperature between 75 and 80° F.

More and more growers use the practice of direct sticking cuttings into the finish container to save labor involved in transplanting. However, the grower must have enough bench space under mist and a means to keep the medium warm.

6-28. Dumbcane or *Dieffenbachia* can be propagated by placing sections of the stem horizontally or vertically in the medium.

Leaf Cuttings

A relatively small number of plants have the ability to produce plantlets on their leaves. Entire leaves or portions of a leaf are removed from the parent plant for use as *leaf cuttings*. Plants propagated by this method include African violet (Saintpaulia ionantha), Mother-in-law's tongue (*Sansevieria trifasciata*), Cape primrose (*Streptocarpus x hybridus*), and Rex begonia.

Propagation of Mother-in-law's tongue, Cape primrose, and Rex begonia involves the placement of a leaf blade or a portion of a leaf blade in a propagation medium. Healthy leaves that have just reached maturity should be used. Those leaves are at a stage when food production and the capacity to produce new plantlets are high.

African violets are easily propagated by *leaf-petiole cuttings*. The leaf blade and the petiole are taken from the parent plant. Under proper conditions, a cluster of plantlets develop where the petiole was cut. When the plantlets have grown large enough to handle, they are separated and potted in individual containers.

6-29. *Sansevieria* is propagated by portions of a leaf.

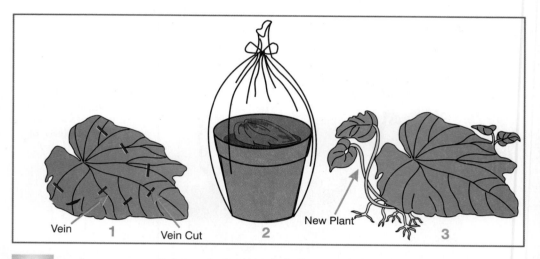

6-30. The leaf blade of the Rex begonia laid on medium will produce plants where leaf veins have been cut.

6-31. African violet propagation is done by leaf-petiole cuttings.

A few plants, including the piggyback plant (*Tolmiea menziesii*), kalanchoe, and the strawberry geranium, produce foliar embryos. Through a complex process, cells in small areas of a leaf develop into plantlets. The plantlets can be removed and planted.

Leaf-bud Cuttings

Many plants cannot be propagated by leaves alone. One option is to take leaf-bud cuttings. **Leaf-bud cuttings** are composed of the leaf blade, the peti-

6-32. English ivy is propagated by leaf-bud cuttings.

6-33. In one day, this Floridian can stick 10,000 leaf-bud cuttings directly into finish pots.

ole, a bud at the base of the petiole, and a portion of the stem. The leaf provides the energy for the development of roots. The roots sprout from the stem and are often concentrated at the node of the stem. The bud develops into the stem of the new plant.

Grafting

A method of asexual reproduction common with woody plants is grafting. *Grafting* is the process in which the stem of one plant is made to grow on the

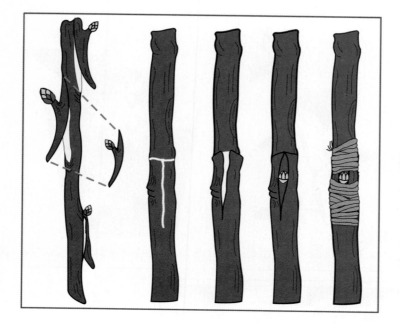

6-34. Budding is a form of grafting.

roots of another plant. The portion of the graft that is to become the stem is the **scion**. The lower portion of the plant that includes the root system is called the **rootstock** or the understock. **Budding** is a form of grafting in which the scion consists of a bud.

Roses are grafted. Usually, a vigorous, cold-tolerant species of rose is selected for the rootstock. Vigorous rootstocks provide an abundance of water and minerals to the scion. A desired rose hybrid that might not have a strong root system is grafted to the rootstock.

Grafting may involve placing individual buds into a stem or a stem being placed onto another stem. In either case, it is important that the cambium wood of both the scion and the rootstock line up. Once placed together, the union should be protected from moisture loss. Also, the scion and the rootstock materials must be capable of growing together for a successful graft.

Layering

Layering is a method of asexual reproduction whereby roots form on a stem while the stem is still attached to the parent plant. The advantage to layering is the parent plant provides the plant-to-be with water and minerals until it produces its own roots. This method is slow as compared to other methods. A form of layering called **air layering** is used with foliage plants including *Dieffenbachia*, *Ficus*, and *Dracaena*.

6-35. Air layering is performed with some foliage plants.

Separation and Division

Propagation of floriculture crops can be done by separating or dividing. This is a common method used with perennials and foliage plants. Some plants produce vegetative plant structures that can be removed intact from the parent plant. Removal and planting of these vegetative structures is *sepa-*

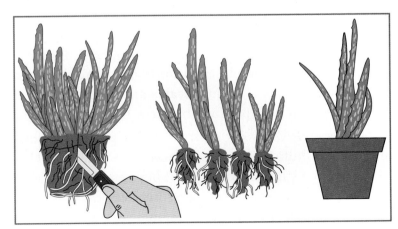

6-36. Separation involves the removal of whole vegetative plant structures from the parent plant.

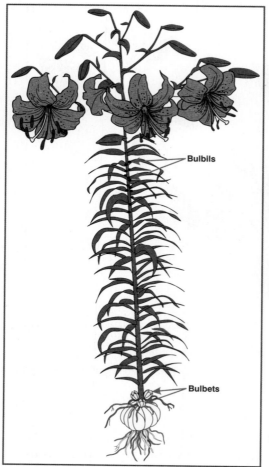

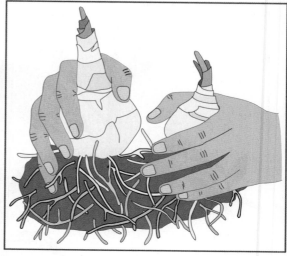

6-38. Narcissus bulbs produce side bulbs that are separated and planted.

6-37. Lilies may produce bulblets below the ground or bulbils in the axils of the leaves. The bulbils can be removed and planted.

ration. With *division,* the plant roots or the entire plant may be cut into sections to make two or more plants from the original plant. Daylilies can be divided by digging a plant and cutting it into smaller portions.

There are several methods used to propagate bulbs. Some species of lilies produce *bulbils* or tiny aboveground bulbs in the axils of their leaves. These can be removed and planted. Lilies also may produce tiny bulbs below the ground called *bulblets*. Some lilies and fritillaries can be propagated by removing bulb scales and placing them in moist medium. In time, they root and produce bulblets that can be separated and planted.

Tulips and *Narcissus* reproduce by natural division. Bulbs are produced off the main bulb. These are separated and planted. Hyacinths are very slow to reproduce by natural division. They can be encouraged to produce bulblets by scooping or scoring. *Scooping* involves the removal of the basal plate of the bulb and the base of all of the bulb scales. Placed upside down in a warm

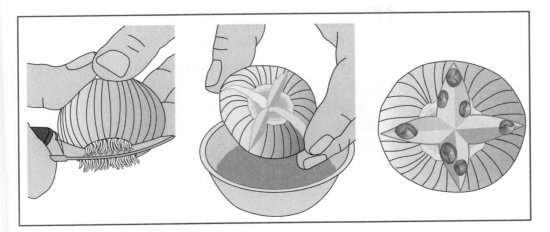

6-39. Scoring, done with hyacinths, involves crossing cuts into the base of the bulb.

dry cabinet, a bulblet will form at the base of each scale. ***Scoring*** is similar to scooping. However, the basal plate is not removed. Two cuts that cross the basal plate are made about a 1/4 inch deep.

Corms, including crocus and gladiola, can be cut into smaller pieces. Each piece of the corm must have a bud that is capable of developing into the stem. Corms also develop small corms called ***cormels***. These miniature corms can be separated and planted.

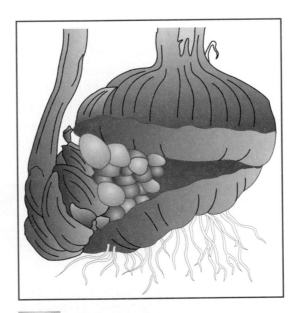

6-40. Gladiolas produce cormels that are separated and planted.

Tissue Culture

A very technical method of asexual propagation is ***tissue culture***. Tissue culture involves the culture or growing of small pieces of plant tissue. It is performed on an artificial medium under sterile conditions. Foliage plants, pot plants and cut flowers are propagated by tissue culture methods.

There are several advantages to tissue culture over other methods of propagation:

1. Large numbers of plants can be produced from a single plant in a relatively small space in a short period of time.

2. Systemic diseases can be eliminated by propagating the quickly dividing cells of the shoot tip.

3. The ability to produce plants with identical flower color is an asset to the cut flower industry.

4. Tissue culture results in excellent basal branching of foliage plants.

5. Horticultural cultivars can be improved by selecting plants, which vary slightly from the mother plant. Examples are leaf shape, disease resistance, growth habit, and flower color.

6. Tissue culture techniques permit the growth of genetically engineered plant cells.

Tissue culture must be done under aseptic or sterile conditions. Tissue culture labs are designed to provide a clean environment. Technicians scrub much like a surgeon does before surgery. Media, tools, and bottles or jars are autoclaved. Autoclaving involves the heating of the materials to 245° F for 15 minutes to kill all bacteria and fungi. Also, to lessen the chance of contamination, work with the cultures is done under laminar air-flow hoods. Laminar air-flow hoods filter bacteria and fungal spores from the air.

Table 6-1. Floriculture Crops Propagated by Tissue Culture

Foliage Plants	Potted Flowering Plants	Cut Flowers
Alocasia	African violet	Alstroemeria
Anthurium	Aloe vera	Asters
Banana	Gerbera daisy	Delphinium
Calathea	Lily	Gerbera daisy
Cordyline	Orchid	Gysophila
Dieffenbachia	Rose	Lily
Dracaena	Rex begonia	Orchid
Fern		Rose
Ficus		Statice
Philodendron		
Spathiphyllum		
Syngonium		

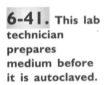

6-41. This lab technician prepares medium before it is autoclaved.

TISSUE CULTURE PROCESS. The tissue culture propagation process can be defined in four main stages. The first three stages must take place under sterile conditions to reduce the chance of contamination from bacteria or fungi.

In the first stage of tissue culture, small pieces of plant material, called *explants*, are carefully removed from the parent plant. Explants are obtained from the growing tip of a desired plant. The explants are cleaned of bacteria or fungal spores. They are then placed on an agar media in glass bottles or test tubes. The agar media is a gel that contains water, sugars, nutrients, and plant hormones to support and promote plant growth.

6-42. Tissue culture is performed under laminar air-flow hoods.

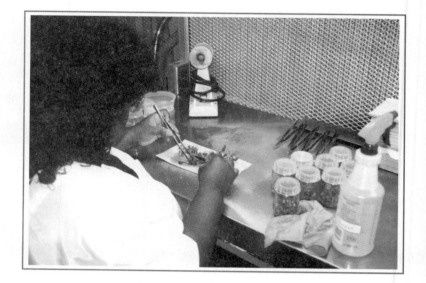

6-43. Plantlets are divided and encouraged to multiply in stage two.

6-44. A single explant can produce millions of plantlets in a year by continually cycling plantlets to new containers.

In stage two, the cells of the explants multiply in one of two ways. They may form a *callous*, which is a group of cells with no particular function. Given the right hormones in the media these callous cells can develop into a normal plant.

The other possibility for stage two involves the rapid multiplication of plantlets. Cytokinins placed in the media encourage an increase in the number of buds on the explants, usually six to eight per shoot. Each bud is capable of becoming a plant and producing more buds. Branching occurs as these buds develop into shoots or *plantlets*. These plantlets are divided and transferred to test tubes or jars. New plantlets are continually cycled to new containers. In this way, a single explant can produce millions of plantlets in a year.

When the plantlets have developed, they are ready for the third stage, the formation of roots. Shoots are trans-

6-45. In stage four, plantlets are removed from the glass container and planted into sterile growing medium.

planted to another medium containing auxins that induce the growth of roots. The plantlets are also given higher light intensity in preparation for stage four.

In stage four, the plantlets are removed from the glass container. They are divided, planted in a sterile growing medium, and placed in a greenhouse. Care must be taken during this transition to acclimatize the plants to their new environment.

The use of tissue culture is growing rapidly in the floriculture industry. It is used to a large extent with herbaceous perennial plants including daylilies,

6-46. Plantlets are misted to acclimatize them to greenhouse conditions.

Hostas, chrysanthemums, and orchids. The importance of tissue culturing in plant breeding will become more significant as the field of genetic engineering expands.

Genetic Engineering

Traditional methods of plant breeding through pollination have left plant breeders dependent on luck. They have had no control over chromosomal division in meiosis. Whether a desired trait would be expressed in a hybrid was in question. Even the benefits of polyploidy have been left to chance. Another disadvantage of traditional breeding is the available genetic material is limited to that found in a certain species. Only a chrysanthemum can be crossed with a chrysanthemum.

However, plant breeding practices are being dramatically changed with new discoveries in biotechnology and genetic engineering. Recent discoveries in science have enabled scientists to select and move genetic material from one plant to another. Genes can even be transferred from one species to another. This process, called *genetic engineering*, holds great potential for improving floriculture crops. Desired results can be obtained much more quickly than with traditional breeding methods. There is also greater control over what characteristics will be expressed in the offspring.

Genetic engineering has already been applied to vegetable crops and grains. Genetically engineered squash that is resistant to viral infection has been developed. Soybeans that are resistant to herbicides have been developed. Genetically engineered corn and cotton have improved defenses against insect pests.

Imagine what could be done in the floriculture industry. The aesthetic value of floriculture crops could be improved. A true blue rose is possible. Cut flowers that have a vase life of a month could be a reality. Crops could be engineered to be resistant to soil-borne diseases, cutting costs and labor involved in disease control. Poinsettias could be engineered to resist white fly infestations. The possibilities are endless.

REVIEWING

Main Ideas

Plants are propagated in two ways. They may be propagated sexually or they may be propagated asexually. Sexual propagation involves flowers and seeds. Pollination of a flower occurs when pollen is transferred to a stigma. Fertilization takes place when sperm carried in the pollen fuses with the egg held in the ovule. The result of sexual reproduction is a seed. The offspring is a hybrid of the parent plants. The significance of sexual propagation is the combining of genetic material from two parents.

Seeds produced through sexual reproduction contain a living embryo and food to help it begin growth. Quality seed is viable and has vigor. Germination or the start of growth happens when the seed receives the right amounts of water, oxygen, temperature, and possibly light. Growers maintain optimum conditions for seed germination.

Asexual propagation involves the vegetative parts of a plant; leaves, stems, or roots. The offspring resulting from asexual propagation are genetically identical or clones of the parent plant. There are many methods of asexual propagation. Methods of asexual propagation include cuttings, grafting, layering, separation, division, and tissue culture. The most widely used method in the floriculture industry is stem cuttings. A newer, highly technical method of asexual propagation is tissue culture. Tissue culture consists of placing explants on an agar gel under sterile conditions.

Recent research in biotechnology has given scientists and plant breeders the ability to improve plants through genetic engineering. Genetic material in the cell of an organism can be removed and placed into another organism through genetic engineering. This technique has tremendous potential for improving floriculture crops.

QUESTIONS

Answer the following questions. Use correct spelling and complete sentences.

1. What is the major difference between sexual and asexual propagation?
2. How does pollination occur?
3. What is the advantage of hybridization?
4. Why are polyploid plants valued?
5. How does fertilization occur?
6. What are the main parts of a seed and their function?
7. What factors are involved in seed germination?
8. What are stratification and scarification?
9. What are the advantages of asexual propagation?
10. How are stem cuttings made?
11. How is tissue culture performed?
12. What are the potential advantages to genetic engineering?

EVALUATING

Match the term with the correct definition. Write the letter by the term in the blank provided.

a. tissue culture
b. explant
c. pollination
d. fertilization

e. polyploid
f. viability
g. stratification
h. germination

i. leaf-bud cutting
j. stock plants
k. grafting
l. asexual propagation

_____ 1. The ability of seeds to germinate under optimum conditions.

_____ 2. Plants from which cuttings are removed.

_____ 3. Beginning of growth from a seed.

_____ 4. Transfer of pollen from the male part of a flower to the stigma.

_____ 5. When sperm carried in the pollen fuses with the egg held in the ovule.

_____ 6. Mechanism that requires a seed to go through a cold period before it will germinate.

_____ 7. Plant reproduction using vegetative parts of a plant.

_____ 8. Cutting composed of the leaf blade, the petiole, a bud at the base of the petiole, and a portion of the stem.

_____ 9. Asexual method of reproduction in which the scion is fused with the rootstock.

_____ 10. Small portion of a plant used in tissue culture.

_____ 11. Plants that have more than the normal double set of chromosomes.

_____ 12. Highly technical method of asexual reproduction involving the culture or growing of small pieces of plant tissue.

EXPLORING

1. Obtain different types of cuttings from various house plants. Place them in a growing medium. Build a tent made of clear poly over the container to maintain high humidity. Set the container by a window. Observe the cuttings for several weeks to determine if adventitious roots begin to grow.

2. Sow bedding plant seeds following the guidelines in the chapter. Schedule the sowing so the seedlings will be ready for planting outside in the spring.

3. Use the World Wide Web to learn more about applications of plant biotechnology in the floriculture industry.

7

Cultural Practices: Light, Temperature, Air, Water

Have you ever heard someone joke about having a brown thumb instead of a green thumb? People who claim to have a brown thumb say that every plant they have had has died under their care. On the other hand, a person with a green thumb appears to grow plants without effort. In truth, the ability to grow healthy plants is not automatic. Care of plants can be learned.

Plants have basic needs. If those needs are met, the plants grow and thrive. If they are not met, they decline and die. Part of the success with growing healthy plants is in knowing what the plant needs. Another part is providing those needs at the appropriate times. Top growers have learned to understand the needs of plants. They draw from knowledge gained in the classroom, from talking with other growers, and by applying their skills in the greenhouse.

7-1. Growers understand the needs of plants.

OBJECTIVES

1 Explain how light influences greenhouse crop production

2 Discuss the plant responses to light duration

3 Express the theory behind DIF

4 Describe the effects of temperature on greenhouse crop production

5 Explain how air quality influences plant growth

6 Explain the importance of water quality

7 Describe recommended watering practices

TERMS

capillary mats
cultural practices
day-neutral plants
drip irrigation
ebb and flood system
electromagnetic spectrum
far-red light
foot candle
hand watering
high-intensity discharge
   (HID) lighting system
intermittent mist system

irrigation
irrigation booms
long-day plants
overhead sprinklers
photoperiodism
saucers
short-day plants
thermoperiodism
turgidity
vernalization
wilting

CULTURE OF GREENHOUSE CROPS

Most of us learned at an early age that plants need water and light to grow. Later we might have learned that temperature and air are also important. Experienced growers know how to control these environmental factors to produce floriculture crops. The control or management of light, temperature, air, and water to promote healthy growth is often referred to as **cultural practices**. Understanding basic cultural requirements of greenhouse crops is of great importance.

7-2. The growth and development of floriculture crops is dependent upon light energy.

LIGHT

The growth and development of floriculture crops is dependent upon light energy. Light energy enables plants to make food through the process of photosynthesis. Light also influences plant growth in other ways. There are three key aspects of light affecting plant growth. They are the color of the light, the duration of the light, and the intensity of the light.

Light Color

Visible light or the light that we see is a small segment of all the radiant energy given off by the sun. X-rays, gamma rays, ultraviolet rays, microwaves, and radio waves are some others. The wavelengths of the different

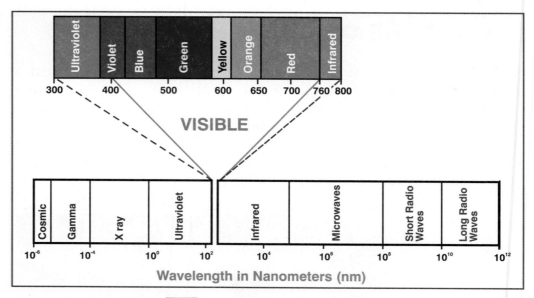

7-3. The electromagnetic spectrum.

rays are measured in nanometers. Based on their wavelengths, the rays have been placed on an *electromagnetic spectrum*.

Sunlight contains a complete blend of visible colors including red, orange, yellow, green, blue, and violet. The rays of visible light fall between 380 and 780 nanometers. Each color has a different range of wavelengths. We can see the individual colors when the light passes through a prism. The prism separates the colors. This phenomenon of separating the colors of visible light occurs naturally with rainbows.

Light is composed of particles called photons. They carry with them energy. The energy level of the photons increases as the wavelengths become shorter. For example, blue light photons have a shorter wavelength than red light photons, and therefore, have a higher energy level. The energy carried by the photons is absorbed by objects and produces heat. Plants through photosynthesis are capable of converting the light energy to stored chemical energy.

The visible rays of light are absorbed or reflected by objects. Objects that appear black absorb all the colors of visible light. Therefore, no colors are reflected into our eyes. White objects, on the other hand, reflect all the colors of visible light. If an object absorbs all the colors but green, it will appear green to us because green wavelengths have been reflected from the object into our eyes. This is the case with green leaf plants. Because most of the green wavelengths are reflected from the leaves, they have less effect on plant growth than the other colors.

7-4. The flowers and leaves of these gerbera daisies reflect colors of visible light into our eyes. (Courtesy, Society of American Florists)

The colors that have the greatest influence on plant growth are blue and red. Both of these bands of light produce a higher level of photosynthetic activity and chlorophyll synthesis than other colors. In addition, red light promotes seed germination, seedling growth, and stem elongation. Red wavelengths influence flowering and anthocyanin formation. Blue light reduces stem length, increases branching, and promotes stem strength. Blue light also improves leaf and flower color.

A wavelength that plays an important role in plant growth and development is called *far-red light*. Far-red light triggers a shade avoidance response in plants when levels of blue or red light are low. Stems stretch and become weak while leaves become thinner and wider. Far-red light also plays a key role in breaking seed dormancy and in photoperiodism.

*L*ight Duration

Plants are responsive to the length of time they are exposed to light. A mechanism within plants detects day lengths. The length of the days or the length of the light period is known to influence different phases of plant growth. Some of these phases are seed germination, enlargement of leaves, development of buds, and flowering. A plant's response to light duration is called *photoperiodism*.

Different plants respond differently to light duration. Chrysanthemums, kalanchoe, holiday cacti, and poinsettias are plants that will begin to flower naturally in the fall when the day lengths get shorter. They are said to be

7-5. Kalanchoes must receive short-day treatment to flower.

short-day plants. Carnations, Shasta daisies, and coneflower plants flower as days lengthen in the summer. They are termed *long-day plants*. A third group of plants is unaffected by day length and are classified as *day-neutral plants*. Day-neutral plants include many foliage plants, African violets, and tomatoes.

Growers control the length of days in a greenhouse to bring on one of two plant responses. The plants will either be kept in a vegetative stage of growth or encouraged to flower. The key is not so much the length of day as the length of uninterrupted darkness. For example, poinsettias will begin to initi-

7-6. This photograph shows black cloth curtains in a partial closed position. (Courtesy, United Greenhouse Systems, Inc.)

ate flower buds when the length of uninterrupted darkness is about 11 hours and 50 minutes. Poinsettias respond to nights shorter than 11:50 by growing vegetatively. If the darkness is interrupted by someone turning on the lights, flowering will be delayed. That is because the poinsettia thinks it is in a long-day situation.

Short-day plants can be made to flower when the days are long. The plants are covered with black cloth to ex-

7-7. Crops are lighted at night to simulate long days.

tend the period of darkness. Thinking it is in a short-day situation, the plant begins to initiate flower buds. This is why you can find flowering chrysanthemums in the stores at any time of the year. To keep a short-day plant in a vegetative stage of growth, they are lighted at night to simulate long days. Managing the day length is critical for getting plants to flower at a time of year they normally would not flower.

Light Intensity

The third effect light has on plants involves intensity or brightness. Intensity of light depends largely on the angle of the sun, clouds, and dust in the atmosphere. Light intensity is greater in the summer months when the sun is higher in the sky. Where artificial light is provided, the source of light and the distance from the light source to the plants are important.

Light intensity is measured in foot candles. A *foot candle* is the amount of light distributed by a single candle one foot away. A sunny, summer day provides about 10,000 foot candles of light.

Different plants have different requirements in terms of intensity of light. The major floriculture crops perform the best when they receive full sunlight. The high light intensity elevates the rate of photosynthesis and the plant is able to produce more food. On the other hand, plants like impatiens, African violets, ferns, and many foliage plants prefer lower light levels. In fact, most foliage plants have been selected because of their ability to tolerate low levels of light. Exposure to full sun can damage these crops.

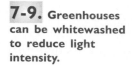 **7-8.** Thousands of hanging baskets create shade on the bedding plants below.

Light intensity influences plant development. Plants receiving the proper level of light will be compact and have good leaf color. Symptoms of lower than optimum light levels include a slower growth rate, thin leaves, small flowers, dull leaf and flower color, and etiolation or stretching. High light intensity can also cause problems. Plants receiving too high of light intensity might have pale leaves, flowers, and stems. Other symptoms include short rigid stems, small thick leaves, and small flowers. Excessive light intensity may even cause death of leaf tissue.

Reducing Light Intensity

Light intensity in the greenhouse can be reduced if necessary. The amount of light that is transmitted varies with the greenhouse covering material. So if a grower knows the crop to be grown prefers lower light, a covering can be selected that blocks more light. If the greenhouse has a covering, such as glass, that provides high light transmission it can be white washed. This is accomplished by mixing one part white latex paint to 15 to 20 parts water. It is then

7-9. Greenhouses can be whitewashed to reduce light intensity.

7-10. Curtains in this photograph have been drawn to reduce light intensity.

sprayed onto the outer surface. White washing also reduces the heat buildup in the greenhouse. Over a period of several months, the paint wears off. A third option is to shade the crops with curtains.

Supplemental Lighting

Supplemental lighting is valued in greenhouse operations located in low light regions of the country. It is particularly important during the months of November, December, and January. Also, artificial lighting during cloudy periods improves plant growth and vigor. One application involves the lighting

7-11. Supplemental lighting is used to get young plants off to a strong start. (Courtesy, P. L. Light Systems)

7-12. Lighting systems, seen through the glass, can be used to supplement natural light.

of plants early in their development. Plugs and newly planted cuttings are given additional light to speed growth and to insure compact healthy growth.

7-13. This incandescent light turned on at night keeps these mums in a vegetative state.

Lighting is also used to promote a long-day response in some crops.

There are a number of light sources that can be used. However, none of them can provide the range of wavelengths given by the sun. Desirable features to consider when selecting a light source include high efficiency, uniform light distribution, and limited shading. Until recently, incandescent and fluorescent lights were the only choices. The development of *high-intensity discharge (HID) lighting systems* have given growers more efficient and effective light sources. Several sources can produce supplemental light. Among these are incandescent lights, fluorescent lights, metal halide lamps, low pressure sodium lamps, and high pressure sodium lamps.

Incandescent lights are considered inefficient, emitting most of the energy as heat. The wavelengths given off are primarily far-red. They are inexpensive and a good choice for photoperiod control.

7-14. Fluorescent lights are used in this tissue culture lab.

Fluorescent lights are cooler and more efficient than incandescent lights. They also have a wider range of wavelengths and longer life. They are often used with incandescent lights to provide a more complete spectrum of light. Because of their large size and shading problems they are used only in special situations.

Metal halide (MH) lamps display a spectrum of light similar to the sun's light. It is the best lamp for plant growth. However, they are not as efficient, long-lived, or cost-effective as other HID lamps.

Low pressure sodium (LPS) lamps are the most efficient HID light source. They are expensive and shading becomes a problem due to their large size.

High pressure sodium (HPS) lamps emit a high level of red, yellow, and orange wavelengths. The combination of features including their light output, efficiency, and long lives makes them the best HID supplemental lighting system.

7-15. High-pressure sodium lamps give off high levels of yellow, orange, and red wavelengths.

TEMPERATURE

Temperature is an important factor governing plant growth. Important biochemical reactions, including photosynthesis and respiration, are affected by temperature. Temperature is a key factor in a number of plant responses. Life processes occur more quickly as temperature rises. They slow down as temperatures become cooler. This is because the enzymes that drive those reactions are sensitive to temperature. If the temperature becomes too warm or too cold, the enzymes are unable to carry out their functions.

7-16. These narcissus, azalea, and Easter lilies have been placed in a cooler to slow their development.

7-17. Holiday cacti are thermoperiodic, meaning temperature plays a role in the initiation of flowers.

Temperatures can be instrumental in triggering responses in some greenhouse crops. ***Thermoperiodism*** is term used to describe a temperature requirement that produces a plant response. Poinsettias and holiday cactus are examples of thermoperiodic plants. A period of cool temperatures along with short days causes them to initiate flowering.

For some floriculture crops, a period of cold temperature is required for flowering. This physiological process is known as ***ver-***

nalization. Bulb crops including tulips, narcissus, and Easter lilies must undergo vernalization. They are exposed to freezing or near freezing temperatures for a number of weeks. Once the cold requirement is satisfied, the plants are moved into the greenhouse for forcing.

Growers use temperature to control the height of plants. They do this by managing the difference between daytime and nighttime temperatures. The mathematical difference between the day temperature and the night temperature is called DIF.

7-18. Easter lilies must undergo vernalization to flower.

DIF can be positive, negative, or zero. A positive DIF results when the day temperature is higher than the night temperature. Positive DIF causes a plant to lengthen its stems. A negative DIF occurs when the day temperature is cooler than the night temperature. Plants grown under negative DIF conditions have limited stem elongation. Zero DIF is a result of identical day and night temperatures.

Table 7-1. Effect of DIF on Stem Elongation of Greenhouse Crops	
Strong or Medium Effect	**Little or No Effect**
Begonia	Foliage plants
Carnation	Kalanchoe
Cyclamen	Rose
Chrysanthemum	Seed geranium
Fuchsia	
Impatiens	
Lilies	
Pansy	
Petunia	
Poinsettia	
Salvia	
Zonal geranium	

EXAMPLES:

Positive DIF—A day temperature of 78°F and a night temperature of 68°F equals a positive DIF of +10°F (78 – 68 = 10). Stems elongate.

Negative DIF—A day temperature of 65°F and a night temperature of 72°F equals a negative DIF of -7°F (65 – 72 = -7). Stem elongation is limited.

Zero DIF—A day temperature of 70°F and a night temperature of 70°F equals a zero DIF or 0°F (70 – 70 = 0).

7-19. These impatiens plugs have been kept compact with the application of DIF. (Courtesy, Ball Horticultural Co.)

Advantages and Disadvantages of DIF

The main advantage to DIF is stem elongation can be increased or decreased on a daily basis. Elongation is slowed with a negative DIF and speeded with a positive DIF. DIF can be used in place of growth retardants. Costs for chemical growth retardants and the labor involved in applying the retardants are reduced. Also, the potential of harming the environment with the use of chemicals is lessened.

One disadvantage of DIF is its application is not always possible in warm regions or during the warm summer months across the country. Warm, sunny days make it more difficult for growers to reduce day temperatures within the greenhouse. Another disadvantage is DIF can result in higher heating and cooling costs to achieve targeted temperatures.

7-20. It is difficult in warm areas, such as Florida, to apply DIF.

AIR

Air has carbon dioxide and oxygen that are critical for photosynthesis and respiration. Exchange of oxygen and carbon dioxide through stomata in the leaves keeps photosynthesis operating at peak efficiency. The ability of air to move in and out of the soil is important in providing oxygen for healthy root growth. Root cells must have oxygen to undergo the vital life process of respiration. Air quality is an ingredient to producing healthy plants in the greenhouse.

Carbon Dioxide Levels

When greenhouse vents are closed, CO_2 levels can drop significantly. Carbon dioxide becomes a limiting factor and photosynthesis is slowed. Ventilation of the greenhouse helps to replenish CO_2 in the greenhouse atmosphere. Supplemental CO_2 is sometimes added to the greenhouse atmosphere when vents are not open. This is accomplished with special burners for the purpose of increasing the rate of photosynthesis. Supplemental CO_2 is most effective when used to give

7-21. Fans help to increase the exchange of gases.

7-22. The sides of this structure can be lowered to increase ventilation.

young plants a boost. The result is higher quality crops and a shorter production time. Carbon dioxide is usually added during the hours between 9:00 a.m. and 3:00 p.m.

Humidity, which is water vapor in the air, affects plant growth. The growth rate of plants increases under conditions of high humidity. Lush, tropical forests exist, in part, because of frequent rain and high humidity. High humidity reduces water stress of a plant so photosynthesis can function smoothly. If the humidity is low, the dryness of the air can put stress on the plant. This is especially true if soil moisture is inadequate and wilting oc-

7-23. Heater gases must be vented to the outside.

curs. One drawback of excessive humidity in the greenhouse is the increase of leaf and flower diseases.

Air pollution can be damaging to plants. Dust in the air can reduce light intensity, slowing photosynthesis. Chemical pollutants, such as sulfur dioxide, can actually kill plant cells or the entire plant. Greenhouse plants grown in urban settings sometimes suffer from air pollution.

Greenhouse heaters must be checked regularly for proper burning of fuel. Heaters need to burn cleanly. It is extremely important to vent gases from heaters to outside the greenhouse. Gases from burning fuel are harmful to plant growth causing foliar damage. Faulty heaters or inadequate venting can create risks to workers as well.

WATER

Watering is the most important cultural practice in the greenhouse. Life processes of the crops depend on water. Photosynthesis and respiration require water. Roots are able to absorb minerals only if the minerals are dissolved in water. Water is the carrier of materials through the xylem and phloem. Water also makes up a large percentage of the plant cells, tissues, and organs.

A lack of water places plants under stress. Plants transpire water through their stomata. If the plant roots cannot supply water quickly enough to replace water lost from transpiration, the plant responds by closing its stoma. This helps the plant to conserve water. However, when closed, the stoma do not permit an exchange of carbon dioxide and oxygen. Without carbon dioxide, photosynthesis, or the manufacture of sugars, cannot occur. Severe water

7-24. The plugs in this photograph will die unless they are watered.

7-25. This person is using acid to lower the pH of the water before irrigating the plants.

loss causes wilting. **Wilting** is a drooping condition and a lack of firmness to the plant tissues caused by inadequate water. Wilting is a result of a loss of *turgidity*, or water pressure, in the plant cells. Wilting is very serious with chrysanthemums. Chrysanthemums allowed to wilt severely never fulfill their full flowering potential.

Water must be given to plants when needed. Timing is critical. Frequent applications of water can keep a growing medium too wet. The result may be damaged plant roots caused by the lack of good air exchange. Allowing soils to become too dry between waterings may also cause root death and lower the quality of the crop. In the greenhouse, it is not unusual for plants to need water more than once during a warm, sunny day. Therefore, the person in charge of watering plants must have knowledge of the crop being grown and good judgment about when to water. A good rule is to water plants thoroughly when they need water and wait until they need water before watering again.

Watering Tips

1. Water when the plant needs water and wait until they need water before watering again.

2. Avoid wetting the leaves and flowers. Moisture can lead to problems with fungal diseases.

3. Never allow the breaker nozzles to touch the floor. Disease organisms on the floor can be picked up and spread to the plants during watering.

4. Water thoroughly to wet all of the growing medium and to leach soluble salts from the growing medium. This sometimes means watering a container more than once.

Water Quality

The quality of the available water is carefully researched and tested in selecting a site for a greenhouse. Water with a favorable pH range of 5.8 to 6.2 is best for most plant growth. If the water supply has a pH outside that range, the pH can be adjusted. A second consideration in determining water quality involves soluble salts. Water with high levels of soluble salts is detrimental to plant growth. Soluble salts damage roots. Removal of soluble salts from the water supply is an expensive operation.

Irrigation Methods

Furnishing plants with water by flooding or sprinkling is known as *irrigation*. There are a number of methods used to irrigate or water plants. With new techniques involving automation, labor has been reduced. Thousands of plants can be watered at one time. Several different watering methods are used.

Hand watering is the most reliable method of watering. However, it is time consuming and great responsibility is placed on the person performing the task. A wand is usually placed on the end of the hose with a nozzle to break the flow of water.

Spaghetti tubing involves small tubes connected to a main line. The end of each tube is placed in an individual pot. When operating, water dribbles through the tubes, watering all the pots on a bench simultaneously. An advantage is foliage and flowers do not get wet.

7-26. Although labor intensive, hand watering is the most reliable method of watering.

7-27. A spaghetti tubing system waters the gloxinias shown.

Drip Irrigation is similar to spaghetti tubing except the tube provides a slow steady drip with little run-off. Less water and fertilizers are used than with spaghetti tubes. Drip irrigation is widely used with hanging baskets.

With the *ebb and flood* method, water is pumped into the system at regular intervals, filling the bench. The pots sit in the water. The medium in the pots slowly absorbs water. After a certain period, the water drains from the bench. Ebb and flow benches conserve water, provide accurate nutrient levels, and allow for optimum spacing of plants.

Capillary mats consist of porous mats laid on a bench and wetted. The medium in the pots absorb the water by capillary action. Capillary mats are

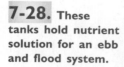

7-28. These tanks hold nutrient solution for an ebb and flood system.

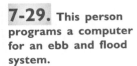 **7-29.** This person programs a computer for an ebb and flood system.

7-30. The leaves of these poinsettias stay dry on an ebb and flood bench.

7-31. Capillary mats are often used to water African violets and plants in small pots.

7-32. Plastic saucers are used with these chrysanthemums to collect water.

frequently used in African violet production and with other plants grown in small pots. The plant foliage stays dry and there is little runoff.

Saucers are used with overhead irrigation systems in a manner similar to capillary mats. As water is applied, it is collected in the saucer and drawn up into the growing medium by capillary action. Saucers reduce water and fertilizer waste.

Computer controlled *irrigation booms* sweep across greenhouse benches delivering overhead water. Large areas of bench space are watered quickly. Irrigation booms are very useful for bedding plant production. Some hand wa-

7-33. An irrigation boom waters these poinsettias.

tering is needed for touch up work. Also, the foliage of the plants does get wet.

Overhead sprinklers are used primarily with bedding plants. Sprinkler nozzles in a fixed position above the crops deliver overhead water. While they water a large area in a short period, application is often uneven. Also, water and fertilizer are wasted and foliage gets wet.

Intermittent Mist Systems for Plant Propagation

An *intermittent mist system* delivers water in tiny droplets for the purpose of keeping plant material moist. Intermittent mist systems are used for plant propagation. When taken, cuttings are without roots to absorb water. The mist system can relieve water stress on the cuttings until the cuttings develop roots. Mist systems permit higher light intensity. The higher light intensity increases sugar production and hence, speeds the production of roots.

7-34. Overhead sprinklers are used primarily with bedding plants.

7-35. Intermittent mist systems are used in plant propagation.

Intermittent mist systems can operate continuously or be set to mist the plants at regular intervals. Since there is less water stress at night, mist systems are set to operate only during the day. A solenoid valve controls the flow of water through the system. The solenoid is activated by one of three control mechanisms.

A time clock can be set to determine the time of day the mist system will operate. It also is set for the frequency and duration of the mists. A typical frequency of operation during the day might be 30 seconds every ten minutes.

A weighted leaf system consists of a fine metal mesh leaf that is balanced with a switch. When the leaf is dry, it triggers the switch to turn on the mist. The leaf system better reflects the conditions in the greenhouse than a clock timer does. It is more active on warm, sunny days, than cool, cloudy days.

A third controlling device involves a computer. Computer devices program the frequency and duration of the mists. They can also take into account the environmental conditions in the greenhouse.

REVIEWING

MAIN IDEAS

Growers manage light, temperature, air, and water in the greenhouse to promote healthy growth. These production practices are referred to as cultural practices.

Light plays a role in many aspects of plant growth and development. The effect of light is a result of the color of the light, the duration of the light, and the intensity of the light. Blue and red wavelengths produce a higher level of photosynthetic activity and chlorophyll synthesis than other colors. A plant's response to light duration is called photoperiodism. Plants are classified based on their response to light duration. They may be short-day, long-day, or day-neutral plants. Growth of the major floriculture crops is most active when they receive full sunlight. Growers can reduce light levels in the greenhouse when needed. They use artificial lighting to alter light duration and to increase light intensity.

Temperature is an important factor in biochemical reactions, including photosynthesis and respiration. In general, life processes are more active under warm temperatures. Thermoperiodism is a term used to describe a temperature requirement that produces a plant response. Some floriculture crops require a period of cold temperature or vernalization to flower. Temperature management is used to control the growth of plants. This is achieved by managing the difference between daytime and nighttime temperatures. The mathematical difference between the day temperature and the night temperature is called DIF. Stems elongate under positive DIF conditions and stay shorter under negative DIF conditions.

Air quality is an ingredient to producing healthy plants in the greenhouse. Carbon dioxide levels influence the rate of photosynthesis. A good air exchange between the greenhouse atmosphere and the outside atmosphere helps to keep CO_2 levels high. Sometimes, CO_2 burners are used to provide additional CO_2 in the greenhouse. Air pollution can be damaging to plants. Greenhouse heaters must be checked regularly for proper burning of fuel. It is also important to vent gases from heaters to outside the greenhouse.

Water is something that must be given to plants when it is needed. A good rule is to water plants thoroughly when they need water and wait until they need water before watering again. Automation has made watering a large number of plants in a short period possible. There are a number of methods used to water plants including hand watering, spaghetti tubing, drip irrigation, ebb and flood, capillary mats, irrigation booms, and overhead sprinklers. Intermittent mist systems are used for plant propagation.

QUESTIONS

Answer the following questions. Use correct spelling and complete sentences.

1. What is meant by cultural practices?

2. How do the colors of light influence plant growth and development?

3. How does light duration impact plant growth?

4. How does light intensity influence plant growth?

5. What are some applications of artificial lighting systems?

6. How do thermoperiodism and vernalization impact floriculture crop production?

7. Why is carbon dioxide sometimes added to the greenhouse environment?

8. Why is watering considered to be the most important cultural practice in the greenhouse?

9. What is a good rule for watering?

10. What are the major methods of irrigating greenhouse crops?

EVALUATING

Match the term with the correct definition. Write the letter by the term in the blank provided.

a. cultural practices
b. DIF
c. ebb and flood
d. high-intensity discharge (HID) lighting systems
e. high pressure sodium lamps

f. photoperiodism
g. short-day plants
h. spaghetti tubing
i. vernalization
j. wilting

_____ 1. The control or management of light, temperature, air, and water to promote healthy growth.

_____ 2. Plants that will begin to flower naturally in the fall when the day lengths get shorter.

_____ 3. A drooping condition and a lack of firmness to the plant tissues caused by inadequate water.

_____ 4. A HID supplemental lighting system that emits a high level of red, yellow, and orange wavelengths.

_____ 5. The mathematical difference between the day temperature and the night temperature.

_____ 6. The physiological process of some floriculture crops whereby a period of cold temperature is required for flowering.

_____ 7. A watering method in which water is pumped into the system at regular intervals, filling a watertight bench.

_____ 8. A plant's response to light duration.

_____ 9. Artificial lighting systems that have given growers more efficient and effective light sources.

_____ 10. This watering method involves small tubes connected to a main line through which water dribbles, watering all the pots on a bench simultaneously.

EXPLORING

1. Make an appointment to visit with a grower at a local greenhouse. Be prepared to ask questions concerning cultural practices involving light, temperature, air, and water. Keep notes on the grower's responses.

2. Conduct a school greenhouse "cultural practice inventory" with your instructor. Identify practices that could be changed to improve crop production. Work to implement approved cultural practices.

8

Growing Potted Flowering Crops

You would find it difficult to go a mall or an office building and not find potted flowering plants used in the interior landscape. They can bring bright colors to ordinarily cheerless surroundings. This is especially true around the holidays when festive looks are desired. Flowering potted plants are closely associated with each of our major holidays.

Can you think of which flowering plants are sold around Christmas? What flowering plants are sold at Valentine's Day, Easter, and Mother's Day? Have you ever wondered where the plants come from? Why are some of them available at certain times of the year and not at other times? There are many more questions that you might think about if you really give flowering potted plants some thought.

8-1. The Opryland Hotel in Nashville uses potted flowering plants for a festive look during the holidays.

OBJECTIVES

1 Identify major flowering potted crops and their origin

2 Describe the importance of flowering potted plants to the floriculture industry

3 Arrange a schedule for a 6½-inch pinched poinsettia crop

4 Set up a growing schedule for a chrysanthemum crop

5 Describe cultural practices in producing an African violet crop

6 Identify basic growing requirements for kalanchoes, cyclamen, and minor potted flowering crops

TERMS

African violet
center bud removal
chrysanthemum
cineraria
cyclamen
disbudding
florist azalea
florist hydrangea
gloxinia
hard pinch

heat delay
holiday cactus
kalanchoe
liners
Persian violet
pocketbook plant
poinsettia
primrose
roll out pinch
soft pinch

POTTED FLOWERING PLANTS

Potted flowering plants consist of plants grown in pots for their showy flowers. The major potted flowering crops are part of everyday life in America. Most people easily identify poinsettias, chrysanthemums, and African violets. Supermarkets, florists, garden centers, and chain stores sell potted flowering plants. Offices, malls, and retail stores use them to brighten their business environments.

Potted flowering plants are sold in all areas of the country. They make up a large portion of greenhouse production sales in the United States. Their segment of the greenhouse production industry is second only to bedding plant production. Based on the 1997 USDA Floriculture Crops Summary, the total value of the potted flowering crops was $701 million.

Table 8-1. Potted Flowering Crop Sales According to the 1997 USDA Floriculture Crops Summary

Crop	Total Pots Sold in 1996-97
1. Poinsettia	59,873,000
2. Chrysanthemum	27,575,000
3. African violet	20,652,000
4. Florist azalea	14,225,000
5. Easter lily	9,148,000
6. Orchid	8,646,000
7. Kalanchoe	6,176,000
8. Cyclamen	5,854,000
9. All others (Cineraria, Calceolaria, Primrose, Persian violet, Gloxinia, Holiday cactus, Florist hydrangea, etc.)	83,953,000

POINSETTIA (Euphorbia pulcherrima)

General Information

Poinsettias are native to Mexico. The U. S. Ambassador to Mexico, Joel Poinset, introduced poinsettias to the United States. Until the early 1900s, poinsettias were used chiefly as cut flowers. Poinsettias are associated with Christmas and are now sold as potted plants only during that time of the

8-2. Poinsettias are associated with Christmas.

year. The Ecke family in California promoted the use of poinsettias. To this day, the Ecke family is recognized as the leader in poinsettia production. They supply stock plants and cuttings for growers around the country.

The first poinsettia plants were much less attractive than today's poinsettia cultivars. They dropped their lower leaves creating a leggy appearance, had small bracts, and failed to hold their color. New production techniques and hybridizing have greatly improved the appearance of poinsettias. Plant breeding has led to new cultivars of poinsettias that hold their color longer, have larger bracts, and are more compact than early varieties. Success in propagation has increased dramatically with mist systems. Also, growth regulators have been affective in keeping plants more compact.

Poinsettia cultivars are available in a variety of colors including the traditional deep red, pink, white, speckled, and even yellow. They are grown as single stem or branched plants. They can be trained to grow as small trees or used in hanging baskets. Pot sizes used range from 4-inch to 12-inch azalea pots.

8-3. Poinsettia cultivars are available in a variety of colors.

Propagation

Poinsettias are propagated asexually. Growers can buy stock plants and take their own stem cuttings. They can also purchase unrooted cuttings, rooted cuttings, or callused cuttings.

When starting with unrooted cuttings, the grower should allow three to four weeks for rooting. Most cuttings are stuck near the end of July as part of the overall crop schedule. A suggested procedure follows:

- Cuttings are taken 3 to 4 inches in length.

- Dip or dust the end of the cuttings in a medium-strength rooting hormone and stick the cutting in a rooting cube or directly in the finish pot.

- Place under intermittent mist for 24 hours the first day. Adjust to 15 to 20 seconds every 3 to 5 minutes during the first week and 10 seconds every hour at night.

- Reduce the period of mist to 10 seconds every 10 minutes as the cuttings form root initials.

- Provide a temperature range of 70 to 75°F during rooting.

Growing Procedures

Poinsettias require a well-drained and well-aerated growing medium with a pH between 5.0 and 6.5. The recommended pot for most production is the

8-4. Some growers buy stock plants in February, plant them to induce branching, and then take cuttings.

8-5. This worker pinches plants in mid-September.

azalea pot. Soilless medium settles so pots should be filled to the top. It is important for all of the pots to have the same amount of medium. This helps with watering practices and in uniform development of the entire crop. Plant the cuttings in the center of the pot and at the same depth. Shallow placement promotes healthy root growth. This is because the top few inches of medium has 20 to 30 percent more air than the lower medium. After planting, drench the pots with fungicide to control root and stem rot.

It is important to understand that poinsettias are both photoperiodic and thermoperiodic. As short-day plants, they initiate flower buds as days get shorter. Flower bud initiation begins when nights reach about 11 hours and 50 minutes of darkness. Lowering night temperatures in the greenhouse to 62 to 64° F during flower bud initiation produces a favorable response.

Poinsettia production can be broken down into four stages of development. They are the vegetative stage, flower bud initiation, flower bud development, and flowering. Lighting and temperatures are adjusted according to the stage. The fertilization schedule also changes with the production stage.

A growing schedule for 6 to 6½-inch multi-flowered poinsettia crop in soilless mix follows:

Late August—Vegetative Stage

Pot poinsettias in a finishing pot. Drench with Lexan and Terrachlor fungicides. Promote vegetative growth by lighting plants from 10 p.m. to 2 a.m.

8-6. These plants were just pinched leaving six leaves.

Fertilize with 300 ppm nitrogen and potassium. Provide 68 to 70° F night temperatures and 70 to 80° F day temperatures.

September 10—Vegetative Stage

Drench with Cycocel. Pinch the plant leaving four to six leaves. Maintain high humidity to encourage breaks. Note, that the longer the period between pinching and flower bud initiation, the larger the plant. Raise fertilizer rate to 350 to 400 ppm nitrogen and potassium. Maintain night temperatures of 68 to 70°F.

8-7. With the removal of the apical meristem, side shoots or breaks develop.

8-8. This photograph shows automatic short day curtains being closed over a crop of poinsettias to ensure short days and long nights.

September 20 to 25— Flower Bud Initiation Stage

Turn lights off and give plants short days. If nearby lights interfere with the natural darkness, cover the crop with short day curtains from 5:00 p.m. until 8:00 a.m. Drop night temperatures to 62 to 64°F and day temperatures to 70 to 72°F. Fertilize at 300 to 350 ppm nitrogen and potassium. Initiation of flower buds occurs over a period of 8 to 10 days. Cell division stops after flower buds initiate. From then on, the cells enlarge. Space plants 15 inches by 15 inches to avoid stretching.

October 10—Flower Bud Development Stage

Flower buds begin to develop. Stop black cloth treatment. Adjust temperatures to 64 to 66°F at night and 70 to 75°F during the day. Fertil-

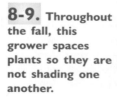

8-9. Throughout the fall, this grower spaces plants so they are not shading one another.

ize at a rate of 300 ppm nitrogen and potassium. Drench with a fungicide, such
as Banol 66.5%, Banrot 40W, Chipco
aliette 80 WDG, Subdue II WSP,
Terrazole 35 WP, or Truban 25EC or 30
WP to control root rot.

November 15—Flowering Stage

Begin to finish plants. Drop temperature to 58 to 62°F nights to deepen
bract color. Reduce fertilizer rate to 200
to 300 ppm nitrogen and potassium.

Pests and Disease Problems

The most serious insect pest on
poinsettias is the white fly. Mites, mealy
bugs, thrips, and fungus gnats can also
create problems. A clean, weed-free
greenhouse and a pest control program
reduce insect problems. Botrytis is a
problem in the propagation area. Poinsettias are also very susceptible to three

8-10. A finished plant has a flower at the
end of each stem that developed after
pinching.

major root rot diseases, *Pythium*, *Rhizoctonia*, and *Thielaviopsis*. Well-timed
fungicide applications reduce losses caused by fungi.

CHRYSANTHEMUM (Dendranthema grandiflora)

General Information

Chrysanthemums (mums) have their origin in China, Japan, and Europe.
There is evidence that chrysanthemums were used in Chinese gardens
around 550 BC. Mums were brought to the United States and used only in
the fall until the 1940s.

Then, it was found that chrysanthemums are photoperiodic and thermoperiodic. Because flower buds set naturally from middle August to late September, chrysanthemums are considered to be short-day plants. They are
lighted for vegetative growth and shaded between March and September to

8-11. A chrysanthemum in flower.

induce flowering. By controlling light duration and temperatures, potted mum crops can be produced throughout the year. Easter and Mother's Day are two holidays that see high sales of potted chrysanthemums.

Chrysanthemum varieties are very diverse. Mums come in many colors and the flower forms differ. There are also physiological differences that influence production schedules. Mums are classified based on these differences:

- **Response group**—One grouping is based on the number of weeks it takes them to flower from the time they begin receiving short days. For instance, a nine-week variety takes nine weeks to flower once it is given short-day treatments. The response groups of mums range from 6 weeks to 15 weeks. Garden mums include six-, seven-, and eight-week varieties. The majority of potted chrysanthemums have a 9- or 10-week response.

- **Plant height**—A second grouping involves the height of the plants. Chrysanthemum varieties are identified as being tall, medium, or short.

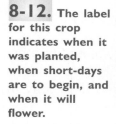

8-12. The label for this crop indicates when it was planted, when short-days are to begin, and when it will flower.

8-13. Chrysanthemums have different flower forms. (Courtesy, Yoder Brothers, Inc.)

Tall varieties grow taller than 15 inches in height. They may receive short-day treatment prior to pinching.

Medium varieties are around 15 inches tall and receive short-day treatment at the time of pinching.

Short varieties grow less than 15 inches in height and need an additional 7 to 14 days growing time after pinching before given short-day treatment.

■ **Flower forms**—Mums are also grouped by their flower forms, which include standard, spray, button, spoon, decorative, daisy, spider, pompon, and anemone.

Propagation

As the popularity of chrysanthemums grew in the 1940s and 1950s, it was discovered that many of the plants were infected with viruses that produced deformed growth. The Yoder Brothers Company began a crusade to

8-14. Chrysanthemums can be purchased as unrooted cuttings. These are dusted with a rooting hormone.

clean infected plants from the industry. They began producing cuttings free of virus and other systemic diseases. Today, a few specialized companies provide over 95 percent of all the chrysanthemum cuttings. The cuttings are sold as rooted cuttings or as unrooted cuttings.

Cuttings are taken 2½ to 3 inches in length with three leaves. They are rooted with bottom heat of 70 to 75°F and lit to maintain vegetative growth. Intermittent mist is provided until roots form. Chrysanthemums are basal rooters. Fast-rooting varieties root in about 18 days.

8-15. These cuttings were graded before planting to get uniform growth.

Growing Procedures

The cuttings are graded or sorted before planting. This is done according to the number of roots, diameter of the stem, and the length of the stem. Failure to grade cuttings results in pots with lopsided growth. Some cuttings in the pot may grow vigorously while others grow more slowly.

Chrysanthemums are grown as single stem or pinched plants. They prefer a growing medium with a pH of 6.0 to 6.5. Azalea pots are the pots of choice for most growers. Typically, one cutting is used in a 4½-inch pot. Three, four or five cuttings are used in a 6- or 6½-inch pot, six to seven cuttings in a 7-inch pot, and 9 to 12 cuttings in an 8-inch pot. Plant cuttings shallow and at a 45-degree angle with the tops extending over the lip of the pot. Planting cuttings too deep is a major problem. Also, the roots should not be pressed down when potting.

There are four main periods of growth and development in producing a potted chrysanthemum crop. The first phase or vegetative phase involves the promotion of root and leaf growth. The vegetative phase lasts three to five weeks depending on the variety and the time of the year. Flower bud initiation, flower bud development, and the finishing stages follow. Each phase requires a different fertilizer rate and temperature.

Vegetative Phase

The vegetative phase is the most critical period of growth. During this time, plants must build up reserves of sugar and produce a strong root system. Begin feeding newly planted rooted cuttings immediately. Use a starter fertilizer with 250 to 350 ppm nitrogen at the first watering. Starter fertilizers are typically high in phosphorous to encourage root growth. Thereafter, use 200 to 300 ppm nitrogen and potassium with each watering. Water when the growing medium approaches drying. Provide 65 to 70°F night temperatures, 75 to 80°F day temperatures, and high humidity. HID lighting in the darker months and carbon dioxide burners help the cuttings get off to a fast start.

Long days must be provided to keep chrysanthemums in a vegetative stage of growth. Interrupt the night darkness from December through February by lighting the plants from 10:00 p.m. to 2:00 a.m. From September through November and March through May, light for three hours. In the summer months, light for one to two hours to be sure plants stay vegetative.

PINCHING. Grow for 7 to 14 days or until roots appear at the bottom of the pot before pinching the plants. Pinching is the removal of the growing point of the stem. Pinching encourages breaks or branching of the plants. Three to four strong breaks from a pinch are desired. Plants with good lower leaf development produce more breaks than weaker plants. The results of pinching include better-shaped plants that appear fuller and produce more flowers. There are three methods of pinching:

The **roll out pinch** involves the removal of just the meristematic tip of the stem. Care needs to be taken to remove the whole tip or growth from the tip resumes. The roll out pinch is recommended in winter when growth is sluggish.

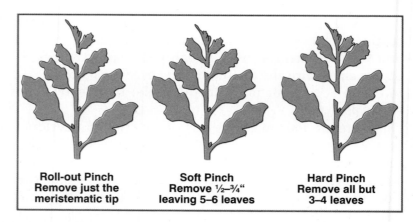

8-16. There are three methods of pinching.

| Roll-out Pinch
Remove just the
meristematic tip | Soft Pinch
Remove ½–¾"
leaving 5–6 leaves | Hard Pinch
Remove all but
3–4 leaves |

8-17. This grower is taking a soft pinch.

A **soft pinch** involves the removal of ½ inch to ¾ inch of the stem. Five to six leaves are left on the cutting. This method is used throughout most of the year.

The **hard pinch** removes everything but three to four leaves. The hard pinch is used in the summer with tall cuttings.

Flower Bud Initiation

Turn off night lighting to provide short-day treatment for the initiation of flower buds. Cover the crop with black cloth if necessary to extend the period of light duration. The desirable temperature range for flower bud initiation is 62 to 65°F nights. Also, lower the humidity levels in the greenhouse. Reduce fertilizer rates to 200 to 250 ppm.

In the summer months, temperatures can build up under black cloth resulting in heat delay. **Heat delay** is caused by day temperatures over 90° F or night temperatures over 80°F. The result is a delay of flowering by several days to weeks.

Use of a growth retardant or DIF effectively controls the height of tall varieties. Typically, a foliar application of B-Nine is applied 7 to 18 days after pinching or when about 2 inches of new growth has occurred. Short varieties and nine-week varieties do not need growth retardant applications. A slightly negative DIF of –1 to –4 has proven effective.

8-18. Disbudding involves the removal of flower buds.

Flower Bud Development

At night, drop temperatures to 60 to 62°F. Continue to fertilize at a rate of 200 to 250 ppm.

As the flower buds develop, they may be removed to improve the overall quality of the plants. This practice is known as *disbudding*. One method of disbudding is *center bud removal*, which involves the pinching off of the most terminal flower bud. This allows the lateral flower buds to develop. Center bud removal is performed with decorative-type mums. Another disbudding practice involves the removal of all the lateral buds. The plant responds by sending all its energy to the remaining bud. The result is larger showier flowers.

Finishing

Drop temperatures to 55 to 58°F at night to increase color intensity and quality. Growth of the plant at this point has stopped. Stop fertilization and allow

8-19. With the lateral flower buds removed, all the energy goes into the terminal flower buds.

8-20. This florist-quality mum nearly ready for sale is 15 inches tall from the lip of the pot, 15 inches in diameter, and it has 15 flowers.

the growing medium to dry a bit more than earlier in the crop before watering.

A quality final product will be symmetrical and have all the flowers opening at the same time. A florist-quality potted mum in a 6½-inch pot will follow a 15-15-15 rule of thumb. That is, it is 15 inches tall from the lip of the pot, 15 inches in diameter, and it has 15 flowers.

Scheduling

Classifying chrysanthemums by response group has made timing of crops for a certain sales date easier. We can look at an example schedule for a Valentine's Day crop using a nine-week, medium-size variety. For marketing purposes, the plants need to begin flowering by February 7. Begin by counting backwards on the calendar nine weeks from February 7. This takes us to the date when plants are pinched and short-day treatment is begun. Count back another two weeks for vegetative growth prior to pinching. The total time for production of a 9-week variety from rooted cuttings is 12 weeks. So, rooted cuttings should be ordered for and planted 13 weeks before February 14th.

Table 8-2. Simplified Growing Schedule				
Tall varieties	Vegetative 1 week	Short days 1 week	Pinch	
Medium varieties	Vegetative 1–2 weeks	Pinch	Short days	
Short varieties	Vegetative 2 weeks	Pinch	Vegetative 1 week	Short days

Pest and Disease Problems

The major pests of chrysanthemums are aphids, whiteflies, spider mites, leaf minors, and cutworms and cabbage loopers. Disease problems include botrytis, mildews, and soil-borne disease including *Pythium*, *Rhizoctonia*, and *Phytophthora*.

AFRICAN VIOLET (Saintpaulia ionantha)

General Information

African violets are native to areas south of the equator on the African continent. They are found on rainy hillsides where temperatures are warm. They are common in many American homes because of their bright and abundant flowers. Flower colors fall in the white-pink-purple range. They are produced for Valentine's Day, Easter, and Mother's Day. African violets are not photoperiodic, but they do develop more quickly under long-day conditions.

Propagation

African violets are usually propagated by leaf-petiole cuttings. Select half-mature leaves. They have active hormone production and the potential for growth still exists. In fact, the leaves will grow while it is rooting. It is desired to have eight to ten plantlets develop from each leaf. Tissue culture is another technique used in propagating African violets.

8-21. African violets are very popular plants for the home.

Leaf petioles are stuck at an angle 1 to 1½ inches into a light medium. Temperatures are kept at 70 to 75°F. Artificial light is provided at 1200 to 1500 foot candles. Roots form in about three weeks. Plantlets form in three to four weeks.

Growing Procedures

The plantlets are carefully separated so only one plantlet is in a pot. Plant African violets in a peat-based growing medium. Care must be taken not to cover the crown of the plant. The pH should be around 6.0. They are typi-

8-22. African violets are usually propagated by leaf-petiole cuttings.

cally transplanted to the 4-inch plastic azalea pots for finishing. African violets have a very fine root system so larger pots are avoided.

Capillary mats and ebb and flood watering systems are applied in African violet production. These systems keep the plant leaves dry and provide humidity around the developing plant. Provide 100 to 150 ppm nitrogen and potassium at every watering. Apply less fertilizer when light intensity is low between October and March. Also, African violets should never be allowed to dry out.

Water overhead every four to five waterings to leach soluble salts from the growing medium. However, care must be taken not to wet African violet

8-23. An ebb and flood system is used to water these African violets.

leaves with cold water. Cold water causes enzymes in the plant cells to coagulate. Leaf tissues are damaged and white spots are created. Never apply overhead water that is more than 5 degrees cooler than the air temperature.

African violets perform best when light levels are between 1,000 and 2,000 foot candles. Below 1,000, they produce large leaves and no flowers. Above 2,000, the leaves are bleached. In many greenhouse operations African violets are given some shade. The preferred temperature range is 65 to 75°F nights.

African violets take different amounts of time to reach marketable size depending on the time of year. In general, total production time from the leaf cutting to sale is eight to nine months. In northern states, it takes 12 to 14 weeks to produce a Valentine's Day crop and 8 to 10 weeks for a Mother's Day crop. A quality plant has a single crown with leaves that are radially symmetrical. The flowers are held above the leaves to the center of the plant.

Pest and Disease Problems

Pests include cyclamen mites, root aphids, and mealy bugs. Nematodes can be a serious problem as African violets are highly susceptible. Phytophthora root rot and mildew are disease problems.

FLORIST AZALEA (Rhododendron obtusum, Rhododendron simsii)

General Information

Two species of *Rhododendron* are grown as florist azaleas. *Rhododendron obtusum* is native to Japan and *Rhododendron simsii* is native to China. Neither plant is considered to be very hardy. Most florist azaleas are grown in Florida, Alabama, Mississippi, and California where temperatures are warm and light intensity high. Different varieties are grown for Christmas, Easter, and Mother's Day. Most growers buy prefinished plants and force them to flower

Propagation

Florist azaleas are woody plants and as such take anywhere between two and three years from propagation to flower. Stem cuttings, 2½ to 3 inches in

8-24. A florist azalea. (Courtesy, Ball Horticultural Co.)

length, are rooted in a peat mix. The rooting process takes about 6 to 12 weeks. The rooted cuttings are pinched four to five times to encourage branching. The resulting small-branched plants are sold as 4-, 6-, or 8-inch diameter *liners*.

Growing Procedures

Received in May, liners are planted in 6-inch azalea pots in pure peat moss. Shredded pine fibers and pine bark humus are alternative medium components. Florist azaleas require an acid medium with a pH ranging from 4.5 to 5.5. The medium should never be allowed to dry completely.

Plants are pinched in June. Chemical pinching agents are sometimes used to kill the apical meristems resulting in breaks. During the vegetative stage of production, they are given 65°F night temperatures and 75 to 85°F day temperatures.

High light intensity is desired for production. Azaleas also respond to light duration. They grow vegetatively under long-day conditions. They will

8-25. These florist azaleas are being held at 40°F to satisfy flower bud dormancy.

initiate flower buds when given short days and 60 to 65°F nights. This process of flower bud initiation takes four to six weeks.

Florist azaleas must be cooled to satisfy flower bud dormancy. Middle to late season varieties are cooled at temperatures less than 40°F for 10 to 12 weeks. If placed in a cooler, the plants need to be lighted to prevent leaf drop. After the cooling period, they are given 50 to 55°F temperatures to force flowering.

Application of gibberellic acid is used to help the plants overcome their dormancy. Gibberellic acid promotes the uniform opening of flowers desired of high-quality florist azaleas. Foliar applications of gibberellic acid can be used as a substitute for the period of cold treatment with some varieties.

Pest and Disease Problems

Pest problems are minimal for the grower who has florist azaleas for a few months of forcing before sale. Major pests include leafminers, spider mites, and aphids. Diseases include *Phytophthora*, *Cylindrocladium* blight and root rot, and *Botrytis* during storage.

KALANCHOE (Kalanchoe blossfeldiana)

General Information

Kalanchoes are succulent plants with thick, fleshy leaves. They are native to Africa and Asia. Their flowers range in color from bright yellow to orange to hot pink. Kalanchoes are short-day plants.

Propagation

Maintaining disease-free stock plants is very difficult, so most growers purchase rooted or unrooted stem cuttings from specialty growers. Stem cuttings, 1½ to 2½ inches long, are stuck without the use of rooting hormones. Cuttings root in one to two weeks. The cuttings are lighted to promote vegetative growth.

8-26. A kalanchoe plant.

8-27. These cuttings were taken from a stock plant.

*G*rowing Procedures

Plant kalanchoes in a well-drained medium with a pH between 6.0 and 6.5. Provide 65 to 68°F night temperatures. Higher temperatures result in taller plants. Kalanchoes respond well to CO_2 enrichment during periods of lower light.

Place kalanchoes on a constant feed program of 300 to 400 ppm nitrogen and potassium at the time of planting and continue until the start of short-day treatment. Then, reduce fertilizer rates to 150 to 200 ppm nitrogen and

8-28. Spaghetti tubing is used to deliver water and fertilizer solution to these kalanchoe.

potassium. Kalanchoes respond well to ebb and flow, spaghetti tubing, and capillary mat watering systems.

Plants in 4-inch pots require no pinching, while those in 5- or 6-inch pots should be pinched two weeks after planting. Plants in the larger pots benefit from a second soft pinching when new shoots are 2 to 2½ inches long. B-Nine is used after the first pinch to keep plants compact.

Allow two weeks after the final pinch before the start of short-day treatments. The crop takes 8 to 10 weeks from the beginning of short days to flower.

Pests and Diseases

Major pests include aphids, cabbage loopers, and leaf rollers. Crown rot, root rot, and powdery mildew are the primary disease problems.

CYCLAMEN (Cyclamen persicum)

General Information

Cyclamen are attractive plants native to the Mediterranean. Their unusual-shaped flowers come in white, pink, carmine, and red. Cyclamen are considered a cool crop. As such, they have been produced in greatest numbers for winter and spring sales.

Propagation

Sexual propagation is used with cyclamen. The first of four stages of the propagation process begins with seeds being sown in plug trays. High humidity, darkness and 63 to 65°F temperatures are provided for three to four weeks. In stage two, the developing hypocotyl (similar in appearance to a radish) is covered with vermiculite for two weeks. The vermiculite is moistened and humidity is kept high. In the third stage, seedlings are given higher light levels and tempera-

8-29. A cyclamen plant. (Courtesy, *Greenhouse Product News*)

8-30. Cyclamen are grown and sold as plugs.

8-31. Note that during potting the hypocotyl is placed above the medium.

tures of 65 to 68° F for six to eight weeks. The final step is the transplanting of plugs into 4-inch pots.

Growing Procedures

Cyclamen prefer a peat-based medium with a pH of 5.5 to 6.3. Plants should be planted high to prevent rot of the hypocotyl, which develops into a tuber. Do not fertilize the crop until the roots reach the end of the pot. Start fertilizing with 100 to 150 ppm nitrogen. Maintain temperatures between 65 and 68°F.

Transplant the plants to 5- or 6-inch finishing pots after 16 to 18 weeks. Fertilize at a rate of 200 to 250 ppm nitrogen. Maintain temperatures at 65 to 68°F. Never let the medium dry completely or the tuber is damaged. Keep the greenhouse humidity high.

Cyclamen are sensitive to high light intensity. They prefer 4,000 to 6,000 foot candles. In northern regions, they should be grown in full sun from November through March. Thirty percent shade is recommended from April through May and September through October. Fifty percent shade is needed June through August. In southern regions, more shading is required.

Flower bud development occurs after the plants have become well established and have 15 to 40 leaves. At this time, reduce fertilizer rates to 100 ppm nitrogen and potassium. Drop night temperatures to 60 to 62°F. The lower temperatures in-

8-32. Cyclamen are grown with their leaves almost touching to maintain high humidity.

crease the number of flowers and keep the flower stalks firm. Gibberellic acid is sometimes used to speed flowering.

Pests and Diseases

Cyclamen mites, spider mites, aphids and thrips cause damage to flowers and foliage. Disease problems include fusarium wilt, botrytis, and phytophthora.

MINOR POTTED FLOWERING CROPS

Minor potted flowering plants collectively account for a large portion of sales nationwide. Some of the more common minor crops include cineraria, calceolaria, Persian violet, gloxinia, holiday cactus, hydrangea, and primrose.

Gloxinia (Sinningia speciosa)

The *gloxinia*, native to Brazil, is in the same plant family as African violets. Its large trumpet-shaped flowers come in red, pink, purple,

8-33. A gloxinia ready for sale.

8-34. This photograph shows leaf damage on gloxinias caused by cold overhead water.

white, and two-tones. Gloxinias are propagated from their tubers or by seed. Most growers buy seedlings from specialty growers. Plant gloxinias in a peat-based medium with a pH around 6.0. Keep the medium moist. Capillary mats, ebb and flood, and spaghetti tubing watering systems reduce the chance of damaging leaves with cold water. Provide 150 to 200 ppm nitrogen and potassium. They prefer 3,000 to 4,000 foot candles so shading is usually required. Gloxinias like 65 to 70°F nights and a humid greenhouse. Seed to flower takes about six months for a spring crop.

Holiday Cactus

Three types of holiday cacti are available: Thanksgiving (*Schlumbergera truncata*), Christmas (*Schlumbergera bridgesii*), and Easter (*Rhipsalidopsis gaertneri*). The natural photoperiodic response of these plants brings them to flower around the holiday for which they are named. **Holiday cacti** are both short-day plants and thermoperiodic. Holiday cacti are propagated by cuttings taken from stock

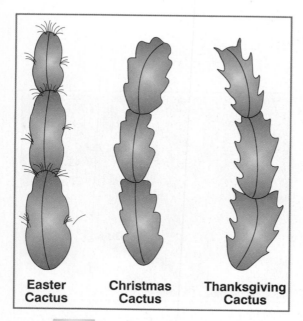

Easter Cactus   Christmas Cactus   Thanksgiving Cactus

8-35. Three types of holiday cacti.

8-36. These people are taking holiday cactus cuttings.

8-37. These Thanksgiving cacti will flower naturally around Thanksgiving.

plants. The medium must have good drainage and a pH between 5.5 and 6.0. Fertilize holiday cacti with 100 to 150 ppm nitrogen and potassium with each watering up until one month before flower buds develop. Thanksgiving and Christmas cacti initiate flower buds at 55°F nights. Easter cactus initiates flower buds when given night temperatures between 47 and 53°F.

Florist Hydrangea (Hydrangea macrophylla)

Florist hydrangeas are native to Japan. They are grown primarily for Easter and Mother's Day. Their long-lasting flowers come in blue, pink, white or red.

8-38. A florist hydrangea in flower.

Production has dropped because of the space they require and the length of time they take to produce. Hydrangeas are propagated by stem cuttings in April and May. They are grown as single stem or pinched plants. B-Nine is used to retard growth. Hydrangeas initiate flower buds from middle to

8-39. Florist hydrangea produce vegetative growth until flower buds begin to develop in late August. (Courtesy, *Greenhouse Product News*)

8-40. This grower adds aluminum sulfate to his hydrangea crop to promote blue coloration.

late August. In October, they are defoliated with ethylene gas. From mid-November to January they are given a cold treatment of 35 to 40°F. They are moved to the greenhouse and forced at 60 to 64°F.

Blue-pink varieties change flower color based on fertilization. Aluminum promotes a blue coloration. Aluminum is available to the plants when the growing media is acidic. Growers will provide medium with a pH of 5.5 or less for blue flowers and raise the pH above 6.5 to produce pink flowers.

Persian Violet (Exacum affine)

Persian violet is from the Island of Socotra off the tip of Somalia. It has pretty violet-blue flowers that cover the whole plant. Most Persian violets are grown in 4- to 6½-inch pots. They are propagated by seed or cuttings. Persian violets are grown for sales ranging from Mother's Day through October. They are long-day plants that like warm temperatures. Preferred growing temperatures are 60 to 65°F nights and 72 to 77°F days. Moderate fertilization rates of 150 to 200 ppm nitrogen and potassium are effective. Since they like 4,500 to 6,000 foot candles, shading is often required. They are very susceptible to *Pythium* root rot and *Phytophthora*.

8-41. Persian violet.

COOL CROPS

Northern growers produce three cool crops that share similar production schedules, cultural requirements, and usually the same greenhouse. Production is for Valentine's Day, Easter, and Mother's Day. They are the cineraria, pocketbook plant, and the primrose.

8-42. A cineraria.

8-43. A pocketbook plant, also known as slipper flower.

8-44. A species of primrose. (Courtesy, *Greenhouse Product News*)

Native to the Canary Islands, the **cineraria** (*Senecio cruentus*) has daisy-form flowers held in a cluster above the foliage. They come in blues, pinks, reds, and white. The native range of the **pocketbook plant**, also known as slipper flower (*Calceolaria herbeohybrida*), extends from Mexico to Chile. Its flowers resemble a woman's purse. The flowers are very colorful yellows, oranges, and reds. There are six species of **Primrose** (*Primula* species) used in greenhouse production. All of these originate in the northern temperate regions of the world. Primroses are available in a wide range of bright, colorful, and fragrant flowers.

Seeds of all three plants are sown in late summer. Soilless media are recommended with a pH around 6.0. Cinerarias and pock-

8-45. These people unload primrose plugs for planting.

etbook plants are grown in 5- or 6-inch azalea pots, while primroses are grown in 4- to 4½-inch azalea pots. Plants are started with 100 ppm nitrogen and potassium. Once in the finish pots, a constant feed program of 200 ppm nitrogen and potassium is recommended. During the vegetative stage, lasting four to six weeks after planting, temperatures are kept at 60 to 62°F nights, 70 to 75°F days. Shade is usually required to limit light to 4,000 to 5,000 foot candles.

Flower bud initiation is promoted after the foliage has grown to extend 2 to 3 inches over the lip of the pots, usually around mid-November. Temperatures are dropped to 45 to 55°F nights. Day temperatures should not exceed 60°F. Fertilization is stopped. It takes six to eight weeks for the flower buds to initiate.

The plants can be forced to flower after small buds become apparent.

8-46. These primrose are grown on the floor of this poly house where temperatures are cooler.

8-47. These cineraria are being grown in 6-inch pots. Note the level of growing medium.

Forcing takes four to six weeks. Night temperatures are raised to 60 to 62°F. Feeding is resumed with 200 to 250 ppm nitrogen and potassium.

REVIEWING

MAIN IDEAS

Flowering potted plants are grown for their showy flowers. As a whole, they rank second in sales only to bedding plants. Some of the major potted flowering crops include poinsettias, chrysanthemums, African violets, florist azalea, kalanchoe, and cyclamen. Some minor crops include gloxinia, holiday cactus, florist hydrangea, Persian violet, cineraria, pocketbook plant, and primrose.

The crops are propagated by seeds or cuttings. The growing media are selected based on what each crop prefers. The same is true with the selection of growing pots. In general, vigorous vegetative growth is encouraged before the initiation of flower buds.

Each flowering potted crop can be brought to flower by manipulating the greenhouse environment. Flowering potted plants are often photoperiodic and thermoperiodic. Therefore, growers adjust the day length and temperatures to promote certain plant responses. Watering practices and fertilizer rates are also adjusted to meet the scheduling needs. Light intensity is increased at times with supplemental lighting and decreased with shade curtains.

QUESTIONS

Answer the following questions. Use correct spelling and complete sentences.

1. What general conditions are given to promote vegetative growth of potted flowering crops?

2. Why are various crops pinched?

3. How are chrysanthemum varieties classified?

4. What does it mean to have a chrysanthemum with a nine-week response?

5. Why are chrysanthemums disbudded?

6. What are the general growing requirements for African violets?

7. Why are cineraria, pocketbook plant, and primrose often grown together?

EVALUATING

Match the term with the correct definition. Write the letter by the term in the blank provided.

a. breaks
b. center bud removal
c. kalanchoe
d. heat delay

e. soft pinch
f. florist azalea
g. cyclamen
h. disbudding

i. potted flowering plants
j. pocketbook plant
k. liners
l. Persian violet

_____ 1. The removal of ½- to ¾-inch of the stem.

_____ 2. Branching of the plants caused by pinching.

_____ 3. Removal of flower buds to improve the overall quality of the plants.

_____ 4. Plants grown in pots for their showy flowers.

_____ 5. A cool crop from the area from Mexico to Chile that has colorful flowers resembling a woman's purse.

_____ 6. The pinching off of the most terminal flower bud.

_____ 7. Rooted cuttings pinched four to five times to encourage branching and sold to growers.

_____ 8. A warm season plant with violet-blue flowers grown for Mother's day through October sales.

_____ 9. Woody plants requiring between two and three years from propagation to flower.

_____ 10. Delay of flowering caused by warm temperatures.

_____ 11. Succulent plants with thick, fleshy leaves native to Africa and Asia.

_____ 12. A cool crop native to the Mediterranean with unusual-shaped white, pink, carmine, and red flowers.

EXPLORING

1. Grow potted flowering crops in your school greenhouse. Determine when you want the crop to flower. Then, schedule the crop from propagation to sale. Purchase seed, plugs, or cuttings. Plant them in the recommended growing medium and in the appropriate pots. Provide them with the recommended light duration, light intensity, temperatures, watering practices, and fertilization rates. Pinch the plants if necessary. Sell the finished crop to students, school staff, and/or the community.

2. Arrange a job-shadowing program with the assistance of you instructor, counselor, school administrators and local greenhouse grower. Visit the greenhouse at least six times during the year. During the visits, observe the production practices employed by the grower. Also, consider whether greenhouse production is the type of career you would like to pursue.

9

Growing and Forcing Bulbs, Corms, and Tubers

Springtime! For many people, it doesn't come soon enough. Winter days seem to last much too long. The outdoor landscape is not as green and colorful as it is during the other seasons. Plants help people to brighten their homes.

If there is one floriculture crop that carries the message of springtime, it is the bulb crop. Tulips and daffodils are associated with the arrival of spring and warmer temperatures to come. They are among the first plants to emerge from winter's sleep to flower in the landscape. Easter lilies, used widely in churches, are another signal of the beginning of spring. Forced to flower in the winter and in the early months of spring, bulb crops uplift the spirits of people tired of winter.

9-1. Bulb crops are forced for winter sales.

OBJECTIVES

1 Identify major crops grown from bulbs, corms, and tubers

2 Differentiate between bulbs, corms, tubers, and rhizomes

3 Explain the major steps in Easter lily production

4 Describe cultural practices in forcing tulip crops

5 Describe production practices associated with daffodils

6 Explain how crocuses, dwarf irises, and grape hyacinths are produced for sale

7 Describe production practices associated with Asiatic and Oriental lilies

8 Discuss how amaryllis crops are produced

TERMS

amaryllis
Asiatic lilies
basal plate
bulb
case cooled by forcer
case cooled by supplier
controlled temperature
  forcing (CTF)
crocus
double nose (DN)
dwarf iris
Easter lily
forcing
grape hyacinth
hyacinth
leaf counting

narcissus
natural cooling
non-precooled
non-tunicate bulbs
precooled
rhizome
rooting room A
rooting room B
scales
scalettes
splitting
tuber
tulip
tunic
tunicate bulb

BULBS, CORMS, TUBERS, AND RHIZOMES

Potted bulb crops are grown for winter and spring sales. Some common bulb crops include Easter lily, tulip, narcissus, and hyacinth. Dwarf irises, crocuses, grape hyacinths, Asiatic lilies, Oriental lilies, and amaryllises are other bulbs. Although these plants are commonly referred to as bulb crops, they technically are not all bulbs.

BULBS

Bulbs are short, flattened stems that bear fleshy, food-storage leaves. The fleshy modified leaves, called *scales,* store food and water. At the base of each scale, there is a bud. The scales can be relatively thin and wrap tightly around the bud, as in the case of tulips and daffodils, or they can be thick and loose, as with lilies.

True bulbs are further classified as tunicate or non-tunicate. A *tunicate bulb* has a dry, papery covering called a *tunic.* Just as a coat protects you from the elements, a tunic protects the bud scales from damage and drying. Examples of tunicate bulbs include tulips, hyacinths, and narcissus. *Non-tunicate bulbs* lack a tunic and the protection a dry, papery covering would provide. Lilies are non-tunicate bulbs.

The bulb scales are held together at the bottom of the bulb by the basal plate. The *basal plate* is a hardened portion of stem tissue. Roots develop along the outside edge of the basal plate.

9-2. Easter lilies have thick, loose scales and are non-tunicate.

9-3. This amaryllis has a dry, papery covering called a tunic. (Courtesy, DeVroomen Holland Garden Products)

9-4. Shown are crocus corms. (Courtesy, International Flower Bulb Centre)

CORMS

Corms, although they look like bulbs, differ in structure. A corm is defined as a short, swollen, underground stem. It lacks fleshy scales. One or two dry leaf bases similar to a tunic cover corms. As with bulbs, new roots grow from a basal plate. Each season of growth depletes all the food and water reserves in a corm. New corms develop from buds located on the top or side of the original corm. Crocuses, freesias, and gladiolas are corms.

TUBERS

A *tuber* is an underground stem. It differs from bulbs and corms in that it has no dry leaf coverings or a basal plate. Tubers are usually flat and rounded. They have a tough outer skin from which roots develop. Tuberous plants include tuberous begonias, gloxinias, and anemones.

9-5. Tuberous begonias have tubers.

RHIZOMES

A *rhizome* is an underground horizontal stem. Buds are produced on the top or sides of the rhizome. Irises and calla lilies are rhizomes.

BULB CROPS

Bulbs and corms are produced in regions of the world that provide optimum growing conditions. Holland produces the greatest number of bulbs. Some other areas that produce bulbs include Israel, the Pacific Northwest, and Michigan. Parts of the United States that have a short spring followed quickly by hot summer temperatures are not good for bulb growth.

9-6. Calla lilies have rhizomes. (Courtesy, International Flower Bulb Centre)

Summer is a very important time in bulb production. A climate that provides long, cool, bright days is best for most bulbs. These conditions are good for vegetative growth. Leaves that stay on a plant for a long period produce sugars that contribute to the enlargement of the bulbs. Food produced is stored in the bulb before it goes dormant.

It is best to pot and root bulbs before they are cooled. Roots that have developed are present to absorb water once the bulbs are moved to the greenhouse for forcing. As a result, rooted bulbs are well prepared to send all their stored energy into the development of leaves and flowers.

Bulbs require a vernalization, or cold period, to flower. Tulips, daffodils, lilies, crocuses, and irises are *precooled,* or given cold treatment, for early forcing. All but the lilies are given some cooling prior to shipment. Bulbs that are not given cold treatment by the supplier are said to be *non-precooled*. Precooled lilies have received all their cooling. Once bulbs have received the required cold period they are forced. *Forcing* is a term used to describe the practices that get bulbs to grow and produce flowers.

9-7. Easter lilies are grown as potted flowering plants in the United States and Canada. (Courtesy, International Flower Bulb Centre)

EASTER LILIES
(Lilium longeflorum)

General Information

Easter lilies are grown in the United States and Canada as a potted flowering crop for the Easter season. They produce a single stem and 1 to 20 large, fragrant, white, trumpet-shaped flowers. They are sold with one flower open. In Europe, Easter lilies are grown and sold as cut flowers. The primary varieties grown as potted plants are 'Nellie White' and 'Ace.'

The Easter lily crop is difficult to grow because Easter falls on a different date each year. Easter is the first Sunday following a full moon after March 21. The earliest Easter can be is March 21. The latest date for Easter is around April 20. Therefore, growers must schedule their crops differently each year.

Propagation

Easter lilies are produced along the Pacific Coast in California and Oregon. The coastal area has cool, wet conditions all year. The bulbs are propagated from bulblets and scalettes. Bulblets form on the underground stem of a mature lily. **Scalettes** are small bulbs that grow on bulb scales that were removed from a bulb and planted.

In the first season, scalettes grow to 1 to 2 inches in circumference or the distance around the outside of the bulb. They are dug, graded, and replanted. A yearling is produced by the end of the second season that is 4 to 6 inches in circumference. They are dug, graded, and replanted. It takes three years to produce a commercial bulb with a 7- to 10-inch circumference. The harvested bulbs are packed in peat moss for shipment to growers around the country.

The forcer has a choice in what size bulbs to purchase. The larger the bulb, the more flowers it will produce. Bulbs are measured in circumference. They are graded and sold as 6½ to 7, 7 to 8, 8 to 9, 9 to 10, and 10 to 11 inches. On average, a 10- to 11-inch bulb produces eight to nine flower buds on an "Ace" and seven to eight flower buds on a "Nellie White."

Cooling

Easter lilies must go through vernalization. Vernalization is sometimes referred to as precooling or cooling. The required vernalization period for Easter lilies is 1,000 hours or around six weeks of cool temperatures. 'Nellie White' is cooled at 44 to 46°F and 'Ace' is cooled at 39 to 41°F. There are four methods of cooling the Easter lily bulbs.

Controlled temperature forcing (CTF)—With this method, bulbs are received by the forcer and potted immediately. The growing medium is kept at 63°F for two to three weeks to promote the development of roots. Then, the bulbs are given 1,000 hours of 40°F temperatures. At the end of the cooling period, they are removed from the cooler and forced. CTF gives the forcer the most control over the cooling period. As a result, crops tend to be of higher quality. Plants produce more flowers and have longer leaves. The crops are easier to force and development is more uniform.

Natural cooling—This involves potting the bulbs as soon as they arrive. They are placed outdoors, or may be kept in a poly house if temperatures drop below freezing. Natural cooling is generally not recommended in middle or southern areas of the continental United States. It too, results in plants with more flowers and longer leaves.

9-8. These Easter lilies are undergoing natural cooling in a poly house.

Case cooled by supplier—The bulbs are cooled in their packing cases by the supplier before they are shipped to the customer. The forcer pots the bulbs upon arrival and begins the forcing process. This product is convenient for forcers that lack cooling space. A disadvantage is the cases at the center of the large coolers may not have been cooled long enough.

Case cooled by forcer—This is similar to case cooled by supplier with the exception that the cooling is done by the forcer. The advantage is the forcer can feel confident that the bulbs have received the required period of cooling.

Growing

Easter lilies are potted in 6-inch lily pots that are similar in size to a standard pot. Some growers plant two to three bulbs in larger pots. The growing medium should have a high bulk density and a pH between 6.5 and 7.0. Lilies are sensitive to fluorides. A symptom of fluoride damage common among monocot plants is leaf-tip burn. Sources of fluorides include perlite, city water, and super and treble phosphate fertilizers. Some growers avoid using perlite in their growing medium because of the fluoride.

The forcer must plant the lilies promptly upon receipt or, if the case is cooled by the forcer, after they have been cooled. Place the bulbs near the bottom of the pot. The bulb is then covered with several inches of growing medium. This potting practice promotes the formation of stem roots. The stem

9-9. Although planted in the center, shoots often emerge at the edge of the pot. At this stage the plant on the right can be corrected.

roots help to stabilize the plant and serve as a backup in case the bottom roots die.

Lilies should be watered sparingly at first. After the shoots have emerged, allow the medium to dry between waterings. Overhead watering is most commonly used with Easter lilies. Root rot can be a problem with wet medium, so capillary mats and ebb and flow systems are avoided. Fertilize lilies grown in soilless media with 250 ppm nitrogen and potassium. Medium with soil should receive 200 ppm nitrogen and potassium. Slow-release fertilizers are often incorporated in soilless mixes before potting. Early fertilization produces vigorous stem growth and leaf development.

Forcing

The simple schedule for CTF and naturally cooled bulbs is to pot the bulbs, keep them at 50 to 60°F for two to three weeks, cool, and force. Precooled or case cooled bulbs are potted, given one to two weeks at 50 to 60°F, and then forced. With six weeks of cooling, expect 110 to 115 days to force the plants.

Temperature affects the speed of forcing. It can be adjusted to speed or slow growth. If the lilies are too advanced, they can be given cooler temperatures to slow their metabolism. If the lilies are behind schedule, temperatures are raised. Generally, if Easter is early, bulbs are forced at 63 to 65°F nights. If Easter is late, the bulbs are forced at 60°F nights. When Easter is

9-10. These Easter lilies show excellent leaf development in the early stages of forcing.

9-11. Temperature has a big effect on the speed of forcing Easter lilies.

somewhere in the middle, they are forced at 62°F nights. Flower buds should be visible by Ash Wednesday or about 40 days before sale.

Long-day treatments can be used as a substitute for insufficient cooling or to induce earlier flower formation. Lighting plants from 10:00 p.m. to 2:00 a.m., beginning when shoots emerge and continuing for 10 to 14 days, speeds development. Each four-hour per day lighting substitutes one full day of cooling.

The height of Easter lilies is influenced by a number of factors. 'Nellie White' is a shorter growing variety than 'Ace.' Light, temperature, humidity and watering practices affect plant height. Lower light levels result in taller plants. The more water or fertilizer the plants receive, the taller the plant. Therefore, high temperatures that increase the frequency of water and fertilizer applications, result in taller lilies. High humidity also produces taller plants.

DIF and growth retardants are employed to control the height of lilies. DIF is a very easy way to maintain the height of lilies. A zero or slightly nega-

9-12. Easter lilies can be grown fairly close together.

tive DIF is the most affective. Large negative DIF causes the leaves to droop and curve down. Growth regulators, including A-rest, can be used as a drench or as a spray when shoots are 6 to 8 inches tall.

The practice of **leaf counting** is the best way to monitor the progress of the crop and to determine whether growth needs to be speeded or slowed. It also allows the timing of the crop to begin on January 15, leaving plenty of time for adjustments.

TABLE 9-1. Leaf Counting
Part 1—Determining the desired rate for leaves to unfold
1. Between January 15 and 20, select three to five plants to be the representatives for the crop.
2. Identify the uppermost unfolded leaf and mark it with a marking pen.
3. Count all of the leaves from the base of the plant up to the unfolded leaf. Record this figure. (Example: 46 leaves)
4. Remove and count all of the unfolded leaves. A magnifying lens and tweezers help with the smallest leaves. Record this figure. (Example: 48 unfolded leaves)
5. Compute the number of leaves that must unfold to meet the schedule. To do this, count backward from Easter to the date flower buds should be visible. Six weeks is the usual time period before Easter. (Example: If Easter is on April 4, flower buds should be visible February 21.)
6. There are 37 days from January 15 to February 21. Divide the total number of leaves yet to unfold by 37. The result is the number of leaves that must unfold per day in order to see flower buds by February 21. (Example: 48 divided by 37 = 1.3 leaves per day)
Part 2—Determining the rate of unfolding leaves
1. Select three to five plants to be the representatives for the crop. Place a label in the pots.
2. Identify the uppermost unfolded leaf and mark it with a making pen or notch it.
3. Wait four to five days and identify the new uppermost unfolded leaf and mark it with a marking pen or notch it.
4. Count the number of leaves that unfolded between the two marked leaves.
5. Calculate the number of leaves unfolding per day by dividing the number of new leaves unfolded by the days. (Example: Five newly unfolded leaves divided by four days = 1.25 leaves unfolding per day.)
6. Previously in the example, we determined that 1.3 leaves need to be unfolding per day to meet the schedule. The rate of 1.25 leaves that are actually unfolding is a little bit slow. Therefore, temperatures should be raised a bit to speed development.
7. By counting the leaves every four to five days, the rate of development can be monitored.

9-13. This grower counts leaves to determine the progress of his lilies.

9-14. The grower holds a leaf identified by having its tip removed and counts the number of unfolded leafs to determine the rate at which the leaves are unfolding.

9-15. These lilies, with white, puffed-up flower buds, are ready for market.

9-16. These Easter lilies are being held in a cooler.

Easter lilies are ready for market when the largest floral bud has ballooned and turned white. If necessary, plants that open early can be held in a cooler with temperatures between 35 and 40°F. They can tolerate cold storage for about two weeks. Warm them slowly when they are removed from storage.

If flower buds have opened, the anthers should be removed. Removal of the anthers prolongs the life of the flower. Also, the anthers produce an abundance of pollen. The pollen discolors the petals and can stain clothes and tablecloths.

9-17. Before packaging for shipment, these people remove anthers from the flowers that have opened.

9-18. Bulb mites caused this lily to become deformed.

9-19. Potted tulips are very popular. (Courtesy, International Flower Bulb Centre)

Pest and Disease Problems

Easter lily pests include the bulb mite. A recommended practice to control bulb mites is to dip the bulbs in a miticide bath before potting. Aphids and fungus gnats can also be problems.

Root rot is a concern for growers of Easter lilies. *Rhizoctonia* fungus can cause root rot especially in wet medium. Another fungus, *Botrytis*, can cause damage to flowers and flower buds. Virus infections can also deform flowers.

TULIPS (Tulipa species)

General Information

Most tulip species are from southwestern Europe and the Near East. They are very popular bulb plants. Tulips are available in practically all colors with the exception of a true blue. They are grown for cut flowers or as potted flowering plants. The season for tulip production extends from early January to mid-May.

Tulips may be purchased as precooled or non-precooled bulbs. Precooled tulips require only 10 to 12 weeks of cold temperatures. For later forcing, approximately 18 to 20 cold weeks are needed. It is recommended that bulbs, 12/14 centimeters in circumference, be used for potted crops. Plan on 3 bulbs in a 4-inch pot, 4 bulbs

9-20. These bulbs are being grown in 8-inch pots.

in a 5-inch pot, 6 to 7 bulbs in a 6-inch pot, and 9 to 10 bulbs in an 8-inch pot. Use a well-drained medium with a pH between 6.0 and 7.0.

*G*rowing

Plant the bulbs upon arrival. In the planting process, remove any bulbils attached to the bulb and remove the tunic. Place the bulbs with the flat sides facing the rim of the pot. By doing so, the big leaf develops to the outside of the pot. The nose or tip of the bulb should be slightly below the surface of the medium.

9-21. Note how the first big leaf unfolds outwards.

Tulip production is divided into two groups based on the forcing program. One group called **rooting room A** involves production for early flowering, before February 14. The other group, **rooting room B**, involves production for later flowering, after February 14. Bulbs for rooting room A should be received and planted in mid-September. Order bulbs for a rooting room B program for planting around the beginning of October. Most tulip varieties require 15 to 16 weeks of cold temperatures followed by three to four weeks in the greenhouse to force them.

Rooting Room

After potting, the bulbs are cooled. This is often accomplished in poly houses or in refrigerated coolers. In the rooting room, bulbs are given 48°F temperatures for four to six weeks, or until roots begin to grow out the bottom of the pots. In this phase, the soil should be kept moist and the humidity maintained between 95 and 100 percent. The temperature is lowered to 41°F, and maintained until the shoots are about 1 inch high. At this stage, temperatures are dropped again to 31 to 35°F for the duration of the cold-week requirement.

Table 9-2. Rooting Room Temperatures and Time

Rooting Room	Flowering Schedule	Treatment
Rooting room A—Early	Early to middle season varieties flowering until February 14	48°F for 4-6 weeks (Nov. 10), 41°F until shoots 1" (Jan. 5), 32-35°F to end of cold requirement
Rooting room B—Later	Middle to late season varieties flowering after February 14	48°F for 4-6 weeks (Dec. 5), 41°F until shoots 1" (Jan. 5), 32-35°F to end of cold requirement

Forcing

In the greenhouse, strive for constant temperatures. Normally, 60°F is good. Provide good ventilation and keep humidity levels low. Tulips force best with light intensity between 1,000 and 2,500 foot candles. Keep the medium moist and water in the morning to reduce possible damage from *Botrytis*. Fertilize with 140 ppm of calcium nitrate.

Move the tulips to market when they are in the bud stage, when at least one bud is showing color. The preferred height is 10 to 14 inches. If neces-

 **9-22.** These tulips have just been removed from the cooler and are ready for forcing.

9-23. This photograph shows four groups of tulips scheduled one week apart in order to provide a steady supply to retailers.

sary, tulips can be stored in the green bud stage at temperatures between 33 and 35°F.

DAFFODILS (Narcissus species)

General Information

Daffodils are very popular bulbs. The typical daffodil brightens any setting with its brilliant yellow flowers. Some varieties are available in white,

9-24. The flowers of large and miniature daffodils brighten the interiors of many homes.

two-tone colors, and peach. Potted daffodils are grown for sale during the months of January through April.

Use only **double nose (DN)** bulbs when growing potted daffodils. DN I bulbs produce more flowers than DN II bulbs and DN II bulbs produce more than DN III bulbs. The number of bulbs planted in a pot depends on the bulb size and the size of the pots.

Growing

Pot daffodil bulbs upon receipt. Use well-drained medium with a pH of 6.0 to 7.0. Plant the bulbs at a depth whereby the widest part of the bulb is below the surface, but the nose is uncovered. Water thoroughly and move to the rooting room.

Table 9-3. Recommended Pot Size and Number of Bulbs Per Pot				
Pot size	4-inch pot	5-inch pot	6-inch pot	7-inch pot
DN I	Not recommended	Not recommended	3	5
DN II	Not recommended	Not recommended	3	5
DN III (Mini-narcissus)	3	5	7	Not recommended

Rooting Room

Provide the potted bulbs with 48°F temperatures for four to six weeks. Keep the growing medium moist, but not wet during this time. When roots are seen growing out the bottom of the pots, reduce the temperature to 41°F until shoots are 1 inch high. Then, lower the temperature to 32 to 35°F until the cold requirement has been satisfied.

9-25. Pictured are a single, double, and triple nose daffodil bulb.

Each cultivar has an optimum number of cold weeks for a specific flowering date. Most varieties require 15 to 16 weeks of cold temperatures. Daffodils that have been precooled by the supplier require a total of 9 to 10 weeks of cold temperatures. Overcooling results in tall plants that are of less value.

Forcing

Move the plants to the greenhouse and force them at 60 to 63°F night temperatures. Temperatures lower than this result in taller plants, which are undesirable. Also,

9-26. Three bulbs are placed in a 6-inch pot with the noses of the bulbs above the growing medium.

9-27. When shoots are 1 to 1½ inches in length, temperatures are lowered to 32 to 35°F.

avoid temperatures above 65°F. Daffodils force best with medium light or around 2,500 foot candles. The growing medium should be kept moist.

Forcing of an early crop takes about three to four weeks at 63°F nights. Later crops require only one to two weeks in the greenhouse. These times vary slightly with the cultivar being grown. Although diseases and insects are seldom a problem, the forcer should watch for *Botrytis* and aphid problems.

Move the crops to market when the plants are in the pencil stage. This is before the flowers show color and enter the bent, "goose-neck," stage. A plant

9-28. These daffodils are being forced at 63°F nights.

height of 8 to 12 inches is preferable. If necessary, store daffodils at temperatures of 33 to 35°F.

Hyacinth
(Hyacinthus orientalis)

General Information

Hyacinths are native to Greece and Asia Minor. They produce a fragrant flower that may be purple, white, pink, or multicolored. Most hyacinths are produced in Holland. The majority of hyacinths are sold between January 3 and Valentine's Day.

Hyacinths are available to forcers as prepared bulbs or regular bulbs. Prepared bulbs require about 10 weeks of cold. They are used for early forcing. Regular bulbs need about 13 weeks to satisfy the cold requirement. Regular bulbs produce a better-looking plant than do prepared bulbs.

Hyacinths come in sizes ranging from 15/16 centimeters in circumference to 19/20 centimeters. They require a very well-drained growing medium. They can be grown with one bulb in a 4-inch pot or a number of bulbs in larger pots. Use of short bulb pans provides a stable appearance.

Count backwards on a calendar the number of weeks to produce the crop, beginning from the sale date. The bulbs might need to be held from the time of their arrival until cooling. Hold prepared bulbs at 48 to 50°F and regular bulbs at 63°F if necessary.

9-29. These paperwhite narcissus are nearly ready for market.

9-30. Hyacinths are fragrant as well as colorful.

9-31. Shown are seven hyacinths in an 8-inch bulb pan.

Rooting Room

Provide rooting room temperatures between 48 and 50°F for about four weeks or until roots grow out the bottom of the containers. Drop temperatures to 41°F until shoots are 1 to 1½ inches high. Lower temperatures to 33 to 35°F until ready to force.

Forcing

The longer the cooling period, the shorter period of time it takes to force hyacinths. December crops can be forced at 73°F greenhouse temperatures.

9-32. These hyacinths are nearly ready for sale.

Force January and February crops at 65°F. Later crops are forced at 60°F. Hyacinths require only a few weeks in the greenhouse. Sell the crop before it flowers, and let the buyer force the plant the last three to four days.

One problem of hyacinths is known as splitting. **Splitting** is a condition where the flower stalk separates from the basal plate. Once separated, the flowers fail to develop. It is caused by changes in temperature that cause the bulb to expand and contract. Freezing of the bulbs can also lead to this problem. Splitting is more common with purple varieties.

CROCUS (Crocus species), DWARF IRIS (Iris reticulata), and GRAPE HYACINTH (Muscari armeniacum)

General Information

Crocuses are a very popular small plant native to central and Western Europe. Crocus varieties offer flowers of bright purple, yellow, and white colors. Dwarf irises are native to the Caucasus region. They are purple in color. Grape hyacinths are native to Asia Minor. Grape hyacinths have clusters of blue or white flowers. The blues can sometimes appear iridescent. The majority of bulbs for these three crops are produced in Holland.

The recommended bulb sizes for crocus and grape hyacinth are 9 cm and larger. Bulb size recommendations for dwarf iris are 6 cm and larger. The bulbs are grown in 4-, 5-, and 6-inch containers. A well-drained growing me-

9-33. Crocus (left), dwarf iris (center), and grape hyacinth (right) all have similar forcing schedules. (Courtesy, International Flower Bulb Centre)

Table 9-4. Suggested Number of Bulbs Per Pot			
	4-inch pot	**5-inch pot**	**6-inch pot**
Crocus	5-6 bulbs	7-9 bulbs	10-12 bulbs
Dwarf iris	7-10 bulbs	10-12 bulbs	12-15 bulbs
Grape hyacinth	5-6 bulbs	7-9 bulbs	10-12 bulbs

dium with a pH between 6.0 and 7.0 is suggested. Plant the bulbs immediately upon arrival. The proper planting depth involves a slight covering over the tops of the bulbs.

Rooting Room

Provide 48°F temperatures for four to six weeks or until roots emerge from the bottoms of the pots. Reduce the temperature to 41°F, and store at this temperature until the shoots are about 1 inch high. Then, lower temperatures to between 32 and 35°F until the completion of the cold-week requirement.

The cold-week requirement for these crops is 15 to 16 total weeks. Precooled bulbs need only 9 to 10 weeks of cold before forcing. During the rooting room treatment, keep the growing medium moist.

Forcing

Crocuses and dwarf irises force very quickly. For early forcing, they develop in only one to two weeks in the greenhouse. Later forcing takes only two to three days. Grape hyacinth, on the other hand, needs about three weeks in the greenhouse for early forcing. Later forcing takes about two weeks.

Provide temperatures of 55 to 60°F nights and 60 to 63°F days. Light requirements for forcing are considered low to medium, 1,000 to 2,500 foot candles. For early forcing, induce the shoots to stretch by keeping them dark for a few days.

Market crocuses and dwarf irises as the sheaths encasing the flower buds become visible. Late-season crops can go right from the rooting room to market. Since these two plants have short shelf lives, it is appropriate to get them to the customer early in their flowering stage. Grape hyacinth should be mar-

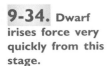**9-34.** Dwarf irises force very quickly from this stage.

9-35. The floral sheaths of these crocus are visible making them ready for market.

keted when the flower buds show the first hints of color. If necessary, short-term storage can be accomplished with temperatures of 33 to 35°F.

ASIATIC AND ORIENTAL LILIES (Lilium hybrids)

General Information

Asiatic and Oriental lilies are, as implied by their name, native to the Asian Continent. They come in a wide range of colors including yellow, white, red, and orange. They are forced throughout the year.

9-36. Asiatic lilies (left) and Oriental lilies (right) come in a wide range of colors. (Courtesy, International Flower Bulb Centre)

Most Asiatic lilies and Oriental lilies are precooled by the supplier. Therefore, no additional cooling is required by the forcer. Asiatic lilies are precooled for six weeks and Orientals for 8 to 10 weeks at 34 to 35°F.

Growing

Pot Asiatic lilies in deep pots. A common practice is to place three bulbs in a 6-inch standard pot and five bulbs in an 8-inch standard pot. The growing medium should be well drained and have a pH within a range of 6.0 and 6.5.

Grow Asiatic lilies at 55 to 60°F nights and 70°F days. Orientals prefer 65 to 67°F nights and 75°F days. Temperatures control timing of the crops. Also, DIF can be used to control the height of the plants. The length of time from planting to flowering varies with the variety from 56 days to 106 days. They are ready for market when the first is swollen and shows color.

AMARYLLIS (Amaryllis belladonna)

General Information

Amaryllises can be found growing naturally in South America. Varieties of amaryllises have been improved through hybridization providing a wide range of large, colorful flowers. Amaryllises are typical of subtropical plants.

As such, they are not cooled, nor do they like cold temperatures. They are actually grown more like a houseplant. Bulbs are produced in Israel, South Africa, and Holland.

The majority of amaryllis cultivars produce four flowers on a stalk. Larger bulbs often produce two flower stalks. Bulbs are available as 20/22, 24/26, 28/30, and 32/up centimeters in circumference.

Growing

Pot amaryllis bulbs as soon as they arrive from the supplier. Use pots slightly larger than the bulbs. Six-inch pots work well with most bulbs. In the process, clean the bulbs of debris and dead leaves, but leave healthy roots undamaged. Place the bulb at a level that will leave its shoulders exposed. A growing medium with a pH of 6.0 to 6.5 is preferred.

Water thoroughly at first, then sparingly for a few weeks. Once the leaves develop, water regularly. Fertilize with a complete fertilizer every two to four weeks. Grow the plant at temperatures from 70 to 80°F. An amaryllis should receive medium light intensity, 2,500 to 5,000 foot candles.

An amaryllis begins to flower about eight weeks after potting. Plants are marketed when a floral stalk is about 12 inches high. It is also desirable to have leaves unfolding and 6 to 12 inches in length. If development needs to be slowed, store them at 48°F. Temperatures lower than 48°F can cause damage.

Reforcing

In September, stop watering the plant. If possible, give the plant 50 to 60°F tempera-

9-37. Amaryllis produce beautiful, large flowers. (Courtesy, DeVroomen Holland Garden Products)

9-38. This amaryllis is being prepared for repotting.

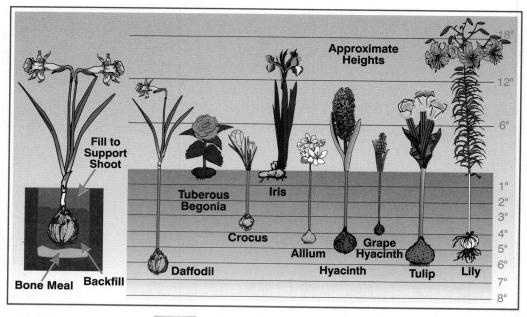

9-39. Planting depths for select bulbs.

tures. The leaves will dry and the bulb will go dormant. Allow 10 to 12 weeks for this downtime. In November/December clean the bulb and repot.

PLANTING OUTDOORS

After flowering, bulb crops can be planted outdoors. Of course, bulbs that require vernalization do well in the northern parts of the country where they receive natural cooling. Tender crops, such as tuberous begonia and amaryllis, do well in the warm areas. Plant the bulbs at the recommended depth. Placement of bone meal fertilizer in the planting hole boosts nutrient levels and promotes plant growth.

REVIEWING

MAIN IDEAS

Bulb crops include those plants that have bulbs, corms, tubers, and fleshy rhizomes. The major crops are Easter lilies, tulips, narcissus, crocuses, dwarf irises, grape hyacinths, Asiatic lilies, oriental lilies, and amaryllises. True bulbs can be further divided as being tunicated or non-tunicated. Bulb crops are typically grown for late winter and spring sales.

A great number of bulbs are produced in Holland, the Pacific Northwest, and Michigan. Long, cool, bright days are ideal for promoting vegetative growth and bulb expansion. Bulbs require a vernalization or cold period to flower. Tulips, daffodils, lilies, crocuses, and irises are precooled. All but the lilies are given some cooling prior to shipment. Bulbs that are not given cold treatment by the supplier are said to be non-precooled.

Easter lilies are grown in the United States and Canada as a potted flowering crop for the Easter season. The primary varieties grown as potted plants are 'Nellie White' and 'Ace.' The bulbs are propagated from bulblets and scalettes. It takes three years to produce a 7- to10-inch circumference bulb. Easter lilies must go through vernalization, referred to as precooling or cooling. Temperature affects the speed of forcing and can be adjusted to speed or slow growth. The rate of growth can be determined through a practice known as leaf counting.

Tulips, daffodils, hyacinths, crocuses, dwarf irises, and grape hyacinths are popular spring flowering bulbs. They are purchased precooled for pot plant production. In general, they are given rooting room temperatures between 48 and 50°F for about four weeks or until roots grow out the bottom of the containers. Drop temperatures to 41°F until shoots are 1 to 1½ " high. At this stage, temperatures are dropped again to 31 to 35°F for the duration of the cold week requirement. They are moved to the greenhouse and forced at 60 to 63°F.

The supplier precools Asiatic lilies and Oriental lilies. Grow Asiatic lilies at 55 to 60°F nights and 70°F days and Orientals at 65 to 67°F nights and 75°F days. Amaryllis are typical of subtropical plants and are grown like a houseplant. They are not cooled, nor do they like cold temperatures.

QUESTIONS

Answer the following questions. Use correct spelling and complete sentences.

1. How do bulbs, corms, tubers, and rhizomes differ?
2. What does a tunicate bulb mean?
3. Why are bulbs precooled?
4. Why are Easter lilies considered a difficult crop to grow?
5. What is vernalization?
6. Why is leaf counting practiced?
7. When are rooting room A and rooting room B used?
8. What is the purpose of the rooting room?
9. Why is it important to get crocus and dwarf iris to the customer quickly?
10. How does an amaryllis differ from the spring bulbs?

EVALUATING

Match the term with the correct definition. Write the letter by the term in the blank provided.

a. hyacinth
b. non-tunicate bulbs
c. non-precooled
d. splitting

e. amaryllis
f. case cooled by supplier
g. corm
h. forcing

i. scalettes
j. leaf counting

_____ 1. Lack a tunic and the protection a dry, papery covering would provide.

_____ 2. Bulbs are cooled in their packing cases by the supplier before they are shipped to the customer.

_____ 3. Defined as a short, swollen, underground stem.

_____ 4. Typical of subtropical plants, they are not cooled.

_____ 5. Small bulbs that grow on bulb scales that were removed from a bulb and planted.

_____ 6. Bulbs that are not given cold treatment by the supplier.

_____ 7. A condition where the flower stalk separates from the basal plate.

_____ 8. Practice used to monitor the progress of an Easter lily crop and to determine whether growth needs to be speeded or slowed.

_____ 9. A term used to describe practices that get bulbs to grow and produce flowers.

_____ 10. Produce a fragrant flower that may be purple, white, pink, or multicolored.

EXPLORING

1. Obtain tulips, narcissus, hyacinths, crocuses, dwarf irises, or grape hyacinths in the fall of the year. Pot them as instructed in the text. Place them in a refrigerator set at the optimum temperatures for the recommended period of cold time. Remove the bulbs and force them in the home or in a greenhouse.

2. Continue to grow potted bulbs from late winter and early spring indoors until the weather warms up enough to safely plant them outside. Plant the bulbs with bone meal at the correct depth. Wait for next spring to see flowers.

3. Propagate your own amaryllis. As the bulbs grow year after year they produce side bulbs. Remove these when you repot the amaryllis and pot them in smaller pots.

10

Growing Cut Flowers and Foliage

Roses are red. Violets are blue. Who hasn't made up a poem beginning with those lines? The familiarity of that poem underscores how roses have a permanent place in American traditions and way of life. People value roses as cut flowers. Cut flowers, easily purchased as a bouquet, can be placed in a vase and brighten a serving table at a party. Gifts of cut flowers can be given to express love, sympathy, and as a request for forgiveness.

Although roses might be the most recognized cut flower in the United States, there are many types of flowers grown for use as cut flowers. As production techniques, marketing and distribution of cut flowers have improved, consumers have been given greater variety. That variety is evident at supermarkets that package cut flowers for cash and carry sales. Florists also have an increased selection of flowers for use in all kinds of design work.

10-1. Roses are the most recognized cut flower and are easily purchased as a bouquet. (Courtesy, Steven E. Newman, Colorado State University)

OBJECTIVES

1   Recognize the importance of the international and domestic cut flower markets

2   Identify major cut flowers

3   Describe cultural practices in growing cut flowers

4   Recognize pest and disease problems of major cut flower crops

TERMS

alstroemeria
freesia
gladiolus
hook cut
hybrid tea rose
leaf drop

mini carnation
single flowering carnation
snapdragon
splitting of the calyx
standard carnation
sweetheart (floribunda) rose

CUT FLOWER OVERVIEW

Times have changed! Before World War II floriculture production in the United States meant cut flowers. If your grandmother or great-grandmother were to go to the market to buy flowers, they would have been shopping for cut flowers. Potted flowering plants, foliage plants, and bedding plants were not common then. Now, cut flower production in the United States is valued at less than 17 percent of the entire floriculture production.

Production of cut flowers and foliage in the United States amounted to $437 million in 1997. That places cut flowers fourth behind the production of bedding plants, potted flowering plants, and foliage plants. Rose, chrysanthemum, carnation, and gladiola are the major cut flower crops in the United States. Minor crops include alstroemeria, freesia, gerbera daisy, orchid, snapdragon, and exotic tropical flowers. The five top cut flower producing states include California, Florida, Hawaii, Colorado, and Pennsylvania. Hawaii is the primary producer of exotic, tropical cut flowers.

Florida is the largest producing state in terms of cut foliage or greens. Cut foliage, which includes leatherleaf fern, asparagus fern, pittosporum, and podocarpus, is used to add greenery to floral work. Florida held an 81 percent

Table 10-1. Value of United States Cut Flower Crops Sold in 1996-1997	
Crop	**Wholesale Value in Millions of Dollars**
Carnations, Miniature	$ 7,042
Carnations, Standard	$ 9,602
Chrysanthemum, Pompon	$ 15,488
Chrysanthemum, Standard	$ 5,794
Gladiola	$ 33,945
Rose, Hybrid tea	$106,317
Rose, Sweetheart	$ 9,762
Other cut flowers (orchid, snapdragon, gerbera daisy, alstroemeria, freesia, anthurium, etc.)	$248,677

market share of the domestic production in 1997. Other states with notable cut foliage production include California, Oregon, and Hawaii. Increasing amounts of cut foliage are being imported from Mexico, Costa Rica, Guatemala, and other countries.

Table 10-2. Value of United States Cut Foliage Crops Sold in 1997	
Crop	**Wholesale Value in Millions of Dollars**
Leatherleaf fern	$60,412
Other cut cultivated greens (asparagus fern, pittosporum, podocarpus, etc.)	$44,818

Table 10-3. Value of Hawaiian Tropical Crops Sold in 1997	
Crop	**Wholesale Value in Millions of Dollars**
Anthuriums	$ 7,421
Birds of Paradise	$ 494
Ginger	$ 1,024
Heliconia	$ 510
Dendrobium orchids	$ 2,543
Other orchids	$ 519
Protea	$ 1,166
Total	**$13,677**

The United States cut flower market relies heavily on imports from other countries. Imports of cut flowers in 1996 totaled $572 million, well exceeding the value of domestic cut flower production. South American exports to the United States accounted for $437 million of cut flowers shipped. The countries with major exports to the United States follow:

- Columbia, $366 million
- Ecuador, $68 million
- Holland, $59 million
- Canada and Mexico combined for $29 million

To remain profitable, growers in the United States have had to change. Some growers refocused their production to potted flowering crops and bedding plants. Some growers invested in technology for more efficient production. Others switched from growing major cut flower crops to specialty cut flowers that would not be in direct competition with imports.

Cut flower production is an international affair for a number of reasons. Modern air travel has made rapid shipments possible. Cut flowers, grown and harvested in one part of the world, can be transported to another part of the world in hours. Production of cut flowers is labor intensive. As a result, some crop production has shifted to parts of the world where the cost of labor is low. Also, in some parts of the world, such as Columbia, the temperatures, light, and other conditions are absolutely perfect for growing certain cut flowers.

PRODUCTION OF CUT FLOWERS

ROSE

Two types of roses are produced, hybrid tea roses and sweetheart (floribunda) roses. About 90 percent of the cut roses produced in the United States are hybrid tea roses. The **hybrid tea rose** is a large, usually solitary flower. The majority of the hybrid tea roses produced are red. Other popular colors include pink, yellow, and white. The **sweetheart (floribunda) rose** is a smaller rose that grows as a spray and is often disbudded. Sweetheart roses are used extensively in wedding work, corsages, and centerpieces. Yellow and pink make up a large percentage of those produced. New cultivars also offer many pastel colors.

Interestingly, most holidays are in sync with rose production. The holidays are spaced about six weeks apart during the year. It takes from six to

10-2. The hybrid tea rose (left) is a large, usually solitary flower, and the sweetheart (floribunda) rose (right) is a smaller rose that grows as a spray.

eight weeks to produce a new crop of roses after a harvest. Eight weeks are required during the darker months of December. There is also a long break in production after June when rose plants are cut back. The two biggest holidays for rose sales are Valentine's Day and Mother's Day.

- Early September—Grandparent's Day

- October—Sweetest Day

- December—Christmas

- February—Valentine's Day

- April—Easter, Secretaries Day

- May—Mother's Day

- June—Weddings

Growing

Roses are an exacting crop. Temperatures must be maintained at optimum levels. In addition, pinching and lighting must be carefully controlled in order for growers to have the flowers ready for specific holidays. Given the right climate, cut roses can be grown successfully outdoors.

Propagation is done primarily by grafting. The most common procedure, t-budding, involves buds from select rose cultivars being placed on multiflora rose rootstocks. Ninety percent humidity is maintained in the greenhouse to

10-3. Roses are usually grown in organic growing medium. (Courtesy, Steven E. Newman, Colorado State University)

help the grafts to take. Plants are planted with the bud union at or just below the soil surface.

Roses like an organic growing medium that is well drained. An organic matter content of 35 to 37 percent provides good drainage, aeration and cation exchange capacity. The expected life of a rose bush in commercial operations is 5 to 7 years, so a medium with stable organic matter is important. A growing medium pH of 6.0 to 6.5 is preferred.

Fertilization requirements are considered medium to high. A suggested fertilization program involves the application of an ounce of granular 10-10-10 or similar fertilizer three times a year. The fertilizer is placed alongside the plant in April, June, and mid-August. A constant liquid feed applied through a drip irrigation system is another option. Feeding at a rate of 100 to 150 ppm nitrogen, phosphorus, and potassium is recommended. It is also recommended that every third watering be clear water.

Roses do best in warm temperatures. They like 62 to 65°F nights and 75 to 90°F days. Cooler temperatures result in larger flowers, but it takes them longer to produce. During periods of low light, the temperature in the greenhouse should be lowered. Roses also require full sun to maximize the production of sugars.

Pruning of roses every year, or at least every other year, helps maintain production levels. A direct prune using lopping shears is performed right after Mother's Day. With direct pruning, stems are cut back to within 18 to 30 inches of the rootstock. Gradual pruning can also be performed. It is a method used in the spring and fall, and it is usually done the first year or the first year after a direct cut. Gradual pruning involves the removal of a portion of the old wood with a flower. The cut is known as a *hook cut*.

Harvesting

Harvest roses when the sepals have dropped and the outer petals begin to open. Growers can expect hybrid tea rose plants to produce 20 to 30 flowers a year. Sweetheart rose plants produce around 40 stems a year. Where the cut is made on the stem influences both the stem length and the growth rate of the bush.

10-4. Harvest roses when the sepals have dropped and the outer petals begin to open. (Courtesy, Hills Floral Products, Inc., Richmond, Indiana)

Generally, the cut is made just above the node of the second five-leaflet leaf from the tip of the stem. Long stems are valued. However, when cuts are made below the second five-leaflet leaf, recovery of the bush and production of the next flowers are delayed. Stems cut 22 inches and longer in length are ordinarily used as gift roses. Those cut to the length of 10 to 14 inches tend to be used for floral work, such as bouquets.

Harvesting is performed in the morning and evening hours to reduce stress on the cut flower. Flowers are placed directly in water acidified with citric acid to a pH of 3.5. They are placed in the cooler set at 34°F. After a few hours, they are graded and placed in bunches of 12 to 25 stems for shipment. Grading classification is as follows:

- Short 10 to 14 inches
- Medium 14 to 18 inches

- Long 18 to 22 inches

- Extra long 22 to 26 inches

- Fancy 26 to 30 inches

- Extra fancy 30 or more inches

Pests and Diseases

One of the main problems with roses is **_leaf drop_** caused by variations in temperature, excessive drying, excessive soluble salts, or wet soil. Cool, moist conditions can lead to problems with black spot or mildew. Major pests include two-spotted mites, aphids, and rose midge.

CARNATION

Carnations are widely used in the floral industry, and rank as the third most popular cut flower in the world. Their long vase life and their tolerance to shipping increase their value. Colors range from red, white, pink, yellow, pastels, and variegated.

Three types of cut carnations are available. **_Standard carnations_** are large, solitary flowers that have been disbudded. Flowers of **_mini carnations_** are 1/2 to 1/3 the size of standard carnation flowers. The terminal flower bud of a mini carnation is usually removed to improve the development of a 2 to

10-5. A standard carnation (left) has a large solitary flower, and the mini carnation (right) has two to four smaller flowers on a stem.

4 flower spray. There are also single flowering types. **Single flowering carnations** produce a flower without the need of disbudding.

In the 1920s, 30s, and 40s, the Chicago area was considered the carnation capitol of the world. Other areas in the United States known for carnation production include Southern California, the mountainous regions of North Carolina, and Colorado. Today, however, the United States imports most of its carnations. Columbia supplies roughly 80 percent of the carnations sold in the United States.

Carnations are propagated from stem cuttings. They are planted shallow in ground beds. The shallow planting helps to reduce verticillium, fusarium, and bacterial stem rot disease problems to which they are very susceptible. The medium must also be sterilized to reduce disease problems. The medium pH should be between 5.5 and 6.5.

Columbia, a mountainous country located near the equator, has perfect conditions for year-round carnation production. The natural temperatures are what carnations prefer, 50 to 55°F nights and 60 to 65°F days. The light intensity at higher elevations is excellent. Carnations are long-day plants and in Columbia, the day lengths are the same throughout the year. Production in the United States requires lighting from September through December. Also, growers in the United States must control greenhouse temperatures.

10-6. Carnations are grown on a one or two year rotation usually in ground beds. (Courtesy, Steven E. Newman, Colorado State University)

Carnations are grown on a one or two year rotation. Flowers in the first year are larger. There are more, but smaller, flowers produced in the second year. Standard carnations are harvested when about ½-inch of the petals show above the calyx. Mini carnations are harvested when two flowers are open and the buds are showing color. The biggest problem with harvested flowers is the **splitting of the calyx**. This condition is caused by fluctuations of temperatures and is more common with some cultivars than others. When the calyx splits, petals spill out and the flower appears misshapen.

GLADIOLUS

Gladioli are valued for their large showy floral spikes. Cultivars are available in nearly every color. As cut flowers, they are long lasting. They can also be harvested when the first bud shows color. Yet unopened buds will open right on up to the top of the stem.

10-7. Gladioli are available in many colors. (Courtesy, Joe Steffen)

Much of the commercial production of gladioli takes place in Florida and California. However, gladioli corms are grown across the United States. In California, production is year-round, while November through June are the prime months of production in Florida.

Gladioli are produced outside in fields. Since they do not tolerate frost, planting in the north is not done until after the frost-free date. Typically, corms for cut flower production are planted about 1 inch apart in 5- to 6-inch deep furrows. Gladioli are relatively heavy feeders. Fertilization with a complete fertilizer at planting and side dressing during the development of the crop is recommended. After flowering and as the leaves die back, corms are dug and placed in dry storage.

Harvested gladioli are kept in an upright position. This is because they respond dramatically to gravitropism. Should they lie on their side for a short

10-8. This field of gladioli is used for hybridizing. (Courtesy, Joe Steffen)

while, their stems bend upwards. The resulting crooked stems are of less value to floral arrangers and designers.

Major pest problems include aphids and thrips. Thrips can be especially troublesome and cause damage to both foliage and flowers. Regular pesticide applications can be used to control thrips.

SNAPDRAGON

The elongated floral inflorescence of snapdragons is very attractive. **Snapdragons** come in a variety of bright colors. White, pink, and yellow are very popular. Other colors available include red, bronze, and purple. Children are often entertained by removing and pinching the sides of a floret to see the "dragon's" mouth open.

Unlike most cut flower crops, snapdragons are propagated by seed. Seeds germinate in 5 to 7 days at 65 to 70°F degrees. The seeds are left uncovered for best results. After they have developed the first set of true leaves, they are transplanted to the growing bed.

10-9. Snapdragons are very popular and come in a variety of colors. (Courtesy, Steven E. Newman, Colorado State University)

The hybrids used have been developed for specific periods of the year. Winter snapdragons have been bred to perform in lower light levels and cooler temperatures, 50°F nights. Spring snapdragons do well in high light and cool temperatures, 55°F nights. Summer snapdragons are bred for high light and warm temperatures. Fall snapdragons like high light and warm temperatures, 60°F nights.

Snapdragons are grown in ground beds or on raised benches. In either case, they like a well-aerated growing medium with a pH between 5.5 and 6.5. They are considered to be light feeders.

10-10. These snapdragons were grown from seed. (Courtesy, Steven E. Newman, Colorado State University)

It is necessary to provide support for snapdragons with netting. Crops require two layers of netting with the top one at a level below the lowest flower. Keeping the flowers upright after harvesting, during storage, and while shipping is critical to maintain straight stems. Laid on their side, snapdragons will bend within half an hour.

The best-quality flowers are cut with a minimum of 5 to 7 florets open. The stems are placed in water as soon as possible. Foliage from the lower 1/3 of the stem is removed before the stems are graded and bunched.

Snapdragons have few serious pest or disease problems. Pest problems associated with snapdragon production include aphids, thrips, and whiteflies. Diseases of note are botrytis, mildews, and damping off of seedlings caused by *Pythium*.

10-11. *Alstroemeria* are long-lasting flowers that have increased in popularity. (Courtesy, Steven E. Newman, Colorado State University)

ALSTROEMERIA

Alstroemeria, also known as the Peruvian lily or Inca lily, has gained popularity in the United States since the 1970s. It is everblooming, produces high yields, and it is easy to grow under cool temperatures. Flowers of the *Alstroemeria* are borne on a cyme, and come in many colors including yellow, orange, red, pink, purple, lavender, white, and bicolor. Another asset is alstroemeria have a long vase life, two weeks or more.

Propagation of alstroemeria is done by division of its white fleshy rhizomes or by tissue culture. Plants are placed in ground beds since they can grow to a height of 6 feet. The medium should have a high percentage of organic matter. The pH should be between 6.0 and 6.5.

Alstroemeria requires high nutrient levels. During spring growth and flower production, they like 600 ppm of a 20-20-20 fertilizer on a weekly ba-

10-12. *Alstroemaria* are long-day plants that require large amounts of nutrients and water. (Courtesy, Steven E. Newman, Colorado State University)

sis. They also require large amounts of water and high light intensity for maximum floral production. Alstroemerias are long-day plants, and as such, require lighting during the darker months to promote flowering.

Flower clusters are harvested when the first flower begins to open. Pests and disease problems are minimal. Aphids, mites, and *Botrytis* are the chief problems.

FREESIA

Freesia is a cut flower that has grown rapidly in popularity. The lily-like flowers, borne on a horizontal spike, come in bright colors including yellow, red, white, blue, and pink. In addition to the visual interest, they are very fragrant. Some people liken their scent to the breakfast cereal, Fruit Loops. Freesias are produced from corms.

Freesias are planted in September in northern regions and as late as December in southern regions of the United States. Corms are planted 2 inches deep in ground beds or raised beds at a spacing of about 12 corms per square foot. Freesia requires a well-drained medium with a pH between 6.5 and 7.2. Perlite must not be used in the medium, as freesias are sensitive to fluorides.

Grow freesias warm (60 to 65°F nights) after planting

10-13. Freesias are fragrant flowers that come in bright colors. (Courtesy, Steven E. Newman, Colorado State University)

10-14. These freesias will be supported with wire and string supports as they grow. (Courtesy, Steven E. Newman, Colorado State University)

until the stems are about 12 inches in height. Then, drop the temperatures to 50 to 55°F nights to trigger flowering. Avoid letting the day temperatures exceed 63°F after the temperatures have been dropped. Freesias like high light intensity and 200 ppm of a 20-20-20 fertilizer every other week. The first flowers appear about eight weeks following the onset of cool temperatures. Each stem produces approximately six flower stalks in the course of a season. Harvest flowers when the first floret opens.

Thrips and aphids must be controlled as they can serve as vectors for viral disease. Other problems include fusarium and spider mites.

REVIEWING

MAIN IDEAS

The floriculture industry has changed. Cut flower production, once the most important aspect of the floriculture industry in the United States, now makes up less than 17 percent of the entire floriculture production. That places cut flowers fourth behind the production of bedding plants, potted flowering plants, and foliage plants. The top five cut flower producing states include California, Florida, Hawaii, Colorado, and Pennsylvania.

The United States cut flower market relies heavily on imports from other countries. The countries with major exports to the United States include Columbia, Ecuador, Holland, Canada, and Mexico. Modern air travel has made rapid shipments possible. Production of cut flowers has shifted to parts of the world where the cost of labor is low. Also, in some parts of the world, such as Columbia, the temperatures, light, and other conditions are absolutely perfect for growing certain cut flowers.

About 90 percent of the cut roses produced in the United States are hybrid tea roses. The hybrid tea rose is a large, usually solitary flower. The sweetheart (floribunda) rose is a smaller rose that grows as a spray and is often disbudded. Propagation is done by grafting. Roses like an organic medium, high fertility, warm temperatures, and high light intensity. Pruning of roses every year or at least every other year helps maintain production levels. It takes from six to eight weeks to produce a new crop of roses after a harvest.

Carnations rank as the third most popular cut flower in the world. Three types of cut carnations are grown; standard carnations, mini carnations, and single flowering types. Columbia has perfect conditions for year-round carnation production. Carnations prefer, 50 to 55°F nights and 60 to 65°F days and high light intensity. The biggest problem with harvested flowers is the splitting of the calyx caused by fluctuations of temperatures

Gladioli are long-lasting cut flowers. Much of the commercial production of gladioli takes place in Florida and California. Gladioli are produced outside in fields from corms. Harvested gladioli are kept in an upright position to reduce bending caused by gravitropism. Thrips can be especially troublesome and cause damage to both foliage and flowers.

Snapdragons are propagated by seed. The hybrids used have been developed for specific growing periods of the year based on temperature and light intensity. It is necessary to keep the flowers upright after harvesting, during storage, and while shipping to maintain straight stems. Snapdragons have few serious pest or disease problems.

Alstroemeria has gained popularity in the United States since the 1970s. It is ever blooming, produces high yields, and it is easy to grow under cool temperatures. Propagation of alstroemeria is done by division of its white fleshy rhizomes or by tissue culture. Alstroemerias are very heavy feeders. They also require large amounts of water and high light intensity for maximum floral production.

Freesia has brightly colored lily-like flowers that are very fragrant. Freesias are produced from corms. Freesias are planted in September in northern regions and as late as December in southern regions of the United States. Perlite must not be used in the medium, as freesias are sensitive to fluorides. The first flowers appear about eight weeks following the onset of cool temperatures.

QUESTIONS

Answer the following questions. Use correct spelling and complete sentences.

1. What has caused the decreased percentage of cut flowers produced by United States growers?

2. Which states are the greatest cut flower producers?

3. Why has cut flower production moved to other countries?

4. How do hybrid tea and sweetheart roses differ?

5. Why are roses pruned?

6. How do standard, mini, and single flowering carnations differ?

7. Why is Columbia a major producer of carnations?

8. Why are gladioli and snapdragons kept upright after harvest?

9. What are three crops discussed in this chapter that have specialized underground stems?

10. Which cut flower crop is grown primarily from seed?

EVALUATING

Match the term with the correct definition. Write the letter by the term in the blank provided.

a. alstroemeria
b. freesia
c. gladiolus
d. hook cut
e. hybrid tea rose

f. mini carnation
g. single flowering carnation
h. splitting of the calyx
i. standard carnation
j. sweetheart (floribunda) rose

_____ 1. Bright, lily-like flowers borne on a horizontal spike that are very fragrant.

_____ 2. A smaller rose that grows as a spray and is often disbudded.

_____ 3. Large, solitary carnations that have been disbudded.

_____ 4. Ever-blooming flowers borne on a cyme, produces high yields, and it is easy to grow under cool temperatures.

_____ 5. A carnation that is 1/2 to 1/3 the size of a standard carnation and is produced with two to four flowers in a spray.

_____ 6. The removal of a portion of the old wood with a flower when harvesting.

_____ 7. A solitary carnation flower produced without the need of disbudding.

_____ 8. A condition caused by fluctuations of temperatures resulting in a misshapen flower.

_____ 9. A large, usually solitary rose.

_____ 10. Long-lasting, large, showy floral spikes from plants with corms.

EXPLORING

1. Visit a local florist or retailer selling fresh cut flowers. Identify the flowers being sold. Are the same flowers available in all the stores? Is there a greater diversity of flowers than you imagined? Less?

2. Arrange a trip to a wholesale florist. Make an appointment with the owner or manager so you can ask questions concerning the handling and care of fresh cut flowers. Determine where the flowers were grown. Ask how they were purchased? Find out how they were shipped and where they will be going.

3. Visit a local operation that produces cut flowers. On your fact-finding tour, learn about how the crop is produced and handled. Inquire as to whether the crops are sold locally or shipped elsewhere.

11

Growing Foliage Plants

Here is a challenge. See if you can go through a day without seeing a foliage plant. It is not easy. Most people cannot help but come in contact with foliage plants every day. They are grown in the home. People keep foliage plants on their desks at work. The interiors of malls are decorated with foliage plants. Foliage plants are everywhere!

Why are foliage plants used so extensively? One reason is that foliage plants bring a freshness and natural beauty to interior spaces. They filter pollutants and dust from the air. They produce oxygen via photosynthesis. They have the quality of being able to soften harsh features in buildings. They grow throughout the year. Most important, they are pleasant to look at.

11-1. Foliage plants bring freshness and beauty indoors. (Courtesy, Jim Frost, Urban Flora, Inc.)

OBJECTIVES

1   Recognize the scope of the foliage plant industry

2   Identify major foliage plants

3   Relate practices used in commercial foliage plant production

4   Describe cultural practices in growing foliage plants

5   Explain techniques for caring for foliage plants indoors

TERMS

foliage plants   **interior plantscaping**

FOLIAGE PLANT PRODUCTION

Foliage plants consist of tropical and subtropical plants selected for their ability to be grown indoors. They are commonly referred to as houseplants because of their wide use in residential homes. The color and interest provided by their leaves make them attractive to people. Some foliage plants produce interesting or colorful flowers that add to their value.

Foliage plants are grown for the purpose of interior plantscaping.

Interior plantscaping involves the use of plant materials to improve the appearance of the indoor environment. Interior plantscaping usually implies a complex design involving many plants. However, use of a single plant or a single type of plant fits the definition.

11-2. Some foliage plants have colorful leaves, like these crotons.

11-3. Interior plantscaping involves the use of plant materials to improve the appearance of the indoor environment. (Courtesy, Jim Frost, Urban Flora, Inc.)

11-4. Foliage plant production ranks third behind bedding plant and potted flowering crop production in the United States.

THE VALUE OF FOLIAGE PLANTS

Foliage plants are an important part of the floriculture industry. According to the USDA 1997 Summary of Floriculture Crops, foliage plant production ranks third behind bedding plants and potted flowering crops. The wholesale value of foliage plants was calculated to be 522 million dollars in 1997. Furthermore, foliage plant production is expected to grow in future years.

Most foliage plants are produced in warm states. Florida leads production with 69 percent of the wholesale market. California is a distant second, followed by Texas and Hawaii. The warm climates and qualities of light found in these states are ideal for growing foliage plants. Heating is often not necessary, so production costs are less than they would be in a colder climate.

Twelve types of foliage plants dominate sales in the United States. Together, they make up 60 percent of the total market. The 12 include *Dracae-*

Table 11-1. 1997 Wholesale Value of Foliage Plant Production	
State	**Wholesale Value (1,000 dollars)**
Florida	$308,827
California	$ 67,063
Texas	$ 15,913
Hawaii	$ 13,200

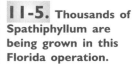**-5.** Thousands of Spathiphyllum are being grown in this Florida operation.

11-6. Three types of *Dracaenas* are shown in the foreground of this photograph.

11-7. Pothos ranks second in production.

11-8. A weeping fig, a rubber tree, and a variegated weeping fig represent three plants in the genus *Ficus* grown as foliage plants.

11-9. Two of the many cultivars of dumbcane that are available.

na, pothos, *Ficus*, dumbcane, palms, Chinese evergreen, peace lily, English ivy, *Philodendron*, *Schefflera* and *Brassaia*, nephthytis, and ferns.

GENERAL INFORMATION

The production of foliage plant crops involves a number of steps. Production begins with the propagation of plant material. Then, plants are grown quickly under optimum conditions and prepared for sale. Once sold, foliage plants are packaged and shipped throughout the country to the retail florists, garden centers, interior plantscapers, and mass market distributors. These retailers have the responsibility of maintaining the health of the plants until they are sold to the public. Maintaining the health and appearance of the plant then rests with the customer.

11-10. Germination of seed is improved when flats are placed on tubing through which warm water circulates.

Propagation

Foliage plants are propagated in a variety of ways. The most common methods are stem cuttings and leaf cuttings. Other methods of propagation include seed, spores, separation, division, air layering, and tissue culture. The selection of the method of propagation depends largely on the species of plant being propagated.

Some foliage plants lend themselves well to propagation by seed. Palms are typically produced from seed. Sexual propagation is also common with Buddhist pine (*Podocarpus macrophylla*), Norfolk Island pine (*Araucaria heterophylla*), False-aralia (*Dizygotheca elegantissima*), Schefflera (*Brassaia actinophylla*)

Tissue culture has grown in importance as a method of propagating foliage plants. Thousands of identical plants can be produced in a relatively short period. In addition, the plants produced are free of disease. Most ferns, including the Boston fern (*Nephrolepis exaltata* 'Bostoni-

11-11. A person transplanting palm seedlings to 4-inch pots.

11-12. This person is seen checking the development of Spathiphyllum tissue cultures.

11-13. Under a laminar air flow hood, this person divides cultures before returning the explants to jars with multiplication media.

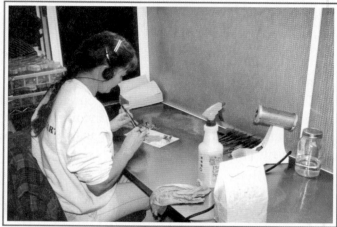

11-14. An explant. (Courtesy, *Greenhouse Product News*)

ensis), are propagated through tissue culture. Peace Lily (*Spathiphyllum* hybrids), dumbcane (*Dieffenbachia* species), and Nephthytis (*Syngonium podophyllum*) are also easily propagated by tissue culture.

Mother-in-law's tongue (Sansevieria) is divided because varieties do not reproduce true to form if propagated by cuttings. This is a disadvantage because of the labor involved in division. Air-layering is another propagation method. It was once

11-15. Small plants produced through tissue culture are moved to the greenhouse for production.

11-16. This worker sticks English ivy cuttings directly into the finish containers, thereby saving the labor involved in transplanting.

used widely with Schefflera and Fig (*Ficus* species). Its use has been in decline because of the intense labor required.

Mist systems have greatly improved propagation success. Cuttings root quickly under mist because plants are kept cooler and water stress is reduced. Many growers save labor by sticking cuttings directly into the finish containers.

Growing

As with other greenhouse crops, the health of foliage plants depends largely on cultural practices. Appropriate growing medium, light, water, nutrition, temperature, and air quality are key factors in production. Attention to pest and disease problems is also important.

11-17. Cacti and succulents prefer very well drained growing media. (Courtesy, *Greenhouse Product News*)

Growing Medium

Growing media are prepared with the needs of the plants in mind. Certain plants, including some ferns, like a 100 percent organic medium. Succulents and cacti prefer a medium with 50 percent or less organic material and a greater amount of sand or mineral matter that provides good drainage. However, the vast majority of foliage plants do well in commercially prepared growing media. Most foliage plants like a slightly acid pH falling between 5.5 and 6.5. Exceptions include the prayer plant (*Maranta*) and ferns. Both do best with a more acidic (4.5 to 5.5) medium.

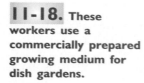 **11-18.** These workers use a commercially prepared growing medium for dish gardens.

Light

Foliage plants have been selected for their ability to withstand low light conditions. Most are found growing on forest and jungle floors. The light in-

11-19. These crotons are being grown under shade cloth to reduce the intensity of the light. They are elevated to reduce ant problems.

tensity for which they are adapted in nature is not too different from the light intensity they receive in an interior plantscape.

Light requirements of most foliage plants fall between 1,500 and 8,000 foot candles. Those levels are lower than what is found in a typical greenhouse. Therefore, most foliage plants are protected from the intense light of full sun during production. Exposure to full sun can cause damage to the leaf tissues and chlorophyll pigments. A symptom of excessive light is faded, or bleached, leaf colors.

Temperature

Since most foliage plants are tropical or subtropical in origin, they are accustomed to relatively warm and constant temperatures. The best temperatures for the production of most foliage plants are 65 to 80°F nights and 75 to 95°F days. Temperatures above 95°F can damage crops. If high temperatures are a concern, shading can be used to help protect foliage plants. Temperatures below 65°F slow plant growth and delay plant development.

Water

To maintain optimum growth, water should be available to plants at all times. A number of environmental conditions influence the frequency of watering. Watering may be necessary daily or weekly. Ebb and flood, spaghetti tubing, and capillary mats work well with foliage plants. Irrigation methods that wet the leaves invite disease problems and spotting. As a result, overhead watering is often avoided.

11-20. This interior plantscaper determines when a plant is in need of water. (Courtesy, Jim Frost, Urban Flora, Inc.)

Watering practices depend largely on the species being grown. Growers must understand the watering needs of the plants they grow. Some foliage plants like a medium that is kept moist and not allowed to dry. Some prefer medium that is allowed to approach drying before irrigation. Others do best when the medium is allowed to dry completely before watering. Whatever the plant prefers, the rule is to water heavily when it is time to water. Heavy watering leaches, or washes, soluble salts from the medium and insures that the medium is completely wetted.

Improper watering is one of the major causes of root diseases of foliage plants. To avoid root rot diseases, start with the appropriate growing medium for the plant and the right size container for the plant. When watering, wait until the plant needs water before watering.

Most foliage plants like a humid environment. In fact, humidity of 50 percent or more is common where foliage plants grow in nature. A relatively high humidity level in the greenhouse improves growth. Growth tends to slow if humidity levels drop below 25 percent.

11-21. Ferns are one of many foliage plants that like a humid environment.

Nutrition

Nutrition during production influences the rate of growth. It also affects the quality of foliage plants after they reach the consumers. One recommended fertilizer program consists of a constant feeding program. With every watering, 150 ppm nitrogen, 25 ppm phosphorus, and 100 ppm potassium are provided. An alternative is to use a slow-release fertilizer in the growing media. Foliage plants grown in soilless medium require fertilizers containing micronutrients. The reason is soilless mix lacks the necessary micronutrients.

Acclimatization

Acclimatization is the process in which a plant becomes accustomed to a new environment. The transition from a warm, humid, well-lit greenhouse to a cool, dry, and dim room in a building is stressful for most plants. A common reaction by a plant under stress from a new environment is to shed its leaves. Few plants demonstrate the shock of being moved as much as the weeping fig. A slight change in conditions causes it to shed most of its leaves.

Studies have shown that the plants that acclimatize the quickest are those grown under low light conditions and that receive light fertilization throughout production. Knowing this, growers can help prepare plants for their ultimate destination.

First, the light intensity given the plants can be reduced for two to six months prior to shipping. The length of time depends on the species. By reducing the light intensity, the plants get accustomed to lower light levels ex-

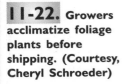 **11-22.** Growers acclimatize foliage plants before shipping. (Courtesy, Cheryl Schroeder)

Table 11-2. Growing Guidelines for Selected Foliage Plants

	Light	Water	Humidity	Problems
Asparagus fern *Asparagus sprengeri*	Medium 2,500-4,500 FC	Let dry slightly	Medium	Spider mites
Baby's tears *Helxine soleirolii*	Medium 2,000 to 4,000 FC	Keep moist	High	
Begonias *Begonia* species	Medium 2,500 to 5,000 FC	Let dry slightly	Medium	Mites
Brassaia (Schefflera) *Brassaia actinophylla*	Medium 3,000 to 5,000 FC	Let dry slightly	Medium	Mites, Mealybugs, Scale, Thrips
Bromeliad Neoregelia species	Medium 2,500 to 4,000 FC	Let dry slightly	Medium	
Cacti Many species	High 4,000 to 8,000 FC	Let dry	Low	
Cast iron plant *Aspidistra elatior*	Low 1,500 to 3,000 FC	Let dry slightly	Medium	
Chinese evergreen *Aglaonema* species	Low 1,000 to 2,500 FC	Keep moist	Medium	Mealybugs, Scale
Croton *Codiaeum* species	High 3,000 to 8,000 FC	Let dry slightly	Medium	Mites, Mealybugs, Scale
Dracaena *Dracaena* species	Medium 2,000 to 4,000 FC	Let dry slightly	Medium	Mites, Mealybugs, Thrips
Dumbcane *Dieffenbachia* species	Low 1,500 to 2,500 FC	Let dry slightly	Medium	Mites, Mealybugs, Scale
English ivy *Hedera helix*	Low 1,500 to 2,500 FC	Let dry slightly	Medium	Mites, Scale
False aralia *Dizygotheca elegantissima*	Medium 2,000 to 4,000 FC	Let dry slightly	Medium	Mites, Mealybugs, Scale
Ferns Many species	Low 1,500 to 3,000 FC	Keep moist	High	Scale, Caterpillars, Mealybugs
Figs *Ficus* species	High 4,000 to 8,000 FC	Let dry slightly	Medium	Mite, Mealybugs, Scale, White fly
Fittonia *Fittonia verschaffeltii*	Low 1,000 to 2,500 FC	Let dry slightly	High	Mealybugs
Grape ivy *Cissus rhombifolia*	Low 1,500 to 2,500 FC	Let dry slightly	Medium	Mites
Jade plant *Crassula argentea*	High 6,000 to 8,000 FC	Let dry	Low	Mealybugs, Scale
Mother-in-law's tongue *Sansevieria* species	Adaptable 1,500 to 6,000 FC	Let dry	Low	

(Continued)

Table 11-2 (Continued)

	Light	Water	Humidity	Problems
Nephthytis *Syngonium podophyllum*	Low 1,500 to 3,000 FC	Let dry slightly	Medium	Mites, Mealybugs
Norfolk Island pine *Araucaria heterophylla*	High 4,000 to 8,000 FC	Let dry slightly	Medium	Mites
Palms Various genus	Low-medium 3,000 to 6,000 FC	Keep moist	Medium	Mites, Mealybugs, Scale
Peace lily *Spathiphyllum* species	Low 1,500 to 2,500 FC	Let dry slightly	Medium	Mealybugs, Scale
Peperomia *Peperomia* species	Low 1,500 to 3,000 FC	Let dry slightly	Medium	
Philodendron *Philodendron* species	Low 1,500 to 3,500 FC	Let dry slightly	Medium	Mites, Mealybugs, Scale, Thrips
Pilea Many species	Low 1,500 to 2,500 FC	Keep moist	Medium	
Pothos *Epipremnum* species	Low 1,500 to 3,000 FC	Let dry slightly	Medium	Mealybugs, Thrips
Prayer plant *Maranta* species	Low 1,500 to 3,500 FC	Keep moist	High	Mites, Mealybugs
Purple passion vine *Gynura sarmentosa*	Medium 3,000 to 5,000 FC	Let dry slightly	Medium	
Schefflera *Schefflera arbicola*	Low 1,500 to 3,000 FC	Let dry slightly	Medium	Mites, Mealybugs, Scale, Thrips
Spider plant *Chlorophytum comosum*	Low 1,000 to 2,500 FC	Let dry slightly	Low	
Strawberry begonia *Saxifraga sarmentosa*	Medium 3,000 to 5,000 FC	Let dry slightly	Medium	
Swedish Ivy *Plectranthus australis*	Medium 3,000 to 5,000 FC	Keep moist	Medium	Mealybugs
Ti plant *Cordyline terminalis*	Low 1,500 to 3,500 FC	Keep Moist	Medium	
Wandering Jew *Zebrina pendula*	Medium 2,500 to 4,000 FC	Let dry slightly	Medium	
Wax plant *Hoya carnosa*	Low 1,500 to 3,000 FC	Let dry	Medium	Mealybugs
Yucca *Yucca elephantipes*	Medium 3,000 to 5,000 FC	Let dry	Low	
Zebra plant *Aphelandra squarrosa*	Low 1,000 to 1,500 FC	Keep moist	Medium	Mites

11-23. Foliage plants grown in Florida are packaged and shipped north.

pected in their new home. Their leaves grow thinner, broader, and produce more chlorophyll for the manufacture of food.

Over fertilization during production lessens the plant's ability to acclimatize to a new surrounding. Fertilization stimulates growth. Foliage plants acclimatize more quickly if growth is slowed. Therefore, to better prepare plants, growers reduce fertility levels to slow plant growth.

Pests and Diseases

Common pests of foliage plants include aphids, mites, caterpillars, fungus gnats, mealybugs, scales and thrips. Pest problems can be reduced with the use of pest-free stock plants. Sanitation and cultural practices also help control pest problems.

Disease problems of foliage plants are most often associated with watering practices. Over watering, usually caused by watering too frequently, often leads to root rot. Fungal and bacterial diseases can attack foliage. They become more of a problem when the leaves are wet.

Fluoride in the water is damaging to some plants. Dracaena, palms, prayer plant, spider plant, and bromeliads are susceptible. Fluoride damage is usually in the form of leaf tip burn or browning. Avoid growing media with perlite and the use of super phosphate fertilizer.

GROWING FOLIAGE PLANTS INDOORS

Foliage plants can be grown successfully indoors by following a few simple guidelines.

11-24. Quality foliage plants are free of pests and diseases. (Courtesy, Society of American Florists)

- Select foliage plants based on their ability to withstand the growing conditions.

- Provide optimum lighting for the foliage plants. Place plants requiring medium to high light near windows. North facing windows have the lowest light intensity. South facing windows provide the brightest light in the winter when the sun is low in the horizon. The further a plant is placed away from a window the lower the light intensity will be.

- Maintain temperatures above 55°F.

- Employ the use of a humidifier in the winter months. Humidity drops significantly in houses with forced-air heat.

- Select containers that are in proportion to the size of the plants to be grown. Plants grown in containers too small, dry quickly. Those in containers too large are subject to root rot. The volume of growing medium in large pots is slow to dry leading to the root rot diseases. For root health, select containers with holes that allow drainage of excess water.

- Repot plants when the roots completely fill the soil ball and if additional

11-25. The sale of these cacti was promoted at Christmas.

11-26. This person disinfects previously used flats before they are used for the propagation of foliage plants.

growth of the plant is desired. Repotting to a larger container stimulates growth. When repotting, plant the plants in the next size container. Use sterile growing medium. Do not reuse growing medium as it can contain disease organisms and high levels of soluble salts.

■ Water when the plant needs it, not on a fixed schedule, such as every Saturday. Water thoroughly, and do not allow the plants to stand in water.

■ Fertilize sparingly to maintain growth. Use of a complete fertilizer every four to six weeks is adequate.

11-27. Select foliage plants on their ability to withstand the growing conditions. (Courtesy, Society of American Florists)

REVIEWING

MAIN IDEAS

Foliage plants, commonly referred to as houseplants, consist of tropical and subtropical plants selected for their ability to be grown indoors. Foliage plants are grown for the purpose of interior plantscaping. Their production in the United States places them third behind bedding plants and potted flowering crops. The state with the greatest production is Florida.

Twelve types of foliage plants make up the majority of the foliage plants grown. They include *Dracaena*, pothos, *Ficus*, dumbcane, palms, Chinese evergreen, peace lily, English ivy, *Philodendron*, *Schefflera* and *Brassaia*, nephthytis, and ferns. Foliage plants are propagated sexually and asexually. The most common methods are stem cuttings and leaf cuttings. Other methods of propagation include seed, spores, separation, division, air layering, and tissue culture.

Cultural practices vary with the type of plant being grown. However, most foliage plants like an organic growing medium with a slightly acid pH falling between 5.5 and 6.5. Light requirements of most foliage plants fall between 1,500 and 8,000 foot candles. The best temperatures for the production of most foliage plants are 65 to 80°F nights and 75 to 95°F days. Watering practices depend largely on the species being grown. A recommended fertilizer program consists of a constant feeding program of 150 ppm nitrogen, 25 ppm phosphorus, and 100 ppm potassium.

It is important that foliage plants be acclimatized. Acclimatization is the process in which a plant becomes accustomed to a new environment. Plants properly acclimatized tolerate new growing environments much better than those that are not acclimatized.

QUESTIONS

Answer the following questions. Use correct spelling and complete sentences.

1. What is interior plantscaping?

2. Why does much of the foliage plant production take place in southern states?

3. How has tissue culture grown in importance for propagating foliage plants?

4. What foliage plants are propagated in large numbers by tissue culture?

5. What are the advantages of mist systems in production?

6. Why are watering methods that wet leaves avoided?

7. How do leaves respond to lower light levels?

8. Why is it important to limit fertilization of foliage plants?

9. How does fluoride affect foliage plants?

10. What is the recommended watering practice for foliage plants in an interior situation?

EVALUATING

Complete the following lists on a separate sheet of paper.

1. List 12 foliage plants that have few if any pest and disease problems.

2. List nine foliage plants that like the growing medium to be kept moist.

3. List five plants that require high levels of light.

4. List five foliage plants that tolerate low light levels.

5. List five foliage plants that prefer the growing medium to dry out between waterings.

6. List 10 foliage plants that can become infested with mealy bugs.

7. List eight foliage plants that do well under medium light and like having the growing medium dry slightly between waterings.

8. List four plants that require humid conditions.

9. List five plants that tolerate low humidity.

10. List seven practices a homeowner can follow to maintain their foliage plants.

EXPLORING

1. Visit a large conservatory. As you walk around observe how foliage plants might grow differently in that setting versus the home environment.

2. The best way to learn how to take care of foliage plants is to care for foliage plants. Obtain foliage plants of different types and care for them in your home. Note how some plants might perform better that others. Consider the growing conditions in your home and the types of plants you have. Then, determine why they perform as they do.

12

Growing Bedding Plants

People love plants that provide color around the home. Cheerful colors stimulate and excite emotions. Flowers and foliage are especially welcome in states where inhabitants have experienced a long, cold winter. The arrival of spring draws people outside where they can reacquaint themselves with nature. Naturally, people want the best display of flowers for the longest period of time. Trees and shrubs may have showy displays of flowers, but they seldom last more than a few weeks. Bedding plants on the other hand provide color from the time they are planted until a killing frost.

Planting bedding plants is one of the most common leisure activities in the country. It is easy! The gardener is also nearly always rewarded with beautiful displays of flowers and foliage.

12-1. Bedding plants add color to the landscape. (Courtesy, *Greenhouse Product News*)

OBJECTIVES

1   Identify major bedding plants

2   Describe cultural practices applied to the production of bedding plants

3   Explain how to start bedding plants from seed

4   Describe the containers used to produce bedding plants

5   Prepare a growing schedule for select bedding plants

6   Explain how plugs are used in bedding plant production

TERMS

annuals
break
cell packs
DIF
fertigation
finished
germination rate
hard basket
leaching

medium
plugs
shelf life
soft basket
sow
toning
transplanted
viable

WHAT ARE BEDDING PLANTS?

Bedding plants include herbaceous annual plants used for ornamental display or vegetable production. Frequently, people will refer to bedding plants as *annuals*, which are herbaceous plants that grow from seed to flower in one season before dying. Bedding plants are selected for their colorful flowers or interesting foliage. A few examples of the bedding plants produced for their flowers include geraniums, petunias, impatiens, and marigolds. Coleus is the most common bedding plant grown for its foliage or colorful leaves. Typically, the vegetable plants included as bedding plants are those started in containers and transplanted to the garden. Some of these include tomatoes, peppers, broccoli, cabbage, and Brussels sprouts.

Impatiens lead the way in bedding plant production accounting for 12.4 percent of the bedding plant and plug crops grown in 1997. Impatiens, petunia, pansy, marigold, seed begonia, and seed geranium production combined for 45 percent of the overall 1997 crop. Together, zonal geraniums, New Guinea impatiens, ivy geraniums, and vegetative begonias accounted for nearly 22 percent of the container crops grown in 1997.

Table 12-1. Average Percentage of Crops Grown in 1997

Crop	Percentage of Bedding and Plug Crops Grown	Crop	Percentage of Container Crops Grown
Impatiens	12.4	Zonal Geraniums	10.3
Petunias	9.1	New Guinea Impatiens	5.4
Pansies	6.8	Ivy Geraniums	4.3
Marigolds	6.6	Vegetative Begonias	1.9
Seed Begonias	4.4		
Herbs	3.1		
Seed Geraniums	3.0		
Vegetables	11.7		
Perennials	13.3		
Others	23.4		

12-2. Bedding plant sales are up.

TRENDS WITH BEDDING PLANTS

The market for bedding plants is bright. Sales are up and the demand is rising. Receipts for bedding plant sales rose from $1.1 billion in 1989 to $1.8 billion in 1996. The $1.8 billion represents 45 percent of the total sales of floriculture crops in the United States. Clearly, the production and sales of bedding plants have very important roles in the floriculture industry.

12-3. Large retail chains sell bedding plants.

Many factors have spurred the increased sales in the bedding plant industry. One factor is marketing. At one time, consumers were limited to garden centers or greenhouses from which to buy their bedding plants. Today, bedding plants are sold nearly everywhere. Large retail chains, such as Wal-Mart, Home Depot and Kmart, have expanded the market. Grocery stores around the country serve as outlets for bedding plant sales. Yet, garden centers remain the top outlets for quality bedding plants.

Research and development have strengthened the industry. Many new varieties resulting from plant breeding programs give consumers higher quality plants and more types from which to choose. Technology and automation have increased the number of plants producers can grow. Biotechnology and genetic engineering are expected to greatly influence the industry, too. Genetically engineered crops will be more resistant to disease and insect pests, will improve floral displays, and will reduce fertilizer requirements because plants would fix their own nitrogen.

The consumer has also played a key role in determining which crops are grown. The United States has experienced a long period of economic prosperity. People are willing to use more disposable income on garden plants. Hence, the demand for bedding plants is high. Consumers have also become more knowledgeable and are willing to try new varieties.

BEDDING PLANT SCHEDULING, SEED, AND GERMINATION

The majority of bedding plants are grown from seed or propagated sexually. One common exception is the zonal geranium, which is usually propagated asexually from stem cuttings. Seeds come in a wide variety of shapes and sizes. The fibrous begonia seed is so small it looks like dust, and an ounce of the seed would include an incredible 2,500,000 seeds. Others, like the salvia, are larger, 7,500 seeds to the ounce, and are easier to handle.

Growers *sow*, or plant, bedding plant seed in late winter or early spring. There are terrific benefits to starting plants early. The rate of seed germination and seedling survival is much greater in the controlled environment of a germination chamber or greenhouse than it is outside. Bedding plants started in a controlled environment receive optimal temperatures, water, and

12-4. Most bedding plants, including impatiens, petunias, and pansies are grown from seed. (Courtesy, Ball Horticultural Company)

12-5. Temperature and humidity can be controlled in a germination chamber.

nutrients important for healthy growth and development. The healthy transplants therefore have a head start. Also, by planting a healthy and vigorously growing plant in the garden, the gardener can enjoy a longer season of flowering pleasure.

SCHEDULING

Production of bedding plant crops really starts with a schedule. The growers must ask when they want the plants for sale based on the consumer.

12-6. A great deal of planning goes into scheduling sowing dates to meet customer needs.

Plants started too soon may be overgrown and less valuable during the prime period of sales. Plants started too late may be too small to attract customers.

Growers determine a date at which they want the plants to have their peak appearance and health for sale. They then count backwards the number

	Number of Weeks to Finish From 390 Plugs			Number of Weeks to Finish From Seed		
	Flats		Pots	Flats		Pots
	48	36	4 inch	48	36	4 inch
Ageratum	5-6	7	8	10	11	13
Alyssum	5-6	7	8	8	9	11
Begonia	6	7	8	15	16	18
Browallia	6	7	7	15	16	20
Celosia	5	6	7	8	9	13
Cleome	3	3	4	9	10	12
Coleus	4-5	5	5	9	10	12
Dahlia	9	10	11	12	13	14
Dianthus	5-6	7	8	10	11	15
Dusty miller	5-6	6	7	11	12	15
Gazania	7	8	9	12	13	15
Geranium	10	10	11	13	14	15
Impatiens	5	5	6	10	11	13
Lisianthus	10	10	11	18	19	20
Lobelia	4-6	7	8	11	12	12
Marigold (French)	4-5	5	6	8	9	10
Marigold (African)	5-6	6	7	11	12	13
Pansy	5-6	7	8	14	15	16
Petunia	5-6	6	6	12	13	15
Portulaca	5	6	7	12	13	15
Salvia	5	6	7	9	11	13
Snapdragon	5-6	6	7	15	16	17
Verbena	6	7	7	12	13	15
Vinca	5-7	8	8	14	15	16
Viola	6	7	8	12	13	14
Zinnia	2-3	3	4	9	10	12

Table 12-2. Finishing Times for Bedding Plants

12-7. The pansies on this bench are ready to be shipped for sale. Note the use of all the growing space in the greenhouse.

of weeks it takes to produce the crop. For instance, if growers know they want to have impatiens ready for a May 14 sale and it takes 10 weeks to grow the crop from seed, they would sow the seed 10 weeks before May 14. When sales are over a period of time, impatiens might be started every week for a period of four to six weeks to maintain a steady supply.

SEEDS

Bedding plant seeds are expensive. Large greenhouse operations might purchase $100,000 of seed for production. Because of the seed cost, it is com-

12-8. Seeds can be kept sealed in their packets in a cooler.

mon for growers to lock their seeds up at night. The value of the seed also makes it necessary to provide proper storage. Proper storage extends the life of the seed. Growers store the seeds in cool dry locations to keep the seeds viable. Storage with a temperature of 40° F and a relative humidity between 20 and 40 percent is acceptable. Small growers often place their seed in sealed containers in a frost-free refrigerator.

Proper storage is one factor that contributes to a high rate of seed germination and plant survival up to sale. Germination is the sprouting of seeds or the beginning of plant growth. Successful germination begins with good seed. Good seed is viable and has vigor. *Viable* is a term used for living seeds capable of germinating under optimum conditions. Vigor describes the seed's ability to germinate under less than ideal conditions.

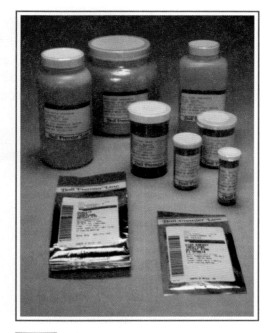

12-9. Germination rates are printed on the seed package. (Courtesy, Ball Horticultural Co.)

Fortunately, research has improved seed quality. Most seeds packaged for the current year have a ***germination rate*** of 90 to 95 percent when given optimum germination conditions. The germination rate is the percentage of seeds capable of germinating. Germination rates drop as the seeds get older. Seeds left over from previous years have noticeably lower germination rates than fresh seed as some seeds die in storage.

GERMINATION REQUIREMENTS

Always check for special germination requirements with each type of seed. Germination requirements include light, temperature, nutrients, moisture, and medium. Each germination requirement can be controlled by the grower for each bedding plant.

Exposure to light influences seed germination. Some seeds must have darkness to germinate. Bedding plant seeds requiring darkness include celosia, cleome, gazania, periwinkle (Vinca), portulaca, pansy, verbena, and viola. It may therefore be necessary to see that the seeds are well covered. Other seeds require exposure to light. Seeds that need light to germinate include snapdragon, begonia, browallia, impatiens, sweet alyssum, petunia, and salvia. Still, others do not seem to be affected by exposure to light.

Proper temperature is important for successful germination. Most seeds germinate quickly with a medium temperature of 75°F. It is important to note that temperature refers to the soil temperature and not the air tempera-

Table 12-3. Germination Guidelines for Bedding Plants				
Common name	Seeds/ounce	Optimum temp. for germination	Light or dark exposure	Days for uniform germination
Ageratum	200,000	78-82	light	8-10
Alyssum	90,000	78-82	light	5
Begonia	2,500,000	75-80	light	5-10
Browallia	125,000	72	light	7-15
Celosia	35,000	75	dark	8-10
Cleome	14,000	80 day, 70 night	dark	10-12
Coleus	100,000	70-75	light	10-14
Dahlia	4,500	60-65	no effect	5-10
Dianthus	25,000	70-75	no effect	7
Dusty miller	7,000	72-75	light	10-15
Gazania	12,000	70	dark	10-12
Geranium	6,000	70-75	no effect	10
Impatiens	46,000	70-75	light	4-5
Lisianthus	624,000	70-75	light	10-20
Lobelia	1,000,000	75-80, then drop to 70	no effect	20
Marigold (French)	9,000	72-75	no effect	7
Marigold (African)	9,000	72-75	no effect	7
Pansy	20,000	65-75	dark	7-10
Petunia	245,000	75-78	light	10-12
Portulaca	280,000	75-80	dark	10
Salvia	7,500	75-78	light	12-15
Snapdragon	180,000	70-75	light	7-14
Verbena	10,000	65	dark	20
Vinca	21,000	78-80, after three days drop to 75-78	dark	7-15
Viola	30,000 to 40,000	65-70	dark	7-14
Zinnia	2,500	70-72	no effect	3-7

12-10. These seedlings are two weeks old. (Courtesy, Ball Horticultural Company)

ture. Check the soil temperatures with a soil thermometer. Soil temperatures that are too cool remain wet for a longer period of time. Wet, cool soil conditions reduce oxygen exchange with the seed and slow germination.

Seeds are started in a special *medium*, a soil or soilless material. The media used for germination purposes are easily purchased as prepackaged mixtures. The mix is fine-textured, uniform, and often consists of a peat moss and vermiculite. It is also free of disease organisms and weed seeds. Medium plays a minor role in germinating seeds. The key is the moisture level within the medium. Most seeds germinate well in a medium with a pH between 5.5 and 5.8. Geraniums, salvia, and marigold like a pH from 6.2 to 6.5.

12-11. Prepackaged medium is being placed in a machine that automatically fills flats.

The most important factor in seed germination is the moisture level in the medium. A rule of thumb is that once the medium and seeds have been moistened they should be kept moist until sprouting. If the medium is allowed to dry out during the germination process, the seeds die. It is best to wet the medium before sowing. After the seeds have been sown, the flats can be covered with a clear plastic cover or sheets of poly to reduce evaporation. The coverings are removed once the seeds start to sprout. Some growers mist their flats regularly to maintain proper moisture levels.

Different seeds prefer slightly different moisture levels. Seeds that prefer a wet medium or one that glistens and is wet to the touch are coleus, begonia, and alyssum. Moist medium that is wet, but not saturated, is prescribed for impatiens, petunia, geranium, salvia, vinca, and pansy. A dryer medium is best for verbena, zinnia, and most perennials.

In general, fertilizers are not used in the germination process. Fertilizers are soluble salts in the medium. Soluble salts inhibit the germination of most bedding plant seeds. Two exceptions are petunia and snapdragon. Low fertility levels actually enhance seed germination for those two crops.

HAND SOWING SEEDS

The depth at which the seeds are planted varies with the size of the seed and their light requirements. Larger seeds have more stored energy in their cotyledons enabling them to push up through the medium as they germinate. Tiny seeds have limited stored energy, and therefore lack the ability to push up through the soil if planted too deep. A rule of thumb is to plant the

12-12. Seeds sown by hand are placed in rows.

seeds at a depth no greater than three times the diameter of the seed. Hand sown seeds are placed evenly in rows rather than being broadcast over the entire flat. This practice protects the loss of all the seedlings by limiting the spread of disease if introduced.

After the seedlings develop their first true leaves, they are ***transplanted*** or moved to pots or cell packs. ***Cell packs*** are molded plastic containers divided into two, three, four, or six separate growing compartments. It is in the pots or packs that they will be ***finished*** or grown to saleable size. During the transplanting process, the seedlings must be carefully divided to avoid damaging the plant. It is recommended that the technician only handle the seedlings by their leaves since the stems are very easily bruised.

THE PLUG REVOLUTION

Propagation of bedding plants has changed dramatically with the industry move toward automation and the increased size of greenhouse operations. Small operations may still rely on hand seeding, but many small operations have moved away from seeding all together. Instead of propagating their own plants, they purchase plugs from large companies. The trays of plugs are easily custom grown for the medium and small greenhouse growers. Today, roughly two-thirds of all the seeded

12-13. Seedlings should be held by their leaves during the transplanting process.

12-14. This greenhouse is full of hundreds of plug trays sown in a day by automation.

12-15. Plugs are produced in plastic trays.

crops begin as plugs. It is safe to say that plugs have revolutionized bedding plant production worldwide.

Plugs are small plants grown in a small amount of medium in divided trays. The cells in the trays determine the size and number of plugs to be produced. The sizes of the plugs are 5/8 of an inch or larger. Plugs are very convenient as they can be popped out of the tray for transplanting to cell packs or pots. Plugs also allow for automated transplanting. The number of plugs grown in a tray varies. Tray designs may allow the grower to grow 800, 512, 390, 384, 288, 162, 144 or 70 plants per tray.

The larger producers of bedding plants use automatic seeders to produce plugs. The automated seeders greatly increase the speed at which plants can

12-16. This automatic seeder places one seed (yellow) into each cell.

12-17. Seeders are computerized.

12-18. The person on the right plants seeds in cells the automatic seeder missed.

be seeded and the number of flats that can be produced. Automatic seeders place a seed in each cell of a plastic plug tray that has been filled with a germination mix or medium. Some growers use more than one seed per cell, especially when germination rates are less than 85 percent. Petunias and begonias may be double-seeded to get a fuller tray. Five to six seeds per cell is common for portulaca or alyssum.

The materials used in the medium are extremely important. The most common material used is peat moss. It has an acidic pH, usually 4 to 5. Peat

12-19. A light covering of vermiculite has been place over these trays with marigold seeds.

moss also absorbs and holds water. Vermiculite is another common plug medium ingredient. It retains water, it has good nutrient exchange, and it provides calcium and magnesium. Perlite is sometimes used to provide aeration. Calcined clay is used for aeration and for its nutrient exchange capacity. In some cases, soil is used in the medium. Lime is added to bring the pH levels up. The optimum pH for most bedding plants is 5.5 to 5.8. Geraniums, marigolds, and salvia prefer a higher pH of 6.2 to 6.5.

Different growers use different mixes. One example of a medium used consists of 80 percent peat, 13 percent vermiculite, 7 percent soil, with lime and fertilizer added. The mix has excellent moisture-holding and aeration capabilities. After the seed is sown, the medium is covered lightly with vermiculite and watered. The key to successful and uniform germination is a medium that pro-

12-20. Plug trays move on a conveyer belt through the seeder and then through this mechanism that waters the tray.

12-21. This person replaces plugs in which seed did not germinate with live plugs so the tray will be full.

vides proper moisture levels and is well aerated. Each tray is labeled with the plant variety to avoid confusion. Some growers then place the plug trays in specially designed germination chambers that provide the optimum temperatures for seed germination.

The goal of the grower is to produce plugs that are uniform, have short internodes, and have a high number of dark green leaves. To accomplish this, the plants move through four growing stages. The type of plant determines how long each stage lasts. Stage one involves germination of the seed. In stage two, the plants are kept warm and given low levels of fertilizers. Stage three in-

12-22. This photograph shows an automatic watering system involving a boom that moves across the entire length of the bench.

12-23. This photograph shows tomatoes wilting along the edges of the tray.

12-24. This person spot waters edges of trays that have dried quickly.

12-25. These plugs were treated with a growth retardant and a warning sign was posted.

12-26. Plugs are moved to greenhouses with retractable roofs prior to shipping so they can be hardened off by exposure to lower humidity, higher light intensity, and lower temperatures.

12-27. These Florida-grown plug trays are packaged for shipping to fill orders around the country.

volves higher levels of fertilizer to promote growth and development. In stage four, plants are prepared for shipping. To slow growth prior to shipping, the plants' fertilizer levels are reduced and they may be treated with a growth regulator. The entire process of producing quality plugs takes 6 to 10 weeks.

GROWING BEDDING PLANTS

At the time of sale, high quality bedding plants are compact, with numerous bottom breaks and with the flower buds just ready to open. The term

 12-28. High quality bedding plants are compact plants, with numerous bottom breaks and flower buds just ready to open at sale. (Courtesy, *Greenhouse Product News*)

break refers to the development of lateral branches that contribute to a bushy appearance. Some vendors require bedding plants to be in flower. The primary factors in producing quality bedding plants are temperature, soil moisture, light, and fertilization. Growth regulators may also be used by growers to produce quality bedding plants.

TRANSPLANTING

Plugs are transplanted to cell packs or pots for growth until sale. One of the trends in the industry has been the move to larger finishing containers. Four-inch pots have become common. Most growers that use cell packs choose ones that hold no more than 48 plants in a standard flat. Higher quality plants can be produced when the larger containers are used. In addition, the plants require less frequent watering and have a longer shelf life. *Shelf life* is the period the plant maintains its health while on display for sale.

 12-29. Many bedding plants are sold in plastic cell packs.

12-30. Labor is reduced by machines that fill pots with growing medium.

12-31. This machine adds osmocote, a slow-release fertilizer, to the growing medium before filling flats.

Transferring the plugs to the pots or cell packs is becoming more and more automated. Nearly all the large greenhouse operations have automatic transplanters. The transplanters are programmed to lift the plugs from the trays and place the plugs in cell packs or pots filled with medium. Some of the transplanters cost more than $100,000. The speed at which they transplant makes them economical for large operations. Most models transplant between 10,000 and 43,000 plugs per hour, which is many more and much quicker than can be done by hand.

12-32. Pots filled with soil and plug trays move on conveyers into the automatic transplanter.

12-33. Technicians oversee the automated transplanter that removes the plugs from the trays and plants them in pots or cell packs.

12-34. This device sprays a bar code and an identifying label on each container as it exits the transplanter.

IRRIGATION

Irrigation or watering of bedding plants is the most important cultural practice in the greenhouse. Watering practices have a direct impact on the quality of the crop. Plants kept constantly moist tend to grow taller and have longer internodes than those allowed to dry out occasionally. Also, wet media reduces the exchange of gases around the roots, thus increasing the possibility of soil-borne diseases. On the other hand, plants allowed to become too dry may experience severe wilting that can stunt growth or cause death of tissues.

12-35. These workers set up the watering boom to fertigate a section of the greenhouse.

The frequency of watering is largely dependent on the weather and the size of the plants. Skilled greenhouse technicians closely monitor the crops in terms of watering needs. Sunny, hot days may require more than one watering. On cool, overcast days the plants may not need to be watered. When the crop is first transplanted, it should be watered immediately. However, it may not require more water for several days. Larger plants, nearing sale size, need more frequent waterings.

When it is determined that water is needed, the crop is thoroughly watered. Thorough watering leaches soluble salts from the medium. Soluble salts are minerals and nutrients dissolved in the water. *Leaching* is a term used to describe the washing of salts from a medium as water passes through the medium. Without thorough watering, these salts build up in the medium and damage plant roots.

Automation has made watering easier in larger operations. The incorporation of automatic watering systems has permitted

12-36. These geraniums in hanging baskets move from one side of the greenhouse to the other. As they do so, they are flooded with water.

many more plants to be watered than could be by hand. One system involves overhead booms that sweep across the benches. Another has hanging baskets on a conveyor system. Each basket passes under a nozzle that floods the medium. Hanging baskets are also watered with spaghetti-tube irrigation systems. Some growers use the ebb and flow system of watering. Ebb and flow systems flood the benches with water. The water is absorbed into the medium from below. Even with the increased use of automation, greenhouse technicians must decide when to water. They must also hand-water plants missed by the automated system or plants that dry more quickly, such as the edges and corners of flats.

FERTILIZATION

Bedding plants respond best to a constant liquid feed beginning at the time of transplanting. This practice of fertilizing while irrigating is known as *fertigation*. Bedding plants require very light fertilizer applications relative to other greenhouse crops. The plants respond well to 200 ppm nitrogen, 100 ppm phosphorus, and 200 ppm potassium. Ageratum and marigolds, however, receive less fertilizer until they are showing color. Secondary macronutrients and micronutrients are added to the solution at much lower rates.

Small growers often depend on packaged fertilizer mixes. These mixes are often formulated to provide all of the necessary macronutrients and micronutrients. Selection of fertilizers that contain the micronutrients makes it easier for the grower. The application of micronutrients is also especially important when the plants are grown in soilless mixes. Soilless mixes do not have the ability to hold nutrients the way clay and silt particles hold nutrients.

12-37. This person is mixing soluble fertilizer with water for fertigation.

TEMPERATURE

Temperature is an important environmental factor in the production of bedding plants. Bedding plants like warm temperatures. Optimum growing temperatures for most bedding plants range from 65°F to 72°F. It is well known that bedding plants flower earlier and grow faster when given warm growing temperatures. However, warm temperatures can result in non-desirable features. The plants may stretch, develop weak stems, and have fewer bottom breaks.

Research has shown that growing bedding plants under cool day temperatures and warm night temperatures controls stretching of the plants. This technique is referred to as *DIF* or the difference between day and night temperatures. Keeping the night temperatures 6 to 8 degrees warmer than the day temperatures actually stops cell elongation. Keeping a cooler day temperature is sometimes difficult, especially in southern regions. This problem can be overcome by focusing on the first one or two hours of the day. If the temperature is kept cool the first hour or two of the day, the plant tends to accept that as the all-day temperature.

12-38. These bedding plants are exposed to cool day temperatures to slow plant elongation.

LIGHT

Most bedding plants grow best in full sunlight. One of the advantages of retractable roofs is the plants receive high light intensities. Even shade-tolerant plants, such as impatiens, wax begonia, and coleus, grow well under full sun in winter and spring. However, as production moves into late spring or early summer, some shading may be necessary.

GROWTH REGULATORS

Growers use growth regulators on bedding plants for several reasons. One reason is to improve the visual quality of the plants by keeping the plants short and stocky. Short and stocky plants are also easier to ship. In some cases, the application of growth regulators provides the side benefit of improved shelf life of plants. The two most widely used growth regulators for bedding plants are A-Rest and B-Nine. The use of growth regulators on vegetable plants is strictly forbidden.

Table 12-4. Recommended Use of Growth Retardants for Bedding Plants		
Either A-Rest or B-Nine	**A-Rest only**	**B-Nine only**
Ageratum	Celosia	Petunia
Browallia	Cleome	
Dusty Miller	Coleus	
Dwarf Dahlia	Dianthus	
Geranium	Snapdragon	
Impatiens	Vinca	
Dwarf Marigold		
Tall Marigold		
Salvia		
Verbena		
Zinnia		

12-39. The pendulous habit of fuchsias make them ideal plants for hanging baskets. (Courtesy, *Greenhouse Product News*)

HANGING BASKETS

Hanging baskets are popular and as a result are being grown in greater numbers. Hanging basket production can be divided into two groups based on the plants used. Growers call them hard baskets and soft baskets. Bedding plants that are propagated by cuttings, such as, fuchsia, geraniums, and New Guinea impatiens, make up the ***hard basket*** group. ***Soft baskets*** consist of bedding plants started from seed. Exam-

12-40. Hand labor is required to hang and remove baskets.

12-41. Growing space is maximized in this house with thousands of fuchsia and New Guinea impatiens baskets being grown over bedding plant flats. Look closely to see the center basket receiving water as it rotates around the greenhouse on an automated rail system.

ples of soft basket plants are petunias, impatiens, browallia, gazania, portulaca, and thungbergia.

Production of hard baskets is a little more involved than with soft baskets. Hard basket plants need to be started earlier, grown longer, and pinched during production to encourage branching. Hard baskets respond very well to DIF conditions. Soft baskets are relatively easy to grow. Soft baskets may only require 6 to 8 weeks to produce a final product versus 12 to 15 weeks for hard baskets. Large plugs are often used for soft baskets. Greenhouse growers maximize profits by growing large numbers of baskets over bedding plant flats.

TONING BEDDING PLANTS

Up to the shipping or sale day, bedding plants have received warm temperatures, optimum fertility levels, and ample water to speed their growth and development. The place they are going, whether it is directly to the garden or to a sales display, is not so cozy. Therefore, the bedding plants must be prepared for a new environment. **Toning** describes the procedures used to prepare plants for a post-production environment.

Toning is accomplished by adjusting temperatures and fertility levels. Temperatures are lowered to tone bedding plants. Lower temperatures slow respiration, resulting in a buildup of carbohydrates in the plant tissues. The stored carbohydrates aid the plant in stressful situations associated with a change of environment. Dropping fertility levels also helps to prepare the plants. A good practice is to reduce fertilizer concentrations by 50 percent when flower buds have become visible.

Table 12-5. Cool Night Temperature Tolerances of Bedding Plants	
Bedding plants toned at 50 to 55°F	**Bedding plants toned at 58 to 62°F**
Ageratum	Begonia
Alyssum	Celosia
Calendula	Coleus
Dianthus	Impatiens
Marigold	Pepper
Pansy	Tomato
Petunia	Vinca
Salvia	Zinnia
Snapdragon	

REVIEWING

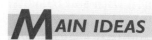 **M** *AIN IDEAS*

Bedding plants consist of annual plants valued for their flowers, or attractive foliage, and vegetables and herbs. Sales of bedding plants have grown significantly. The increased use of automated systems and larger greenhouse operations has significantly increased bedding plant production.

Production of bedding plants begins, in most cases, with sexual propagation or the use of seed. Growers schedule the sowing of seed to meet sales dates. Seed is carefully stored to maintain viable seed and to insure high germination rates. Small growers rely on hand seeding, while larger operations have automatic seeders. The grower must be aware of the requirements of water, light, and temperature for successful germination of seed.

Plugs have revolutionized the bedding plant industry. Roughly two-thirds of all bedding plants are grown as plugs. Seeds are planted in individual cells in a plastic tray that might hold between 70 to 800 plants. Commonly used growing media have mostly peat moss, with some vermiculite, perlite, or soil added. The goal of the grower is to produce plugs that are uniform, have short internodes, and have a high number of dark green leaves. The entire process in producing quality plugs takes 6 to 10 weeks. The plugs are sold and shipped to operations around the country or transplanted to larger containers for finishing.

The industry trend has been to finish bedding plants in 4-inch pots or cell packs with no more than 48 plants per flat. The larger containers extend the shelf life of bedding plants. Plugs in large operations are automatically transplanted from the plug trays to the pots or cell packs. Irrigation or watering has the greatest impact on the quality of the crop. Most growers employ the practice of fertigation. Bedding plants like warm temperatures. Optimum growing temperatures for most bedding plants range from 65 to 72°F. Stretching of bedding plants can be reduced by growing bedding plants under cool day temperatures and warm night temperatures. This technique is referred to as DIF or the difference between day and night temperatures. Most bedding plants grow best under full light conditions, with shading only necessary in late spring and early summer. Hanging baskets are divided into two groups, hard baskets and soft baskets. Before plants leave the greenhouse for sale, they are toned to prepare them for a change of environment and to extend their shelf life.

QUESTIONS

Answer the following questions. Use correct spelling and complete sentences.

1. What have been the recent trends in the bedding plant industry?
2. How are bedding plants scheduled?
3. What characteristics do quality seed possess?
4. What factors influence seed germination?
5. How have plugs revolutionized the bedding plant industry?
6. What are the characteristics of a quality plug?
7. Why is irrigation considered to be so important?
8. How does the technique DIF influence bedding plant growth?
9. Why are growth regulators used with bedding plants?
10. How are bedding plants toned?

EVALUATING

Match the term with the correct definition. Write the letter by the term in the blank provided.

a. bedding plants   e. shelf life   i. toning
b. DIF   f. break   j. plugs
c. cell pack   g. hard baskets
d. fertigation   h. finished

_____ 1. Refers to the development of lateral branches that contribute to a bushy appearance.

_____ 2. Bedding plants, such as fuchsia, geraniums, and New Guinea impatiens, that are propagated by cuttings and used in hanging baskets.

_____ 3. A term used to describe procedures that prepare plants for a post-production environment.

_____ 4. Molded plastic containers divided into two, three, four, or six separate growing compartments.

_____ 5. The practice of fertilizing while irrigating.

_____ 6. The final pots or packs in which bedding plants will be grown to saleable size.

_____ 7. Technique used that involves the difference between day and night temperatures.

_____ 8. Include herbaceous annual plants used for ornamental display or vegetable production.

_____ 9. Refers to the time the plant maintains its health while on display for sale.

_____ 10. Small plants grown in a small amount of medium in divided trays.

EXPLORING

1. Use the knowledge gained from this chapter to schedule, start, and grow bedding plants at home. Transplant the plants to the home landscape when weather permits.

2. Visit a local greenhouse in the spring of the year. Observe their growing techniques, the plants they produce, and the supplies they use. Record your observations.

3. Ask your instructor to allow you to conduct an independent study project in the school greenhouse or to be a greenhouse assistant. Keep records on your experiences, and if applicable, maintain a supervised agricultural experience program.

13

Pest and Disease Management

No problems can make a floriculture product less valuable than pests and diseases. Who wants to buy a plant covered with aphids, a plant with spider mite webs, or a plant with stem rot? People will buy lopsided plants. They will buy plants with broken stems. But they will not touch plants with visible pest problems.

Growers dislike pests for different reasons. They know what a quality plant should look like and strive to produce the highest quality possible. They also know the damage pests and diseases can do to growth and development. Unless they control pests and diseases, their crops lose value and the business loses potential revenue.

13-1. Growers need to be on the lookout for pests and diseases.

OBJECTIVES

1 Describe plant health and causes of plant disorder

2 Define integrated pest management

3 Explain how crops can be monitored for pest and disease problems

4 Identify major pests in the greenhouse

5 Identify major plant diseases in the greenhouse

6 Describe methods of control for the major greenhouse pests

7 Demonstrate methods of safe chemical pesticide application

TERMS

aerosol
aphids
bactericide
biological control
botanical insecticides
Botrytis blight
chemical control
cultural/physical
  control
damping-off
dip
disease
drench
Erwinia
fumigant
fungicide
fungus gnats

granular
greenhouse
  sanitation
herbicide
horticultural oils
infectious disease
insect growth
  regulators
insecticidal soaps
insecticide
integrated pest
  management (IPM)
leaf miners
mealybugs
mites
miticide
noninfectious disease

pathogens
pest
pesticide
powdery mildew
Pythium
Phytophthora
plant health
Rhizoctonia
scale
spray
Thielaviopsis
virus
western flower thrips
whitefly
worms
yellow sticky traps

MANAGING PLANT HEALTH

In the process of producing greenhouse crops, growers must address plant health. ***Plant health*** refers to plants that are free of pests and disease. Plant health is important during the production of the crop. It is also important that plants continue to be healthy after they are sold. Healthy plants have clean foliage and flowers, and they have a good rate of growth.

Pests and diseases can jeopardize plant health. A ***pest*** is a living organism that can cause injury or loss to a plant. Common greenhouse pests include insects, mites, bacteria, fungi, viruses, and weeds. Some pests can be the cause of disease. ***Disease*** is defined as a disturbance to the normal, healthy growth and development of a plant. Diseases are generally classified as being infectious or noninfectious. Bacteria, fungi, or virus can cause ***infectious disease***. These organisms are often referred to as disease ***pathogens***. An infectious disease can be spread to other plants. ***Noninfectious diseases*** are caused by environmental imbalances and cannot be spread to other plants. Examples of noninfectious disease include over watering and air pollution damage.

Plants are most susceptible to disease when they are under some type of stress. The stress is usually associated with environmental factors. While the environmental condition itself may or may not cause a noninfectious disease, the stress it creates can reduce a plant's ability to fight off infectious

13-2. Healthy plants are free of pests and diseases.

13-3. Proper watering practices reduce disease problems

disease. For instance, over watering alone can cause the death of root tissues, but it also weakens the plant's defenses against soil-borne disease organisms.

Growers have control over many environmental factors that can keep a plant healthy. Care can be taken to provide growing medium with desired drainage, aeration, and pH. Plants can be planted at the proper planting depth. Optimum nutrient levels can be maintained with fertilizers. One of the most important factors to control is recommended watering practices. Also, temperature, light intensity, and air quality can be adjusted to meet the needs of the specific crop.

No matter how well crops are grown, pests and diseases will become problems from time to time. The very nature of greenhouse crop production leads to some disease problems. In most cases, crops are of the same species, variety, and cultivar. Being of identical genetic makeup, they are vulnerable to infectious disease. An infectious disease can easily spread from one plant to another. Greenhouses tend to be humid. Humid conditions are ideal for many fungal diseases. Successful growers produce crops with a plan for dealing with pests and diseases.

INTEGRATED PEST MANAGEMENT

Control of pests and diseases in the modern greenhouse is accomplished with well thought-out strategies. Use of a wide range of strategies to control pests and diseases is known as *integrated pest management (IPM)*.

MONITORING FOR PESTS

The key to successful IPM programs is the careful monitoring for pests. This involves casual observation while performing other tasks, as well as, scouting for pest problems on a weekly schedule. Weekly inspections should be made by randomly selecting plants at the middle and sides of benches. The number of plants checked should total a minimum of 1 percent of the crop during each study. Thoroughly check the plants by looking at the top, middle, and bottom leaves of plants. Often pests are located on the undersides of leaves, so be sure to look there.

Yellow sticky traps are effective in monitoring pest populations. Brightly colored, they attract whitefly, western flower thrips, aphids, leaf minors, and fungus gnats. The insects land on the traps, get stuck, and die. The sticky traps are useful as general indicators of a pest population. They also help provide early de-

13-4. Yellow sticky traps are an effective means to monitor insect pest populations.

tection of insect problems. Early detection gives the grower time to prepare an IPM program. Sticky cards should be put in horizontal positions just below the tops of the crops. All the cards in a house should face the same direction, too.

MAJOR GREENHOUSE PESTS AND DISEASES

Correct identification of the pest or disease cannot be understated. How can a pest be controlled if it is unknown? Unless the pest is known, proper treatment cannot be administered. For instance, a doctor would not prescribe cold medicine to treat athlete's feet. Following are a number of the more common pests and diseases found in the greenhouse:

Pests

Aphids—Aphids are pear-shaped, soft-bodied, usually wingless insects. They are often green or yellowish in color. Aphids have the ability to reproduce very rapidly. Astonishingly, they give birth to live young that are pregnant! Aphids use their mouthparts to pierce the plant and suck out juices. Aphids attack a wide variety of greenhouse plants.

13-5. Ladybugs feed on smaller yellow-green aphids. (Courtesy: USDA, Agricultural Research Service)

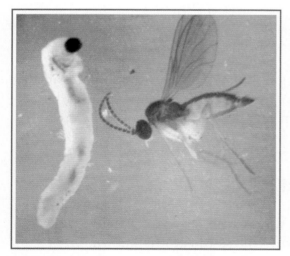

13-6. Shown are a fungus gnat larva and adult. (Courtesy, Fredric Miller and Phil Nixon, University of Illinois Extension)

Fungus gnats—Fungus gnats are long-legged, winged, gray-black insects less than an eighth of an inch long. The larvae of fungus gnats feed on root hairs and tunnel into plant stems. They prefer growing media that is constantly moist.

Leaf miners—Leaf miners are small stocky flies. The adult deposits eggs inside a leaf. The eggs hatch and the larva feeds on the interior of the leaf, making tunnels as it moves along. Chrysanthemums are subject to leaf miner damage.

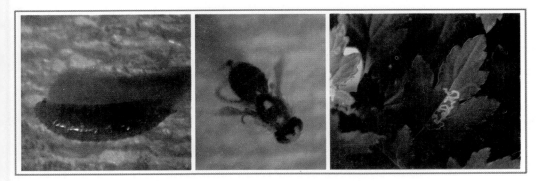

13-7. Leaf miner larva, adult, and damage caused to a chrysanthemum. (Courtesy, Fredric Miller and Phil Nixon, University of Illinois Extension)

Mealybugs—Mealybugs are slow-moving, oval-shaped, whitish insects. They have a waxy finish and produce small cottony masses. Mealybugs pierce plant leaves and suck the plant juices. As with aphids, they give birth to living nymph.

13-8. Mealybugs are often found in the axils of leaves. (Courtesy, Fredric Miller and Phil Nixon, University of Illinois Extension)

Mites—Mites are not insects. They have eight legs and are related to spiders. Mites pierce plant leaf tissues and suck juice. Symptoms include a yellow speckled appearance to the leaf, and in severe cases, yellowing of the leaves and defoliation. Two-spotted or red spider mites are among the most serious greenhouse pests. Two-spotted mites have two dark spots on their back and appear as tiny specks. Cyclamen mites infest a broad range of

13-9. Spider mites on an acacia and a *Ficus*. Notice the speckled appearance of the leaves caused by feeding. (Courtesy, Fredric Miller and Phil Nixon, University of Illinois Extension)

plants and are not visible to the naked eye. Bulb mites damage lily bulbs and the developing shoots. Spider mites create a complex network of webbing as they move about a plant.

Scale—Many types of scale insects infest greenhouse plants. Typically, they have flat, oval, often brown bodies. They may or may not be covered with an armored shell. Scale insects pierce plant leaves and stems and suck juices.

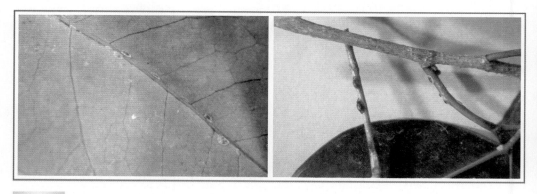

13-10. Photographs of scale on a *Ficus*. (Courtesy, Fredric Miller and Phil Nixon, University of Illinois Extension)

Western flower thrips—Western flower thrips are small insects with two pairs of fringed wings. They are dark brown in color. Western flower thrips have rasping mouthparts that scrape plant tissue. The damage they cause to many kinds of plants often appears as whitish discoloration.

13-11. A thrip. (Photo by M. Herbut, Courtesy of Applied Bio-monics, Ltd., contributed by Mike Cherim, The Green Spot, Ltd.,)

Whiteflies—Whiteflies are small insects that are not surprisingly, white. They generally camp out on the undersides of leaves where they pierce the tissues and suck juices. Their flat, scale-like larvae feed on the undersides of the leaves. The whitefly is a major pest of poinsettias and fuchsias.

13-12. Shown is a whitefly greatly magnified. (Courtesy, USDA Agricultural Research Service)

Worms or caterpillars—Caterpillars are the larva of various moth species. They damage greenhouse crops by eating the plants.

Diseases

Botrytis blight—*Botrytis* blight is a fungal disease that can attack nearly all greenhouse crops, and is a common problem with cut flower storage. It causes a brown rotting and develops fuzzy, gray mold as it produces spores. *Botrytis* is most common when temperatures are between 60 and 70°F, air circulation is poor, and humidity is high.

13-13. *Botrytis* on an impatiens. (Courtesy, James E. Schuster)

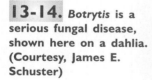

13-14. *Botrytis* is a serious fungal disease, shown here on a dahlia. (Courtesy, James E. Schuster)

Erwinia—*Erwinia* is a bacterial disease that causes rotting of plant tissues. The bacteria enter the plant through wounds. It is a common problem on *Dieffenbachia, Philodendron,* chrysanthemum, and cyclamen.

Powdery mildew—Powdery mildew is a fungal disease. Characteristic symptoms include a white dusty coating to leaves and flowers. Infected plants can become stunted. High humidity contributes to powdery mildew problems.

13-15. Powdery mildew can be a problem with roses. (Courtesy, James E. Schuster)

Pythium—*Pythium* is a fungal disease that attacks greenhouse plants under cool, wet conditions. It is one fungus that can cause damping-off. *Damping-off* is a term used to describe the early death of seedlings that have germinated. More mature plants can develop root and stem rots as a result of *Pythium*, particularly when growing medium has poor aeration.

13-16. Damping-off is often caused by *Pythium*. (Courtesy, James E. Schuster)

Phytophthora—*Phytophthora* is a fungal disease similar to Pythium. It causes crown and stem rots in cool, wet conditions.

13-17. Stem rot is shown in this photograph. (Courtesy, James E. Schuster)

Rhizoctonia—*Rhizoctonia* is a fungal disease prevalent under wet and warm conditions. It is a common disease problem in the southeastern region of the country. *Rhizoctonia* causes damping-off, as well as, root and stem rots.

Thielaviopsis—*Thielaviopsis* is a fungus that causes root and stem rots. Problems caused by *Thielaviopsis* are favored by cool, moist conditions.

Virus—Tobacco mosaic and aster yellows are two common viral diseases associated with greenhouse crops. Symptoms of infection include discolor-

13-18. The streaking of this tulip is caused by a virus. (Courtesy, James E. Schuster)

13-19. Aster yellows, a virus disease, has caused discoloration of the foliage of this marigold. (Courtesy, James E. Schuster)

ation of plant tissues, stunting of growth, and deformed growth. The spread from one plant to another is primarily by feeding greenhouse insects. Tobacco mosaic virus can be spread to the plants from the hands of workers who smoke.

PEST CONTROL STRATEGIES

For successful management of pests, the IPM program must be a year-round program. Also, IPM control measures for a specific crop, poinsettias for example, should begin before the plants enter the greenhouse. The strength of IPM is the combination of control measures used. Four broad areas of control include sanitation, cultural/physical control, biological control, and chemical control.

Greenhouse Sanitation

Many pest problems can be greatly reduced, if not eliminated, with greenhouse sanitation. *Greenhouse sanitation* is simply the efforts made to keep a greenhouse clean. Many modern greenhouse ranges have been built with concrete floors partly because they are easier to keep clean than gravel floors.

One aspect of greenhouse sanitation involves the removal of weeds from the interior of the greenhouse and the immediate area outside the greenhouse. The importance of weed control cannot be understated. Weeds harbor

13-20. The concrete floors as in this greenhouse are easy to keep clean.

pests. Control measures applied to a crop fail to control pests that find safety on the weeds. After awhile, the pests migrate to the crop to cause damage. Only a few herbicides are labeled for use in the greenhouse.

Another important sanitation practice is the removal of plant debris and other debris from the floors and benches. Debris often houses disease organisms and pests. Severely infested or infected plants should also be removed and disposed of properly.

13-21. Weeds are controlled in this greenhouse with a fabric weed barrier.

13-22. Diseased or infested plants should be removed from the greenhouse and disposed.

Cultural/Physical Control

Cultural/physical control methods are those methods that physically prevent activities of pests. Used alone they probably will not provide complete control of pests. However, they can significantly reduce certain problems. Cultural/physical controls are also safe to humans and relatively easy to implement.

Stop the introduction of pests to the greenhouse when possible. Inspect all plants thoroughly before moving them into the greenhouse. Accept only clean plants purchased from reputable suppliers. Admitting infested plants to the greenhouse usually leads to serious control problems.

Maintain the ideal growing environment for the crops. Plants that are healthy are better able to fight disease organisms and pests. A good analogy is people and colds. People who eat right, exercise, get plenty of rest, and are under little stress are more resistant to colds. People who get run down, are out of shape, and eat a poor diet are more susceptible to colds.

Fungal diseases can be reduced by providing good air circulation around the plants. Fungi rely on moisture to grow and spread. Air circulation helps to keep plant leaves dry.

One physical control method that has gained in popularity is the use of screens over greenhouse openings. The fine mesh of the screens prevents pests from flying into the greenhouse environment. The one drawback with insect screening is it can restrict the airflow somewhat.

The yellow sticky traps used as monitoring tools also serve as a means of physical control. Flying insect pests attracted to sticky traps fly onto the trap and get stuck. In a short while, they die.

13-23. Good air circulation reduces fungal disease problems.

13-24. Insect screens over greenhouse openings can help keep harmful insects out. (Courtesy, Ludvig Svensson, Inc.)

*B*iological Controls

Biological controls involve the use of living organisms to control pests. They may be microbial organisms, parasitic organisms, or predators. Biological control organisms for greenhouse use are found in nature and are considered environmentally safe.

13-25. A parasitoid wasp, *Aphidius* species, laying eggs in the abdomen of aphids. (Photo by M. Badgley, courtesy of Buena Biosystems, Inc., contributed by M. Cherim, The Green Spot, Ltd)

Microbial organisms include bacteria and fungi. A bacteria, *Bacillus thurengiensis*, effectively controls caterpillars. Aphids and whitefly can be controlled to an extent by species of bacteria and fungi. The bacteria and fungi are natural diseases of those insects. However, high humidity in the greenhouse required for the beneficial fungi also promotes the growth of disease-causing fungi.

Parasitic organisms help to control some pests. The parasites are natural enemies of the pest and live off the pest organism. An example is a tiny parasitic wasp that lays its eggs on the whitefly larva that feeds on plant leaves.

13-26. A parasitoid wasp, *Encarsia formosa*. It lays eggs in the larva of whitefly. (Photo by B. Costello, courtesy of Applied Bio-nomics, Ltd., contributed by M. Cherim, The Green Spot, Ltd)

The eggs hatch with the wasp larva inside the whitefly larva. The wasp larva proceeds to eat the whitefly larva. The wasp matures, emerges from what is left of the whitefly, mates, and looks for whitefly larva on which to lay the next generation of eggs. There are some restrictions with the use of parasitic insects. Chemical pesticides cannot be used in the greenhouse without killing the beneficial parasites. The parasites are also not effective with heavy infestations of plant pests.

13-27. The big-eyed bug is a predator with mouthparts that allow it to inject white fly larvae with a digestive enzyme. It then sucks out their insides. (Courtesy, USDA, Agricultural Research Service)

Predatory organisms can be released in the greenhouse to devour certain plant pests. A beetle attacks whitefly larva and adults. A mite is used to control thrips. Ladybugs eat aphids. As with parasitic organisms, chemical pesticides should not be used with predatory organisms. Also, predatory and parasitic organisms should be released when pest populations are small.

Chemical Control

The use of chemicals to control pests and diseases is ***chemical control***. The chemicals used are called ***pesticides***. Although once used almost exclusively, control of pests with the use of pesticides is now viewed as only one component of an IPM program. In fact, use of chemical pesticides is now often done only when it is absolutely necessary. Application of pesticides must be done safely to reduce potential injury to people and the environment.

Different types of pesticides are used to control different pests. ***Insecticides*** are used to control insects. Mites are controlled by ***miticides***. A grower would use a *fungicide* to control fungi, *bactericide* for bacteria, and *herbicide* for weeds.

Pest control has been made safer with the introduction of less toxic pesticides. This group of "soft" pesticides includes botanical insecticides, horticultural oils, insect growth regulators, and insecticidal soaps. *Botanical insecticides* are natural materials obtained from plants that are toxic to the insect pest. *Horticultural oils* are sprayed on the insects and clog the breathing pores of the insect, causing suffocation. *Insect growth regulators* disrupt the growth and development of the insects. *Insecticidal soaps* dissolve the protective membranes of insects, bringing on death.

There are several methods used to apply pesticides in the greenhouse. The key is to get the pesticide to the pest that is to be controlled. The methods vary with the formulation of the chemical.

Aerosols—Aerosols consist of atomized spray or smoke particles distributed through the air. Cans containing the pesticide can be set to release the aerosol that creates a fog in the greenhouse. Once started, the applicator can safely leave.

Dip—Plants can be dipped or submerged in a pesticide that has been mixed with water. Easter lily bulbs are dipped in a miticide prior to planting to control bulb mites.

Drench—Some materials are used as a drench. A common practice is to drench poinsettias with a fungicide to control soil-borne disease. The material, mixed with water, is simply poured into the pots.

Fumigants—Fumigants are poisonous gases that are distributed through the air to all parts of the greenhouse. They are particularly effective with flying insects and pests exposed to the gas.

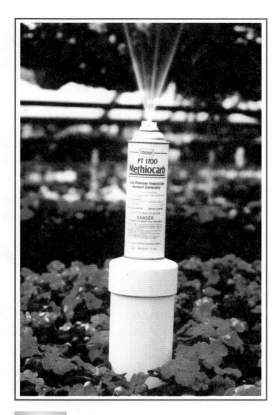

13-28. Aerosols release pesticides into the air. (Courtesy, *Greenhouse Product News*)

13-29. A granular pesticide has been placed in the pot of this chrysanthemum.

Granular—Some pesticides are in a granular or pellet form that is carefully measured and applied on the surface of the growing medium. These pesticides are referred to as systemic because the plant's roots absorb them into their systems.

Spray—Pesticides may be sprayed on the plant. The small droplets of the spray cover the surface of the plant. Care must be taken with sprays to cover parts of the plant where the pest is found, such as the underside of the leaves.

13-30. The most important time spent in pesticide application is the time reading the label.

SAFE USE OF PESTICIDES

There is potential danger when pesticides are used. The applicator can be poisoned. Plants can be damaged. The environment can be polluted and ground water contaminated. Therefore, caution must be practiced whenever pesticides are used.

Some rules to observe when applying pesticides follow:

- Use pesticides only when needed.
- Select the least toxic pesticide that is labeled to control the pest.
- **Read the label of the pesticide carefully.**
- Wear protective clothing when mixing and applying pesticides.
- Apply pesticides when the weather is good (not too hot or windy).

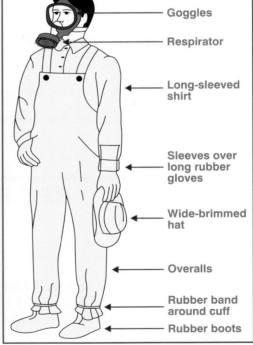

Goggles

Respirator

Long-sleeved shirt

Sleeves over long rubber gloves

Wide-brimmed hat

Overalls

Rubber band around cuff

Rubber boots

13-31. This person is shown preparing a fungicide for application.

13-32. Protective clothing must be worn when working with pesticides.

13-33. Application equipment must be clearly marked as to its use and treated crop areas properly labeled to remind workers of pesticide application.

■ Apply the amount that is called for on the pesticide label.

■ Apply pesticides so complete coverage of where the pests are located is provided.

■ Use equipment that is properly calibrated.

■ Label holding tanks indicating what type of pesticide has been used.

■ Dispose of old pesticides and empty pesticide containers properly.

■ Label crops that have been treated and note the safe time for workers to re-enter the area.

REVIEWING

*M*AIN IDEAS

Plants that are free of pests and disease are important during the production of the crop and after they are sold. Healthy plants have clean foliage and flowers, and they have a good rate of growth. Pests and diseases can jeopardize plant health. Common greenhouse pests include insects, mites, bacteria, fungi, viruses, and weeds. Pests can be the cause of disease or a disturbance to the normal, healthy growth and development of a plant. Diseases are generally classified as being infectious or noninfectious.

Control of pests and disease problems in the modern greenhouse is accomplished with a wide range of strategies known as integrated pest management (IPM). The key to successful IPM programs is the careful monitoring for pests. Yellow sticky traps are effective in monitoring pest populations. Common greenhouse pests include aphids, fungus gnats, leaf miners, mealybugs, mites, scale, western flower thrips, whitefly, and worms or caterpillars. Common disease pathogens include *Botrytis* blight, *Erwinia*, powdery mildew, *Pythium*, *Phytophthora*, *Rhizoctonia*, *Thielaviopsis*, and virus.

IPM programs must be year-round programs. Four broad areas of control include sanitation, cultural/physical control, biological control, and chemical control. Many pest problems can be greatly reduced with greenhouse sanitation, which is simply keeping a greenhouse clean. Cultural/physical control methods are those methods that physically prevent activities of pests. Examples include stopping the introduction of pests to the greenhouse, maintaining the ideal growing environment for the crops, and using screens over greenhouse openings. Biological controls involve the use of microbial organisms, parasitic organisms, or predators to control pests. Chemical control of pests and diseases involves chemicals called pesticides.

Different types of pesticides are used to control different pests. Insecticides control insects. Mites are controlled by miticides. A grower would use a fungicide to control fungi, bactericide for bacteria, and herbicide for weeds. A group of safer materials known as "soft" pesticides include botanical insecticides, horticultural oils, insect growth regulators, and insecticidal soaps. Methods used to apply pesticides in the greenhouse include aerosols, dips, drenches, fumigants, granules, and sprays. There is potential danger when pesticides are used. Therefore, caution must be practiced whenever pesticides are used.

QUESTIONS

Answer the following questions. Use correct spelling and complete sentences.

1. What is meant by plant health?
2. How do infectious and noninfectious diseases differ?
3. What can be done to help a plant fight off pests and diseases?
4. Why are crops monitored for pests and diseases?
5. What are some common greenhouse pests?
6. What are some common greenhouse pathogens?
7. Why is integrated pest management effective?
8. What are four control methods applied in an IPM program?
9. Why are pesticides often considered to be a last resort?
10. Why is safety so important when using pesticides?

EVALUATING

Match the term with the correct definition. Write the letter by the term in the blank provided.

a. aphids
b. *Botrytis*
c. drench
d. fungicide
e. granular
f. greenhouse sanitation

g. horticultural oils
h. integrated pest management (IPM)
i. mites
j. pest
k. *Pythium*
l. yellow sticky traps

_____ 1. A pesticide, mixed with water, is simply poured into the pots.

_____ 2. A living organism that can cause injury or loss to a plant.

_____ 3. The efforts made to keep a greenhouse clean.

_____ 4. Use of a wide range of strategies to control pests and diseases.

_____ 5. Clogs the breathing pores of insects on which it is sprayed, causing suffocation.

_____ 6. A pellet-form pesticide that is carefully measured and applied on the surface of the growing medium.

_____ 7. A pesticide that controls fungi.

_____ 8. A fungal disease that can attack nearly all greenhouse crops; it causes a brown rotting and develops fuzzy, gray mold as it produces spores.

_____ 9. Pear-shaped, soft-bodied, usually wingless insects that are often green or yellowish in color.

_____ 10. A fungal disease that attacks greenhouse plants under cool, wet conditions and may cause damping-off.

_____ 11. Effective in monitoring pest populations.

_____ 12. Pests with eight legs and related to spiders.

EXPLORING

1. Set up your own scouting activity at home or in the school greenhouse. Monitor the plants for pest and disease problems. Record your observations. Suggest ways in which the problems can be managed.

2. Study the safe use of pesticides in greater depth than is presented in this chapter. Obtain study manuals from your state extension office. Attend training sessions if they are offered. Once you feel competent, test your knowledge by taking the state-licensing exam on pesticide use.

14

The History of Floral Design

Floral design has a rich and varied history dating back to very early cultures. Flowers were used to beautify surroundings, for personal enjoyment, to express feelings, and to enhance religious ceremonies or other important festivals and events. The study of the history and traditions of floral design throughout the ages can give great insight into the use of flowers today.

14-1. Flowers have played an important role in all civilizations since the beginning of recorded history.

OBJECTIVES

1 Identify major influential periods of floral design history

2 Identify the major design style(s) for each influential period

3 Relate the influence of those earlier periods to today's designs

TERMS

American Colonial period
chaplet
Dutch Flemish period
English tradition
Egyptian period
free form
French period or Grand era
garland
Georgian era
Greek and Roman period
ikebana
Italian Renaissance period

Japanese influence
language of flowers
line arrangement
line mass
mass arrangement
nosegay
strewing
topiary
tussie mussie
Victorian era
wreath

EARLY FLORAL DESIGN PERIODS

EGYPTIAN PERIOD (2800 – 28 B.C.)

The Egyptians were the first people recorded in history to use flowers for decorative purposes. Cut flowers were placed in bowls, vases, or jars to use in religious ceremonies and for festivals during the **Egyptian period**. Flowers also served decorative purposes in the home.

14-2. Garlands and wreaths were first fashioned by the Egyptians.

The Egyptians valued simplicity and highly stylized repetition. A typical arrangement would be in a wide-mouthed bowl with an orderly sequence of a fully opened water lily, a leaf, and then a bud, repeating around the rim of the bowl.

Flowers, foliage, and fruits were often woven together into wreaths, garlands, flower collars, and chaplets. A **wreath** forms a circular shape; a **garland** is a strand or roping of plants, which can be shaped depending upon the place and the designer. **Chaplets** were either garlands or wreaths worn on a person's head.

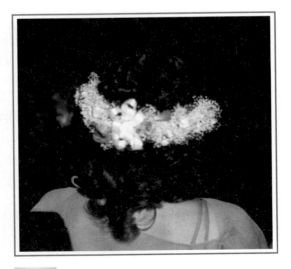

14-3. Chaplets, originally given by the Greeks to honor their heroes and athletes, may today adorn members of a bridal party.

THE GREEK AND ROMAN PERIOD (600 – 146 B.C. AND A.D. 28 – 325)

The Greeks and Romans were greatly influenced by the Egyptian period. Garlands, wreaths, and chaplets were the main floral designs during the **Greek and Roman period**. Flowers were given to honor their heroes and gods during festivals, athletic events, and religious ceremonies. The **strewing** (scattering) of flowers and loose petals at banquets and festivals was a trademark of this period. Flowers arranged in vases or bowls was uncommon during this era.

Influence on Today's Designs

Wreaths and garlands are still very popular today. The wreath is a popular door decoration at the holidays or year-round. Wreaths may be placed either on a wall or on a table as a centerpiece. Garlands are popular for adorning cake tables or head tables at weddings. Evergreen garlands (or roping) add a festive touch to stairways and banisters at the Christmas season. The strewing of petals by a flower girl at a wedding is a common practice.

JAPANESE INFLUENCE

Ikebana or Japanese flower arranging has been practiced as an art form since 621 AD. This form of floral design was influenced by early Chinese art. The floral designs of the **Japanese influence** emphasize careful and significant placement of every flower, branch, or leaf. Space and flowing rhythm also characterize this design style. The placement of three main flowers or branches signifies heaven (shin), man (soe), and Earth (tai).

The three main classifications are as follows:

1. Formal or classical style (Rikka and Shoka)

2. Informal or naturalistic style (Nageire and Moribana)

3. Abstract or freestyle

Ikebana designs are used for religious ceremonies and tea ceremonies as well as for home decoration.

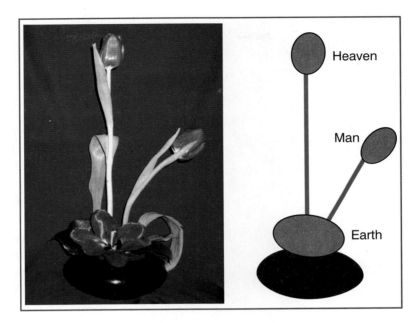

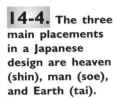

14-4. The three main placements in a Japanese design are heaven (shin), man (soe), and Earth (tai).

Influence on Today's Designs

Japanese flower arranging has influenced the contemporary line and line mass designs of today. The use of space in contemporary floral design was given greater importance due to the influence of this design style.

EUROPEAN PERIODS

MIDDLE AGES (5TH TO 15TH CENTURIES)

The flower arranging of the Middle Ages in Europe continued with the traditions of the Greek and Romans. Flowers were strewn on the floor and were made into wreaths and garlands. Although flowers were important during this period, very little information is known about additional uses, except for their use in food, beverages, and medicine.

ITALIAN RENAISSANCE (15TH AND 16TH CENTURIES)

The *Italian Renaissance period* signifies a greater interest in the arts. This period is considered the beginning of flower arranging as it is known today. Flowers were placed in vases, urns, and bowls for their beauty and for

14-5. The design style of the Renaissance period is symmetrical with no flower stems showing.

their symbolic meanings. The rose portrayed love; the white lily meant chastity. The white lily became known as the Madonna lily because it appeared in so many paintings of the Annunciation, showing the angel Gabriel and the young Mary.

For church and state occasions, the floral design styles were colorful, large, full, and symmetrical with no stems showing. Casual arrangements for the home included short-stemmed, tight clusters of colorful flowers. Colorful arrangements of fruits, vegetables, and flowers placed casually on trays or in baskets were introduced during this period. Wreaths and garlands were still popular.

Influence on Today's Designs

Today's designs are greatly influenced by this period and the use of many flowers in a vase. Incorporating fruits and vegetables within flower arrangements is still a common sight for banquets, buffets, and other festive events. To some extent, people today still attach meanings to certain flowers. Roses are the flowers most commonly given at Valentine's Day. Roses continue to signify love.

DUTCH FLEMISH PERIOD (17TH CENTURY)

The **Dutch Flemish period** was a time of great horticultural interest. Flowers were introduced from all parts of the world and were used to create elaborate mixed designs during this period. The designs were carefully styled, large, and flamboyant arrangements with either symmetrical or asymmetrical balance. Careful attention was paid to the selection and placement of the flowers. Fruit, shells, bird nests or birdcages, and other objects of nature were also added as accessories. During the latter part of this period, flowers were shown in all views—front, sides, and back. Space and depth were emphasized more as compared to the Renaissance style. Many containers were used, including urns, glass vases, goblets, low baskets and bowls, and Delft vases.

Floral designs during this period were favored both for the wealthy and the middle class and for both formal and informal occasions. Many paintings of this period show floral designs as an important part of the scene.

Influence on Today's Designs

The lavish, colorful mixtures of the Dutch Flemish floral designs have influenced many contemporary floral designs, including banquet centerpieces and hotel lobby designs. The use of accessories is still a prominent part of many arrangements. Today's designs also use depth and display flowers from many angles, which originated in the Dutch Flemish period.

FRENCH PERIOD OR GRAND ERA (17TH AND 18TH CENTURY)

The *French period or the Grand era* was influenced by the French monarchy beginning with Louis XIV. The emphasis during this period was on classic form. Floral designs were refined and elegant compared to the often overdone flamboyance of the earlier Dutch Flemish ar-

14-6. Dutch Flemish designs were large and extravagant mixtures of flowers with accessories placed near the vase.

14-7. Highly ornamented vases and classic, refined style characterized the Grand era of France.

rangements. Fan-shaped, round, and crescent-shaped designs were favored. Other designs featured in the Grand era were tall designs (two to three times the container height) as well as small casual bouquets (equal to or shorter than the container height). Roses were very popular along with all the spring bulb flowers—lilacs, lilies, and the newly introduced gladiolus.

Containers, including vases, urns, and flasks, were very ornate and made of porcelain, metal, or glass. Shell and leaf-shaped dishes and baskets or bowls were also characteristic of this period.

Influence on Today's Designs

The fan and crescent arrangements of the Grand era are still designed today. The emphasis on classic form and not the extravagance of the earlier period is also commonly chosen for today's designs.

14-8. Nosegays or tussie-mussies were created and carried by fashionable English ladies as a defense against any unsavory odors.

ENGLISH TRADITION

The English have a long history and love for flowers and plants. The conquering Romans introduced decorating with wreaths and garlands. Tending of kitchen or cottage gardens dated back to the Middle Ages. In the 15th and 16th centuries, the English picked flowers for casual bouquets to bring into their homes. An early requirement for flowers in the **English tradition** was their fragrance. The English favored fragrant flowers because they believed that the perfume would rid the air of pestilence. Fashionable English ladies carried **nosegays** (handheld bouquets) for their fragrance as well as for decoration. Another name for the nosegay was **tussie-mussie** (tuzzy-muzzy). Tuzzy is an old English word for a knot of flowers.

The English enjoyed both casual and formal designs. The William and Mary reign from 1689 to 1702 marked the height in popularity of the very formal and symmetrical style of gardening. With the popularity of formality, the *topiary* form was developed, first in the garden by pruning shrubs into symmetrical shapes, and then later in floral design.

EARLY ENGLISH PERIOD— GEORGIAN ERA (18TH CENTURY)

The *Georgian era* was named for the English kings, George I, II, and III. During the Georgian period, floral designs varied from small, casual, mixed bouquets in glass, or metal, bud vases or vases and small tussie-mussies to large, mixed flower arrangements in urns, baskets, and vases. The arrangement height of the tall designs was usually one and one-half times the container height. These smaller bouquets are also believed to be the first centerpieces. Dried flower arrange-

14-9. Topiary forms became popular in England during the reign of William and Mary.

14-10. The English created the first centerpiece during the Georgian era.

14-11. A variety of containers were used by the English to arrange flowers. (Tussie mussie holders, stem cups with handles, and enclosed bricks with flower holes)

ments also became popular during this time. The English are also credited with inventing the miniature arrangement.

The containers were numerous, such as urns, bud vases, stem cups with handles, baskets, jars, jugs, bowls, bottles, vases, and five-fingered posy-holders. Ceramic wall pockets and Delft enclosed bricks with holes for flowers were introduced for flower arranging during the Georgian period.

Influence on Today's Designs

The English developed many popular items for today's flower enthusiasts, such as the centerpiece, the nosegay (the forerunner of the wedding bouquet), the topiary, and also the miniature. Flowers arranged in a bud vase are still a simple but pleasant way to display a few select blossoms. Dried flower arrangements are still enjoyed today.

LATER ENGLISH PERIOD—VICTORIAN ERA (19TH CENTURY)

The **Victorian era** was named for Queen Victoria who ruled England from 1837 to 1901. The Victorian era contributed the most to establishing floral design as an art. The art of floral design was taught and thoroughly covered in books and magazines of that era. This era established many rules and techniques of floral design. Two design styles were popular—large, abundant,

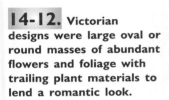

14-12. Victorian designs were large oval or round masses of abundant flowers and foliage with trailing plant materials to lend a romantic look.

masses of flowers and small, mixed, informal bouquets. The larger designs were generally round or oval with draping or trailing plant materials, such as fuchsias or bleeding hearts, to give a touch of the romantic. No obvious center of interest was created. Flowers of all types, especially new or unusual flowers, were favored. Foliage was prominently incorporated into designs, often at the edges to soften the framework.

The *language of flowers* was studied and used to convey meaning—to communicate with others, especially during courtship. The tradition of sending flowers to ladies before social events was begun during this period. The Victorians were much more elaborate and thorough in attaching meanings to plants. Rosemary for remembrance was a Victorian example of a plant's meaning. Roses varied in their meaning depending upon the color. For example, red was love, white was silence, and yellow meant infidelity. Heliotrope meant eternal love; larkspur was fickleness.

Popular containers were urns, vases, bottles, epergnes (see Figure 1-12), tussie-mussie holders, wall pockets, cornucopias, and baskets. Glass was very popular although many containers were also made out of metal, ceramic material, and porcelain. The Victorians loved accessories, such as fans, figurines, shells, knickknacks, and glass paperweights.

14-13. Epergnes were popular Victorian containers with multiple levels to hold flowers, foliage, and fruit or vegetables.

Influence on Today's Designs

The romantic look of the Victorian era is still a popular one today. Draping or trailing material added to soften an arrangement's silhouette makes a beautiful contemporary romantic design. The addition of foliage is an important component of today's designs.

The Victorian era marked the beginning of floral design as an art form. Floral design became a creative field to study. The emphasis on the art and necessity of training during the Victorian era set the stage for the modern day florist.

AMERICAN STYLES

COLONIAL PERIOD (18TH CENTURY)

The European design styles greatly influenced the early American floral styles. *American Colonial period* styles were much simpler and also contained flowers and foliage that were native to the United States. The addition of grains, grasses, and dried flowers made American design styles very unique compared to their European counterparts. Colonial ladies often arranged flowers of the same kind in bowls or baskets and then added filler flowers, such as baby's breath. Other casual designs for the home were generally very colorful mixtures of simple naturalistic styles in vases, pots, or jars. Fan-shaped and triangular arrangements were very popular for more formal events for the home or church. Five-fingered vases, epergnes, urns, and stem cups were other commonly used containers.

Influence on Today's Designs

The incorporation of dried materials with fresh flowers was introduced during this period and is still a popular technique today. Simple, naturalistic arrangements of one kind or simple colorful mixtures continue to be popular designs for the home.

14-14. Line mass designs combine the line and space of the Japanese influence with the colorful masses of the European style.

20TH CENTURY AMERICA

The floral designers of the 20th century enjoyed the simplicity of the Japanese ikebana designs and adapted them to a form called the **line arrangement**. The large, colorful mixture of flowers of the European arrangements were simplified and called **mass arrangements**. The mass designs were based on geometric shapes.

The **line mass** style (also called Western line arrangements) was created by the 20th century American designers. Line mass blended the colorful mass style of the Europeans with the spacious and dramatic line style of the East.

Free form styles were invented in the 1950s. The use of line and expressiveness brought a new dimension to floral design. Unique, individual expression allowed for creative uses of flowers, foliage, and accessories. Often, the rules of design were reinvented or ignored to allow for creativity.

Influence on Today's Designs

The line mass style and the free form style added a new dimension to the florist industry beginning in the 1950s and 1960s. Variations of these design styles are still popular today. The space and linear component of the line mass continue to add vitality and drama to designs. Expressiveness is still important and allows for unique interpretations and uses of plant materials.

REVIEWING

MAIN IDEAS

Throughout history, flowers and floral design have been an important part of religious, community, and home decoration and enjoyment. Learning about the past can help us to relate our current floral practices and techniques to other cultures and periods of history.

The first people to design with flowers were the Egyptians who made wreaths, garlands, and chaplets. The Romans and Greeks strewed numerous flowers and petals at banquets. The Japanese influence gave us beautiful line and spaciousness in floral art.

The Europeans were very influential floral designers. The Italian Renaissance is considered the beginning of appreciation of flowers placed in containers and used in the home. The Dutch Flemish period added a flamboyance and extravagant style to floral design. The Grand era of France emphasized elegance and classic form. The English, including the Georgian period, contributed many design styles, such as the nosegay, centerpiece, topiary, and the miniature. During the Victorian era, floral design rules and techniques were established and floral design was considered an art after that period.

The American Colonial period was responsible for the addition of dried grains or flowers to the fresh flower arrangements. The line mass was developed as a blend of the Japanese line and the European mass arrangements during the middle 1900s by the Americans. Free form designs were invented to allow for creative expression and unique use of plant materials.

QUESTIONS

Answer the following questions. Use correct spelling and complete sentences.

1. Why should a floral designer of today know about the history of floral design?

2. What were the floral decorations of the earliest cultures?

3. What style has three major placements of flowers or branches?

4. What period is considered the beginning of the appreciation of flowers placed in containers and brought into the home?

5. What are the characteristics of the Dutch Flemish style of floral design?

6. Who developed the first centerpiece?

7. Why were the forerunners of today's wedding bouquets developed? Who developed these bouquets?

8. Who first developed the "rules" of floral design?

9. What is the language of flowers and when was it used?

10. Who added dried flowers or grains to fresh flower arrangements?

11. What is a line mass design and what influenced its creation?

12. What design style has very few rules, if any?

EVALUATING

Match the term with the correct definition. Write the letter of the term in the blank provided.

a. chaplet
b. Egyptians
c. Victorian period
d. garland

e. ikebana
f. Dutch Flemish
g. strewing
h. mass arrangement

i. Grand era
j. tussie mussie

_____ 1. The scattering of petals and flowers.

_____ 2. Fragrance was an important aspect of these tightly clustered flowers.

_____ 3. Created designs with very stylized and repetitive flower and leaf placements.

_____ 4. Worn on the head as a decoration or to honor a person.

_____ 5. Emphasizes line and significant placement of every flower or piece of plant material.

_____ 6. Extravagant, colorful arrangements with accessories, such as shells, bird nests, or fruit.

_____ 7. Roping or strands of woven flowers and foliage.

_____ 8. Designs with geometric shapes and numerous flowers.

_____ 9.   Floral design became an art.

_____ 10. Design emphasis was on classic form and elegance, not flamboyance.

EXPLORING

1. Visit a local florist. List the general types of floral designs that are available for sale. Determine the period(s) of history that influenced each type of floral design.

2. Choose a favorite period of floral design history. Gather the plant materials, container, and accessories (if applicable) and make an authentic floral design for that period.

3. Visit a museum and note the use of flowers in the paintings. Choose five paintings from different periods and sketch the floral designs. For each painting, list the floral design style and shape, types of flowers, container, and accessories and determine the period in history.

Care and Handling of Fresh Flowers and Foliages

All floral designers want their flowers to last as long as possible. Although every type of flower has an inherent genetic life span, each flower type can be enjoyed for the maximum time by learning more about its after-harvest care. Floral designs can be enjoyed days longer by understanding some key aspects of the care and handling of fresh flowers and foliages. Using floral preservatives and other pre-treatments and practicing good storage techniques, extends the life of fresh-cut flowers.

Floriculture has an international scope. Flowers and foliages are grown in many parts of the world. Packaging and shipping are a very important part of the care and handling process. The flowers in just one arrangement may have originated in such diverse places as Ecuador, Holland, Israel, Italy, California, and Australia.

15-1. Extend the enjoyment of fresh flowers and flowers by learning proper care and handling techniques.

OBJECTIVES

1 Know the basic requirements of cut flowers

2 Understand the causes of deterioration and death of flowers

3 Describe the steps of effective conditioning of flowers and foliages

4 Explain the importance of using floral preservatives

5 Learn about commercial packing and shipping

TERMS

acidic
alkaline
bent neck
conditioning
deionizer
ethylene inhibitor
grades
green rose
hard water
harden
highly buffered

phloem
photosynthesis
precooled
respiration
salinity
senescence
softened water
stem blockage
total dissolved salts (TDS)
transpiration
turgid

BASIC CUT FLOWER REQUIREMENTS

Even though a fresh flower has been removed from the plant, it continues living (and sometimes, growing), like tulips and anemones. With special care, fresh flowers can be enjoyed for the longest possible time. The basic needs of fresh-cut flowers and foliages are high-quality water, sugars for food, healthy environment, and sanitation.

H IGH-QUALITY WATER

Flowers are 90 percent water. It is important that all parts of the plant—stems, leaves, flowers—be **turgid** (filled with water). As the flowers transpire or give off water, additional high-quality water is needed to supplement that loss.

To check for water quality, a water analysis can be determined by a trusted water treatment company. Adding the correct kind and amount of floral preservative is usually sufficient to make minor adjustments in water quality. In severe cases, a water purification system may be needed.

The pH of the water is important. The pH refers to the relative concentration of hydrogen ions in a solution and ranges from 1 to 14 with 1 through 6 being **acidic**, 7 neutral, and 8 through 14 being **alkaline**. Water pH varies by region and may be alkaline or acidic. Since acidic solutions are better for water uptake, an alkaline pH would need to be lowered by the use of floral preservatives.

Water is also classified as hard or soft. **Hard water** is water that contains high amounts of minerals, which also make the water alkaline. If the pH is on the lower end of alkaline (8 or 9), the water can be efficiently corrected with floral preservatives. Hard water with very high pH values of 11

15-2. As the fresh flower transpires (loses water), sufficient water must be taken in through the cut end of the stem.

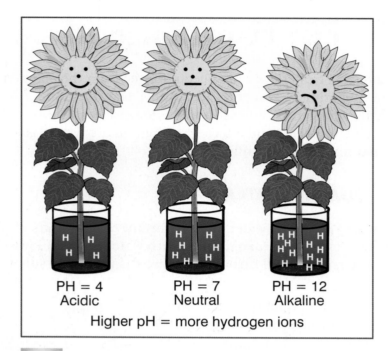

PH = 4   PH = 7   PH = 12
Acidic   Neutral   Alkaline
Higher pH = more hydrogen ions

15-3. Water with an acidic pH is ideal for fresh-cut flowers. Adding floral preservatives will correct alkaline and neutral pH.

through 14 is also *highly buffered* or very resistant to change in pH. Additional acid may be needed to reduce the pH or the use of a *deionizer* may be needed to remove the minerals in the water. *Softened water* is water that has been treated with salts in the form of sodium to remove the minerals. Softened water is not the answer to water quality because of the added salts; it actually does more damage to flowers than hard water.

A water analysis also measures the water *salinity* or the *total dissolved salts (TDS)* in the water. A high salt content (TDS) in the water is very detrimental to flowers; the salt clogs the xylem (the water-conducting tissue within the stem) and may cause weakened stems and wilting. High-quality water should have readings of less than 200 parts per million (ppm).

Food—SUGARS

Sugars, namely sucrose and dextrose, are the food source for cut flowers. Flowers have two ways of getting the sugars (or carbohydrates) that they need.

1. from stored sugars in the plant at the time of harvest

2. from supplemental sugars provided by using the proper amount of floral preservative

HEALTHY ENVIRONMENT

The fresh flowers that you harvest need the proper environment to last for the longest possible time. Provide a clean air environment within the workroom or cooler to avoid ethylene gas exposure. Ethylene is a colorless, odorless gas that is emitted by aging fruit (especially apples), foliage, or flowers and from exhaust and faulty or incomplete burning of fossil fuels.

Provide the proper temperatures for both conditioning and storage. *Conditioning* is the preparation of cut plant materials for arranging by allowing for adequate solution up-take. The temperature of the water in which to condition the flowers upon arrival or after harvesting should be a comfortable bath water temperature, approximately 100 to 110°F. Use a thermometer the first time to be sure of the proper temperature. The warm water is more easily transported up through the xylem and also contains less air than cold water. Never use hot water since it may damage or scald the stem. The use of cold water may result in stem blockage because of the trapped air within the water.

15-4. Condition flowers in warm (110°F) preservative solution.

Allow flowers to condition and take up water at room temperature for several hours. Placing buckets of freshly conditioned flowers into the cooler will slow the uptake of water. Room temperature is preferable for efficient up-take of the conditioning solution.

Table 15-1. Basic Needs for Fresh-Cut Flowers

Needs	Notes
High-Quality Water	
Proper pH of 3 to 4.5 (acidic)	Acidic solutions 1) inhibit bacterial or microbial growth and 2) allow for more efficient movement into and through stems than acidic or alkaline solutions.
	Usually corrected by proper amount and kind of floral preservatives.
Low total dissolved salts (TDS) of 200 ppm or less	Pure water is the best for flowers. Water with high salts causes wilting and weakening of stems. Avoid softened water.
Food	
Sugars	Harvest when flower has the most stored foods, usually late afternoon. Supplement with floral preservatives.
Healthy Environment	
Clean air—avoid ethylene exposure	To avoid ethylene exposure, keep fruit (especially apples) out of the cooler or any confined place with flowers. Other sources include faulty heating units, aging flowers. Practice sanitation.
Proper temperatures Conditioning—warm water and room temperature Storage—cool temperatures	Warm water is quickly transported up the xylem. Room temperature is ideal to allow flowers to take up water and to open.
Sanitation	
Provide clean water Use clean tools (knives, shears) and containers	Avoid the buildup of bacteria and other microbes that cause the stems to be clogged.

Once the flowers have been conditioned or **hardened** (filled with water and ready to be arranged), the flower buckets should be keep in a cool place, such as a cooler. The ideal temperature to store flowers is 34 to 38°F. Flowers will freeze at temperatures below 32°F; check the cooler and watch for any fluctuations. Foliages, especially boxed ones, will store well at 32°F. Store flowers and arrangements in cool areas away from sunlight and drafts of cold or hot air.

SANITATION

Cleanliness or sanitation is important to a long life for a fresh flower. A designer should always clean their hands, their tools, such as knives or floral shears, and the containers for storing or arranging the flowers. Avoid introducing bacteria or other organisms into the vase solution.

Disinfected work areas and clean coolers or storage areas are also important to eliminate the production of ethylene.

CAUSES OF FLOWER DETERIORATION AND DEATH

Once the flower or foliage has been harvested from the mother plant, its source of nourishment is cut off. It is up to the conscientious floral designer to supply all of the needs of the cut flower to make it last for the longest possible time. Take note of the causes of deterioration and death of plant materials.

GENETIC LIFE

Each flower or foliage has an inherent or "built in" length of life depending upon its genetic makeup. Proper care of plant materials will allow them to last their maximum genetic life span. Different varieties or types will last varying amounts of time because of breeding; choosing the longest-lasting kinds is beneficial. For example, many new rose varieties are bred to be longer lasting.

Let's look at the wide range of lasting qualities that differing flowers have.

Flower	Inherent Genetic Life (Approximate)
Daylily	1 day
Dutch iris	3–5 days
Spring bulbs	
Tulips, Daffodils	3–5 days
Roses	5–7 days
Snapdragons	5–7 days
Carnations	10–14 days
Chrysanthemums	14–21 days

| Daffodils (3–5 days) | Carnations (10–14 days) |

15-5. Be aware of the varying genetic life spans of different cut flowers.

Since a floral design may have several kinds of flowers, the lasting qualities of the flowers may vary. In an arrangement with both snapdragons and chrysanthemums, the snapdragons will fade first and need to be replaced. A vase arrangement of spring flowers may all last the same amount of days. In some cases, the filler flowers (statice, sea lavender, or baby's breath) or the foliage may last longer than the flowers.

WILTING

Wilting is the most noticeable symptom of the deterioration of a flower. The causes of wilting may be unavoidable, as in the cause of an aged or spent flower, or may be totally avoidable by practicing proper care and handling techniques. Some causes of wilting are excessive water loss and lack of absorption.

Excessive Water Loss

A fresh flower loses water through ***transpiration*** (plant water loss) due to warm temperatures and low relative humidity (air moisture). Store flowers in a cooler or other cool place at or near 34 to 38 degrees F with high humidity of 80 to 90 percent. Avoid drafty areas of either hot or cold. Also avoid over-handling flowers when arranging. Hot hands can damage flowers and increase transpiration. Do not position a flower by holding the flower head; always handle the flower stem.

Lack of Absorption

A common cause of premature flower wilting is *stem blockage.* Blockage results when the xylem becomes clogged at the stem end by air, bacteria or other microorganisms, salts, undissolved floral preservative powder, or

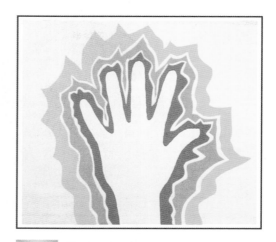

15-6. Avoid over-handling or mishandling fresh flowers while arranging them.

other debris, like sand or soil. The stem end may also begin to heal at the original cut and block the flow of water up the xylem.

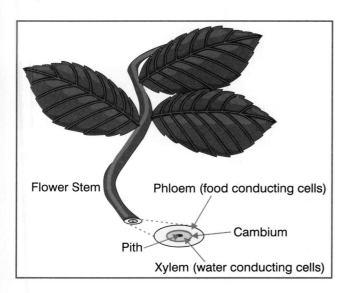

Flower Stem

Phloem (food conducting cells)

Cambium

Pith

Xylem (water conducting cells)

15-7. Xylem moves water up through the stem; phloem supplies food (carbohydrates, sugars) manufactured in the leaves to the rest of the plant.

TIMING OF HARVEST

Knowing the proper time of day and the proper stage of development at which to harvest flowers will also extend the life of fresh flowers.

Late Afternoon Best   **Early Morning Next Best**

15-8. Harvest flowers when the most stored foods are present—late afternoon or evening. Early morning is the next preferred time because the flowers are full of water (turgid).

Time of Day

Never harvest flowers when they are wilted! Avoid cutting flowers during the middle of the day on a hot day. It is important that the flowers and foliages have the highest amounts of stored foods and water.

Harvesting the flower or foliage at the proper time of day ensures that the most stored foods are present in the plant. Late afternoon or evening is an optimum time to harvest because the plant has been engaged in *photosynthesis*, the process of making sugars (food for the plant) from water and carbon dioxide, all day long. The *phloem*, the food-conducting tissue of the flower stem, is responsible for supplying the rest of the plant with its food, that is, the sugars that keep the cut flower healthy, colorful, and alive.

Morning is the next best time to cut flowers from the garden or greenhouse. At that time of the day, the plant is turgid or full of water. In the morning, the cut flowers are not experiencing water stress and can take up water (preservative solution) well.

Stage of Flowering

The ideal stage to cut the majority of flowers is just before the flower is fully open. Exceptions to this rule are daisies, which should be cut fully open, and the spring bulb flowers, such as tulips, daffodils, or iris, which may be harvested in the bud stage. Harvesting the spring bulb flowers in bud will al-

15-9. Most flowers are harvested just before peak—just before the flowers are fully open.

15-10. The exceptions (to harvesting just before peak) are daisies, which should be cut at the stage of development desired (fully open), and spring bulb flowers, which may be harvested in the bud stage.

low a few extra days of vase life. Callas should be harvested at exactly the desired stage of opening because the flowers (from "tubes" to fully open) do not continue to develop after harvesting.

Improper Environmental Conditions

The flower's food supply is used up more quickly in higher than optimum storage temperatures. The rate of *respiration*, the process of the plant using its stored food, increases with warm temperatures. An increased respiration rate leads to an early death or *senescence* of the flower. To prolong the life of a fresh flower, respiration must continue but at a slower pace. Cool temperatures reduce the respiration rate. Other benefits of cool temperatures are less ethylene is produced and the development of bacteria or other clogging microbes is slowed down.

ETHYLENE GAS EXPOSURE

Ethylene gas is a natural plant hormone that is produced by aging flowers, foliages, fruits, and vegetables. Keep flower storage areas clean and free of aging, decaying plant materials. Use clean containers, buckets, and tools. Avoid exposing fresh flowers to ethylene gas by never placing fruit, especially apples, in the flower cooler. Have the heating system in the building checked for efficient operation since incomplete or faulty burning of fuels or improper venting may also produce ethylene.

Another way to combat the influence of ethylene gas is to purchase ethylene sensitive flowers from reputable growers and wholesalers who pretreat their flowers with *ethylene inhibitors*. These products block or tie up the ethylene within the flower and reduce its impact. Storing the flowers at proper cool temperatures also decreases the influence of ethylene on flowers.

15-11. Ethylene damage on chrysanthemums.

Not all flowers are affected by ethylene gas. However, it is important to know the symptoms and to take precautionary measures, as previously mentioned, to reduce the effect of ethylene-induced disorders. Symptoms of ethylene gas exposure include:

- "sleepy" carnations (flower appears wilted or the petals feel soft or mushy—uniformly, not just the outer petals)
- large amount of falling or already fallen petals or florets
- standard or football—drop petals
- snapdragons—drop florets
- uniformly yellowing leaves

Table 15-2. Ethylene Sensitive Flowers	
Alstroemeria	Cornflower
Anemone	Delphinium
Baby's Breath	Freesia
Bouvardia	Lily
Carnations, standard and mini	Snapdragon

DISEASED OR DAMAGED

When purchasing flowers or selecting them to cut from the garden, the best quality ones should be selected. Plant materials with evidence of disease, insect damage, or broken or damaged plant parts should be avoided. Choose flowers and foliages that have good color; inspect the leaves and stems for any disease or damage.

PROPER STEPS TO CONDITION PLANT MATERIALS

HARVESTING TIPS

The two best times to harvest are late afternoon and morning. Wilted flowers should not be cut. Harvest flowers just before they fully open and at their peak of color. Spring bulbs may be cut when in bud stage. Use clean, sharp scissors or knife and cut the flower slightly longer than needed for the chosen floral design.

BUYING TIPS

When purchasing flowers, choose the freshest ones by looking for good typical color, green undamaged leaves, and a turgid appearance and feel (for carnations). Flowers, like roses, should be purchased at the proper stage of development, which is when at least half of the sepals have unfurled. A *green*

Green rose (too soon)   Proper stage of development

15-12. Look for roses to buy or harvest that are at the proper stage of development.

15-13. Avoid buying old roses with many opened petals.

rose, which is a rose with the green sepals still prominently enclosing the bud, may not open at all because it is not fully developed.

Roses that are past their prime will have many loosened petals or may have changed or "blue" coloring. "Old" bunched roses will appear to be buds but are soft, not firm. A gentle touch will confirm it.

Buy from florists or wholesalers who provide a quality product and practice proper care and handling, including pretreating the appropriate ethylene-sensitive flowers. Interview your flower sources to find out if they use floral preservatives.

STEPS FOR CONDITIONING FLOWERS AND FOLIAGE

The following steps for conditioning flowers will increase both the longevity of your flowers and the efficiency of your operation.

1. Unpack and inspect (for proper amount and quality) the flowers immediately upon receiving them. Report any missing or poor-quality flowers.

2. Prioritize the order of processing the flowers—condition wilt-prone (gerberas, bouvardia, baby's breath) and expensive (lilies, orchids, roses) ones first.

3. Remove sleeves, ties, and any foliage that will be below the water level to prevent rotting and bacterial formation.

4. Recut all stems; remove ½ to 1 inch (under warm water is the ideal situation, especially for roses).

5. Use specific treatment solutions as needed, such as a hydration solution or an ethylene inhibitor solution.

6. Place in a floral preservative solution mixed at the proper concentration.

   - Too little—increased bacterial growth, which causes stem blockage and shortened vase life
   - Too much—may result in toxicity (yellowed leaves, petal dropping) and reduced vase life
   - For bud opening—some products will give specific directions for the proper amount to use to effectively open bud-harvested flowers, such as standard carnations and gladiolas

7. Let the flowers remain at room temperature in a well-lit area for 2 to 3 hours to allow for the uptake of the floral preservative solution.

8. Place the flowers in a cooler set at 34 to 38°F, with high humidity (80 to 90 percent), and constant lighting.

9. The flowers are ready to be used in a design!

SPECIAL TREATMENTS

As you become more interested and familiar with different types of flowers and foliages, you will need to know some special treatments that will benefit certain types of plants.

Underwater Cutting

Cutting stems under water will ensure that water, not air, enters the stem (xylem). Individual flowers can be held underwater in a sink or bucket and recut. Also, commercial underwater cutters are available that will allow you to recut an entire bunch of flowers. Underwater cutting is especially suggested for roses.

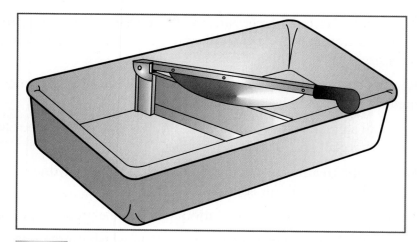

15-14. Cutting flowers under water is highly recommended to extend their life, especially for roses.

Woody Stems or Branches

Plant materials that have woody stems should be conditioned in preservative solution mixed with very warm water. The use of warmer water will maximize water uptake.

Flowering branches may be forced into flower earlier by pruning them from flowering trees (crab apples, forsythia, apple, cherry, or plum trees) before the tree flowers outdoors. Recut and place the branches into very warm preservative solution. The solution may need to be changed periodically (very warm water each time) until the desired opening of the flower buds is reached.

Stems with Milky Sap

Some flowers exude a milky sap when cut from the mother plant. Examples are poinsettias, the related spurges or euphorbias, and poppies. If not conditioned quickly or properly, the sap will solidify at the cut end and block the uptake of preservative solution. The following techniques will allow optimum water uptake of stems with milky sap:

1. A quick dip (5 seconds) in boiling water with the flower heads protected. The stems are then placed into a regular preservative solution immediately.

2. Placement into very warm preservative solution.

3. Careful use of heat near the cut flower end (a match flame)—do not burn the cut end!

Reviving Roses

A rose bud may be just a few days old when the entire bud obviously wilts and bends down. This wilted condition is referred to as a ***"bent neck"*** rose. It is caused by blockage of the xylem by air or debris.

If you notice the condition quickly (within 24 hours), you can revive the flower. Remove the bent neck rose from the arrangement. Place the entire

15-15. A "bent neck" rose is a common site.

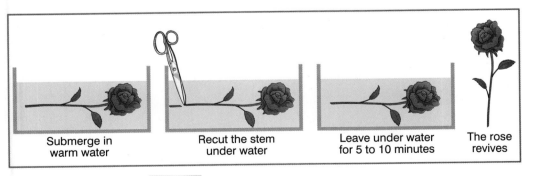

| Submerge in warm water | Recut the stem under water | Leave under water for 5 to 10 minutes | The rose revives |

15-16. A bent neck rose can be revived.

stem into a warm preservative solution, either in a sink or pan, and immediately recut the stem under water. Allow the rose to remain submerged for 5 to 10 minutes. When the rose has revived, place it in the design.

FLORAL PRESERVATIVES

WHY USE THEM?

Using floral preservatives can almost double the vase life of most fresh flowers. Numerous university and corporate tests have shown these results consistently over the years with a variety of flower types.

INGREDIENTS AND THEIR FUNCTION

Effective floral preservatives have three main ingredients. Each of these ingredients has an important function in keeping flowers and foliages fresh and long lasting. Either powder or liquid formulations should be used in high-quality water.

Ingredient	Function
A sugar source	Supplemental food source
An acidifier	Inhibits stem plugging by preventing future microbial growth
A bactericide	Kills any bacteria present in the vase or on the stems

PRETREATMENTS

Pretreatments are specific solutions into which newly harvested or newly arrived flowers are placed or dipped before using the floral preservative solution. Pretreatment solutions may be ethylene reducing or may be valuable for quickly hydrating the stems. Both of these treatments will help to prolong flower life.

Ethylene Reduction Treatments

Ethylene reduction treatments should be used for ethylene-sensitive flowers. An ethylene reduction treatment is only needed once. So check to see if the grower or wholesaler treated the floral product before shipping the flowers.

Hydrating Solutions

A hydrating solution can be beneficial for nearly every flower but is specifically great for flowers that are slow in their water uptake or wilt-prone, such as gerberas, roses (helps with bent neck), bouvardia, or anthuriums. The use of hydrating solutions is valuable for extending flower life for flowers in general everyday enjoyment, but also for important floral displays or functions lasting for several days to a week.

Solutions are available premixed (quick and ready to use) or in concentrate (mixed as needed). Various solutions can be used as a quick 5 to 10 second dip while others suggest 30 to 60 minute treatments. Careful reading and following of the instructions will be very important to their proper mixing and use.

HOME REMEDIES

Over the years, various home remedies have been used to make flowers last longer. Some have been moderately successful; some do not work at all. A few home remedies that will work when added to water include 1) non-diet, non-cola soft drinks, 2) lemon juice, and 3) mouthwash. In our unscientific but fun classroom experiments, soft drink "floral preservatives" are tested compared to commercial floral preservatives and plain tap water. The soft drinks are mixed equally by volume with tap water. Winners for different years have tied or come in second place to commercial preservatives. Examples of some of the home remedy winners are lemon-lime drinks, root beer, iced tea with lemon, grape and orange sodas, and fruit juice-based soft drinks. Each of these winners has two common ingredients—sugar and citric acid. Tap water usually finishes in last place, except for the year that a salty sport drink was included in the experiment. The highly concentrated salty drink was so harmful to flowers that the stems broke at the nodes within three to four days.

Other home remedies that do not work include aspirin, pennies, and plant fertilizer. Always evaluate a home remedy to see if it has sugar and citric acid (and a bactericide) before using it. Many of these home treatments will actually clog the stem and do more harm than good.

COMMERCIAL PACKING AND SHIPPING

International Scope of Floriculture

The flowers sold in florists shops in the United States may have been grown both domestically (within our country) or internationally. The countries where flowers are commonly grown for shipment to the United States and all over the world include:

Region	Countries
North America	United States—California, Florida, Hawaii
Europe	Holland (The Netherlands), France, Italy, Spain
South America	Columbia
Middle East	Israel
Asian	Australia, Singapore
Africa	South Africa, Kenya, Ivory Coast
Central America	Mexico, Jamaica, Guatemala, Costa Rica, Honduras, Ecuador

Packing

Individual growers harvest flowers in the field or greenhouse. The flowers are separated into groups or *grades* before they are bunched. Grades may be based on quality, such as unblemished flowers and foliage, uniformity, or size. Roses and other crops are also graded according to stem length, stem strength, and uniformity. Roses are commonly purchased as shorts, mediums, long, fancy, and extra fancy. The stem lengths start at 9 inches and are graded by 2-, 3-, or 4-inch increments, depending upon the grower. Utility grade roses have blemished foliage, off-color flowers, or possibly weak stems.

Flowers are then bunched before shipping. Bunches are made up of flowers of all the same color. The stem ends are usually bound with a string, rubber band, or a twist-tie. Sleeves are placed over the bunch for protection. Some flowers, such as Fuji mums and gerberas, are individually sleeved to protect the delicate flower.

Knowing the commercial size of bunches for major types of flowers is very important when ordering or buying flowers from a wholesale florist. Roses and carnations are packaged as a bunch of 25; other major crops, such as irises, gladioli, standard chrysanthemums, snapdragons, tulips, and larkspur are packaged in groups of 10. Pompon chrysanthemums and filler flowers are bunched according to weight.

Table 15-3. Common Bunch Sizes for Major Floral Crops	
Bunch Size	**Examples**
25	Roses, carnations, foliages, such as leatherleaf, palms
10	Bulb crops—tulips, daffodils, irises Delphinium, larkspur, snapdragons Standard & Fuji chrysanthemums Gladioli, lilies (unless noted), liatris Dendrobium orchids
Variable by weight	Pompon chrysanthemums (usually at least 5 stems) Filler flowers—baby's breath, sea lavender, Monte casino asters
Single	Gerberas, many tropical flowers

From the grower, the flower bunches are packaged in boxes for shipping. Flower heads are usually packaged at both ends of the box to use the space wisely. Wooden supports are secured at one or several places across the box to keep the flowers from shifting. These boxes are quickly **precooled** before shipping and kept cool throughout the shipping process. Precooling allows cool air to flow through the box of flowers and quickly replace the warm air. Flowers that are packed in this fashion to the wholesaler and then florist are referred to as being shipped dry or drypacked. Dry pompons chrysanthemums and mini carnations can be kept cool, shipped quickly, and then con-

15-17. Drypacked flowers are securely packed with flower heads at both ends of the box to use the space wisely and to avoid shifting or damage.

ditioned by the florist or floral design instructor. Less handling actually insures a less damaged product.

Other flowers, such as gladioli and snapdragons or specialty crops, are packed upright in boxes called hampers. Some crops will also be shipped this way with the stem ends placed in water.

Shipping

Since flowers are perishable, it is important that the product reaches its destination very quickly. Most crops are shipped by air from the grower to the wholesaler. From the wholesaler to the retailer, flowers are shipped in different ways depending upon the distance to be traveled. The flowers may again travel by air; however, shipping by truck usually completes the trip.

REVIEWING

MAIN IDEAS

Fresh flowers and foliages can last for days longer by learning about their needs and after-harvest care. Provide cut flowers with high-quality, acidic water, sugars for food, a healthy environment such as clean air and cool storage temperatures, and proper sanitation.

The causes of flower deterioration and death include an inherent genetic life span for each flower, wilting due to excessive water loss or lack of absorption (stem blockage), used food supply, and ethylene gas exposure. To counteract some of these causes, flowers should be harvested at the proper times and conditioned properly.

The steps for conditioning begin with unpacking and inspecting the flowers after receiving them. Sleeves, ties, and lower foliage are removed; the stem ends are recut; the flowers are placed into a warm floral preservative solution. The flowers should remain at room temperature for 2 to 3 hours for efficient uptake of the solution. Flowers may then be placed in a 34 to 38°F cooler. Other special treatments include underwater cutting, treating woody stems or stems exuding milky sap, and reviving roses.

Floral preservatives are very important for increasing longevity of fresh flowers. They have three main ingredients, including a sugar source, an acidifying agent, and a bactericide. Combining the use of floral preservatives with other pretreatments can benefit many different types of flowers. Pretreatments are used to reduce ethylene and for quick hydration. Home remedies that contain citric acid and sugar can be effective (and expensive) as floral preservatives when mixed 1:1 by volume with water.

Floriculture has an international scope. Flowers are grown and shipped all over the world. Individual growers grade, bunch, and package their flowers in a efficient manner so the flowers will arrive at their destination undamaged. Flowers are bunched by specific bunch sizes according to type. Knowledge of bunch size helps when ordering or buying flowers.

QUESTIONS

Answer the following questions. Use correct spelling and complete sentences.

1. What three factors are important when considering water quality for fresh flowers?

2. What is pH? What pH is recommended for fresh flowers in solution?

3. Why is softened water not recommended for conditioning flowers?

4. What are the proper temperatures (air and water) for conditioning and storing flowers?

5. What length of time should the flowers remain at room temperature? Why?

6. What are some causes of deterioration and death of flowers due to natural aging processes? What are some causes of premature deterioration of flowers?

7. What is ethylene gas? What causes it to form? What effect does it have on flowers?

8. When should the perfect rose be harvested?

9. What are the basic steps to properly condition flowers?

10. Why is underwater cutting recommended?

11. How do you revive a "bent neck" rose?

12. Why should floral preservatives be used for fresh flowers? What are the three main ingredients and their function?

13. Why do some home remedies work reasonably well and others fail miserably? Give examples.

14. What are drypacked flowers? How are they packaged?

EVALUATING

Match the term with the correct definition. Write the letter by the term in the blank provided.

a. acidic

b. transpiration

c. phloem

d. turgid

e. green rose

f. highly buffered

g. bactericide

h. pH

i. xylem

j. bent neck rose

k. salinity

l. precool

_____ 1. Salt content in the water.

_____ 2. The water-conducting tissue within the stem.

_____ 3. A rose that is not fully developed.

_____ 4. Being resistant to change in pH.

_____ 5. The loss of water from a plant due to high temperatures and low relative humidity.

_____ 6. Kills bacteria.

_____ 7. The food-conducting tissue within the plant stem.

_____ 8. Quickly lowering the temperature.

_____ 9. Full of water.

_____ 10. pH of 1 to 6.

_____ 11. A rose that is prematurely wilted.

_____ 12. The relative concentration of hydrogen ions in water.

EXPLORING

1. Set up your own floral preservative experiment. Choose five types of soft drinks (diet and non-diet) or mouthwash or lemon juice to compare with a commercial floral preservative as well as tap water. Mix the treatments 1:1 by volume with tap water. Place three to five flowers in each solution. Evaluate the flowers daily or every other day. Record and determine the winner(s).

2. Visit a wholesale florist and watch flowers being conditioned (processed).

3. Test the pH of tap water. Compare it with the pH of several commercial floral preservative solutions mixed according to the directions. Customize your own floral preservative to reach a pH of 3 to 4.5.

16

The Principles of Design

The principles of design are basic, fundamental truths to follow in creating floral arrangements. Although the principles for floral design were first outlined by the English during the Victorian Era, these principles are still valuable to us today. These design principles should not be regarded as mere rules; they are the foundation of every good design despite changing trends and new plant materials.

16-1. The major principles of design are proportion and scale, balance, rhythm, and dominance.

OBJECTIVES

1 Define floral design

2 List the principles of design

3 Explain the concept of proportion

4 Explain how the concept of balance is applied to floral design

5 Describe how rhythm is applied to floral work

6 Explain how the principles dominance and focal point are used in floral design

TERMS

asymmetrical balance
balance
center of interest
centering
contrast
counterbalancing
dominance
floral design
focal area
focal point
free, variable rhythm
Golden mean
physical balance

principles of design
proportion
radiation
regular, repeated rhythm
repetition
rhythm
scale
symmetrical balance
transition
variety
visual balance
visual weight

FLORAL DESIGN DEFINED

Floral design is the art of organizing the design elements inherent in plant materials, container, and accessories according to the principles of design to attain a composition with the objectives of beauty, simplicity, harmony, suitability, and expression. Flower arranging is another commonly used term for floral design. However, floral design is the more accurate term because the word design implies that the person arranging the plant materials is applying the principles of design.

PRINCIPLES OF DESIGN

The *principles of design* (or art) are rules and guidelines to help a floral designer create a beautiful composition. The design principles are fundamental truths upon which to make accurate floral design decisions. The major principles of design are proportion and scale, balance, rhythm, and dominance. Other minor design principles include radiation, repetition, transition, variation, contrast, and focal point.

Not only learning the principles, but also using them well is essential in creating any kind of art, including arranging plant materials. The proper application of each of these principles will lead to artistic, pleasing floral arrangements. Each principle is important and interrelated to the others and can impact the entire arrangement.

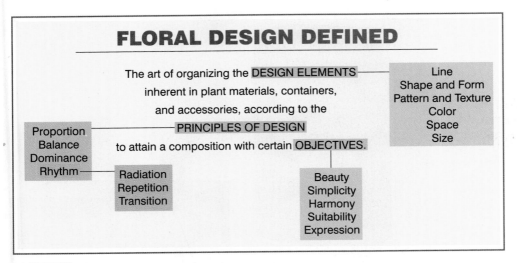

16-2. Floral design is an art that requires the knowledge of the principles of design.

16-3. Proportion is the pleasing relationship in size and shape among the components in a design.

PROPORTION

Proportion is the principle of art that is the foundation of all the other principles. Good **proportion** means the pleasing relationship in size and shape among objects or parts of objects. **Scale** is a part of proportion, dealing with relative size only among things, not shapes.

Three aspects of proportion are very important in floral design. The aspects are:

■ Proper proportion of the ARRANGEMENT to its SURROUNDINGS

■ Proper proportion of the FLOWERS AND FOLIAGES to the CONTAINER

■ Proper proportion of the FLOWERS AND FOLIAGES to EACH OTHER

Proportion to Surroundings

The floral design must suit the intended placement in its surroundings. The arrangement should fit the area in size and in shape, as well as in style. Imagine a massive wooden table with a petite rose arrangement placed on

16-4. A floral design that looks too small on a massive table is more in proportion in a small niche.

Correct   Incorrect

16-5. These bouquets show the importance of proper proportion. On the left, the bouquet is too small; in the center, the bouquet is overwhelming and too large; on the right, the bouquet is just right.

top of it. The size of the table would overpower the arrangement, diminishing its visual impact. The small arrangement would be more in proportion in a book shelf niche or on a small table.

Determining proper proportion for flowers that will be carried or worn is also very important. The flowers should not overwhelm the person, yet should be large enough for visual impact. Imagine a bride who expects a beautiful bouquet. If the bouquet is either too small or too large, the effect is awkward and out of proportion.

Proportion is very important when designing for any event, whether it is a wedding or a birthday party. Not only should the floral designs be in proper scale to the room, but they should also be suitable and in harmony with the theme and the location. To design an arrangement for an event that has proper proportion as well as harmony and suitability, find out the following information:

	For Proper Proportion	**For Harmony and Suitability**
Room	size of the room ceiling height	style of room furnishings color of room furnishings
Tables	size and shape of tables	number of tables color of tablecloths
Designs	centerpieces needed one-sided designs needed accessories	colors theme

Proportion of the Flowers and Foliages to the Container

The Greek's **Golden Mean** (a ratio of 1 to 1.6) and Japanese traditions are used to attain a pleasing proportion between the plant material and the con-

16-6. The height of an arrangement should be at least 1½ times the container's greatest dimension.

16-7. A floral design that is too short makes a beginning designer easy to spot. The container is too prominent in this arrangement.

tainer. Floral designers have learned that proportion will be pleasing if the height of the arrangement is at least 1½ times the height or width of a container, whichever is greatest.

Beginning floral designers often create designs that are too short. The flowers, not the container, should be highlighted. In general, upright arrangements should be taller than they are wide and horizontal centerpieces will be wider than they are tall.

A maximum dimension is not stated however, because that depends upon the background, the type of plant material, the theme, the container, and the skill and artistic expression of the designer. If thin, wispy plant materials are used, the arrangement height may be 2 or 2½ times the container height. An arrangement placed on the floor in a entryway may need to be 2½ or 3 times the container height to provide the visual impact and proper scale for the site.

The container plays a significant role in determining the maximum height of a design. Consider four factors of the container when determining the proper proportion of the flowers to the container:

- physical dimensions (height, width, volume)
- color (dark vs. light)
- material and texture (pottery, glass, ceramic, wicker)
- shape (ginger jars, carafes, coffee cups)

Containers that are visually heavy, such as a dark, bulky pottery vase, can visually support a taller, larger design than a clear carafe-shaped glass vase. If the same container is available in many colors, the lighter colored or clear ones will support arrangements that are shorter than their darker colored counterparts.

Exceptions

Centerpieces are a major exception to the 1½ times the container height rule-of-thumb. In a dining situation, the centerpiece should not obstruct the view of the people sitting at the table. It is ideal to be able to see over, through (or around), or under a centerpiece. Bud vases or small vase arrangements, placed in the center of a dining table, may also be shortened to allow viewing over them.

16-8. A dark, bulky pottery vase can visually support a taller, larger floral design than a clear carafe-shaped glass vase of the same height.

16-9. This showy centerpiece with a circus theme is designed to be seen over (the votive candles and round mirror), around (the mirrored column), and under (the flowers).

Proportion of the Flowers and Foliages to Each Other

The individual flowers and foliages within the floral design should complement each other in size. Variation in sizes of flowers is pleasing and interesting, but huge jumps in size may not be in proper proportion to each other. An arrangement containing only very small flowers, such as baby's breath, and very large flowers, such as Fuji chrysanthemums, does not display proper proportion. Flowers of intermediate size would provide a more pleasing scale relationship within the arrangement.

Steps to Pleasing Proportion—A Checklist

■ Determine where the arrangement is to be displayed
■ Select the container (consider shape, color, size, type and texture)
■ Select plant material to yield the planned design
■ Establish height
■ Establish width
■ Establish the outermost contour
■ Note changes in proportion that occur as various pieces of plant material are added
■ Make necessary adjustments to yield planned design
■ Prune

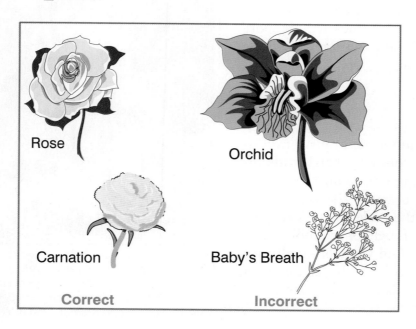

Rose

Orchid

Carnation

Baby's Breath

Correct   Incorrect

16-10. Avoid large jumps in flower size for pleasing proportion among flowers within an arrangement.

- Add taller material
- Use less or more of various plant materials as they interact within the design to maintain color, size, shape, pattern or space balance

BALANCE

Balance is a key part of the beauty of an arrangement. Balance is the physical or visual stability of a floral design. Balance refers to the arrangement's equilibrium or equality in weight, both physical and visual.

Physical balance is the actual stability of plant materials within the container. A design with physical balance has secure mechanics (the foam and the flowers do not move or shift) and can stand on its own in a stable manner and not fall over.

Visual balance refers to the perception of an arrangement being in balance or being equal in weight on both sides of the central axis. A floral design lacking balance is visually unsettling like a crooked picture or a shirt buttoned the wrong way. Poor visual balance in the floral design will overshadow other attractive aspects of the design, such as proper proportion or an effective center of interest.

Physical and visual balance must both occur for a design to be successful. An arrangement may be physically secure through good mechanics, yet lack visual balance. A beautiful visually balanced design may even topple over during a banquet because the physical balance is poor.

Visual balance in an arrangement should be evident in three views:

- From side to side
- From top to bottom
- From front to back

Floral designs exhibit two types of visual balance. They are symmetrical

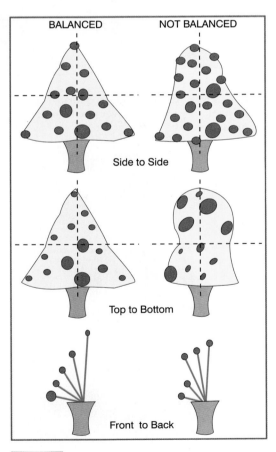

16-11. Check each floral design's visual balance from side to side, top to bottom, and front to back.

16-12. Symmetrical balance is formal and dignified. Avoid a mirror image in flower placement, which can be monotonous.

16-13. Accessories and clever flower placements can vary the predictable nature of a symmetrical design.

and asymmetrical balance. To check a floral design for balance, image lines dissecting the design into four equal quadrants, vertically and horizontally. Both symmetrical and asymmetrical designs should have equal visual weight on either side of the central axis (side to side). The upper portion of the design (above the imaginary line equally dividing the upper and lower parts of the design) should be lighter in weight. The greater weight of the arrangement should be located in the lower portion, near the container rim. Next, turn the design to the side and check for a smooth transitional flow of flowers from front to back. At the top of the arrangement, the flowers should not be leaning too far forward or too far backward. The outline of the flowers should follow the line of the designer's gently curved hand. The top flowers should not "umbrella" or lean out over the lower flowers.

Symmetrical Balance

Symmetrical balance in a floral design occurs when both sides of the design have or seem to have the same physical weight. The weight and appearance of the materials on either side of the imaginary central vertical line are similar. Although the design should have equal weight on each side, it should not be an exact mirror image. Symmetrical balance is a European inheritance and is called formal balance. This type of balance is dignified, restful, predictable, and even grand and impressive.

Although symmetrical balance is called formal balance, clever additions can make it interesting and not so predictable. The use of a dynamic center of interest, clever flower placements (groupings), and accessories can "jazz up" this formal design.

A symmetrical arrangement is usually displayed against a symmetrical background and with symmetrically placed accessories. For example, place a pair of candles, one on each side of a symmetrical centerpiece, or have one, two, or three candles centered within the design.

Asymmetrical Balance

Asymmetrical balance is a dynamic, informal balance, which has its roots in Japanese and Chinese flower arranging. The plant material and manner of placement are different on each side of the central vertical axis; however, the arrangement must appear to be in balance. An asymmetrical design achieves balance through compensation or counterbalancing. The combined weight on one side equals that on the other with the differences com-

16-14. Asymmetrical balance is informal, creative, and dynamic.

16-15. An asymmetrical background looks very appropriate for an asymmetrical design.

pensating or counterbalancing visually. This type of balance is active, creative, and stimulating. Suggesting movement, asymmetrical balance strongly attracts and holds attention. Space is very important and contributes to the achievement of balance.

Asymmetrical designs are usually displayed in a less formal setting. If accessories are used, place them in an asymmetrical way; do not use equal amounts of accessories on each side.

Examples of Symmetrical and Asymmetrical Design Styles

Many geometric shapes can be designed as either symmetrical or asymmetrical. For example, a triangle can be designed in a symmetrical way, such as an equilateral (all sides equal) triangle or an isosceles (two sides equal) triangle or in an asymmetrical manner, such as a scalene triangle (all sides unequal). Centerpieces can also be traditionally round or oval or can be varied with asymmetrical placements of branches or flowers.

Symmetrical designs include round or oval centerpieces, topiaries, one-sided styles—oval, round, equilateral or isosceles triangle, inverted T, fan-shaped, and vertical arrangements. Typical asymmetrical styles are crescent, Hogarth curve, scalene or right triangle, diagonal, and vertical.

Table 16-1. Typical Symmetrical and Asymmetrical Design Styles

Symmetrical	Asymmetrical
Oval and round centerpieces	Centerpieces
Topiaries	Topiaries
Vase arrangements	Vase arrangements
One-sided designs:	One-sided designs:
Oval	Crescent
Round	Hogarth curve
Fan	Fan
Triangle—equilateral, isoceles	Triangle—scalene, right
Inverted T	Diagonal
Vertical	Vertical

Understanding Visual Weights

The **visual weight** of a flower or foliage is its perceived lightness or heaviness based upon its combined characteristics of color, shape, pattern, etc. An

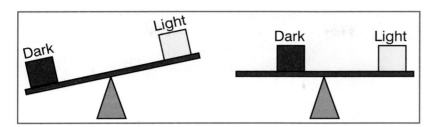

16-16. Dark colors appear heavier and should be placed nearer to the center of an arrangement to achieve visual balance.

understanding of how to determine visual weights of plant materials is important when balancing a floral design. A good floral designer must learn to judge and place materials of differing visual weights to achieve balance within an arrangement.

Visualize a seesaw at a playground. Two children of equal weight are perfectly balanced on the seesaw; however, a larger, heavier child must move closer to the center of the seesaw to balance the smaller, lighter child at the other end. The same concept applies to placing flowers in a design of differing visual weights. Darker colors appear heavier and are placed lower and closer to the center of an arrangement; lighter colors appear more light in weight and can be placed higher and in the outermost positions. There is a transition zone where plant materials of differing visual weights should be subtly combined to create a unified look.

Knowing the specific characteristics of differing visual weights helps a designer to organize and position flowers in the proper way for balance. The following chart can be used as a guideline. Remember that flowers may not have clear-cut characteristics, neither all heavy or all light, so there must be some additional judgement calls made to use the flower properly. For example, a white fully open rose would be heavy because of its size even though its white color is visually light. A dark red rose bud would probably be used higher in the design because of its smaller

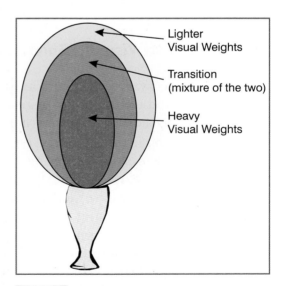

16-17. In a floral design, lighter weights are generally placed higher and in the outermost areas while heavier weights are placed lower and closer to the center of the arrangement.

Table 16-2. Visual Weights Guideline for Plant Materials		
Design Element	**Visually Lighter**	**Visually Heavier**
Size	Small	Large
Color		
Hue	Cool	Warm
Value	Light	Dark
Intensity	Dull, grayed	Bright
Shape	Linear	Round
Space		
Single flower description	Airy and open petals	Dense and full petals
Flower placements	Spacious	Clustered
Pattern	Fine	Bold (in size and color)
Texture		
Surface quality	Rough or Hairy	Shiny
Visual quality	Fine	Bold or coarse

size, even though it is a dark color. With time and experience, judging visual weights of plant materials will become easier.

Ways to Visually Balance a Design

For both symmetrical and asymmetrical designs, a good designer should learn tips and techniques to visually balance their designs. The keys to beautifully balanced floral designs are centering and counterbalancing.

Centering is the technique of placing dominant plant materials along the central vertical axis. Centering allows heavier plant materials (large, dark, round) to be placed higher in the design. Standard carnations, football mums, bird of paradise, gerbera daisies, and Fuji chrysanthemums can all be centered for a dramatic and beautifully balanced design.

Understanding *counterbalancing* is absolutely necessary for the beginning designer. Counterbalancing means to balance plant materials on one side of a design with visually equal materials on the opposite side. It is essential to the visual stability of the outline of an asymmetrical design, but it is also a valued technique for visually balancing flowers within both symmetrical and asymmetrical designs. Use counterbalancing to avoid making symmetrical designs a mirror image.

16-18. Centering dominant and visually heavy plant material is a dramatic and easy way to balance a floral design.

For an asymmetrical design, counterbalance a main line (the primary line), positioned in the upper left side of the arrangement, by placing a shorter line (the secondary line) in the lower right side. The secondary line should be approximately one half the length of the primary line.

Visually balancing similar materials within an arrangement uses the technique of counterbalancing with upper left and lower right placements (also upper right and lower left) and the technique of equalizing. The first example is illustrated with the placement of a hot pink mini carnation on the upper left side of a design and counterbalancing it with a similar hot pink mini carnation in the lower right side. Using the equalizing technique, one large red carnation on the lower left side of an arrangement can be counterbalanced by placing two red mini carnations on the upper right side.

Counterbalancing dissimilar materials requires more thought and judgement. Using the visual weight chart will help the decision-making process. For example, a large, bicolor lily on the lower left side of a

16-19. The main line of an asymmetrical design is counterbalanced with a shorter line (the secondary line) placed low on the opposing side.

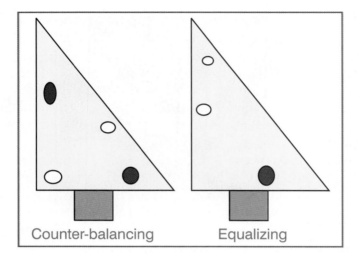

Counter-balancing   Equalizing

16-20. A common counterbalancing technique is to balance a dark flower on the upper left side with one on the lower right. Another technique is to equalize one large flower with two smaller ones place higher on the opposing side.

design can be counterbalanced beautifully with a small pink rose bud and a white unopened tulip on the upper right side. Foliage can also help in counterbalancing each side.

RHYTHM

Rhythm is related, orderly organization of the design elements to create a dominant visual pathway. The related aspects of the design (colors, shapes) tie the design together and gives it flow. Rhythm is "frozen motion" and suggests movement. A floral design with pleasing rhythm has continuity that invites the eye to view the entire design.

16-21. Regular, repeated rhythm is strong, predictable, and compelling (left); free, variable rhythm is subtle, unstructured, and flowing (right).

Rhythm can be regular and repeated or free and variable. ***Regular, repeated rhythm*** is characteristic of a marching band with bold, repetitive beats. In nature, the horizontal branching of the spruce tree or the strong radiating leaves of the yucca plant display regular, repeated rhythm. In floral design, flowers placed at regular intervals from the top to the bottom of the design create the strong regular, repeated type of rhythm. Regular, repeated rhythm is an easy-to-use beginning technique that is strong and compelling but monotonous if overused

Free, variable rhythm is subtle like the spontaneous chirping of birds in the woodland. In nature, the irregular branching patterns of honey locust and cloud patterns in the sky display free, variable rhythms. In floral design, this subtle, flowing style can used in almost any design including line arrangements, centerpieces, and vase arrangements. The unstructured use of branches, filler flowers, and flowers with multiple florets, such as alstroemeria, lilies, and freesias, add interesting lines and forms to achieve free, variable rhythm.

When the viewer's eye flows smoothly and completely through the parts of an arrangement, the viewer is reacting to the rhythm of the design. When the viewer's eye moves jerkily from one group of unrelated plant materials to another, the design's rhythm is choppy and ineffective. Flowing rhythm can be beautifully created by the use of radiation, repetition, and transition.

Radiation

In floral design, ***radiation*** gives the illusion that all of the flower stems are coming from one point. Radiation gives a strong sense of unity and naturalness to an arrangement because this is the way that plant materials grow in nature. To understand and create radiation in a floral design, ponder the yucca plant. The leaves emerge from a single point and project out from the

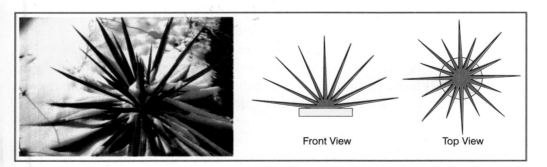

Front View   Top View

16-22. The yucca plant displays perfect radiation. Floral designers can take tips from this plant and its perfectly radiating leaves when creating floral designs with pleasing radiation.

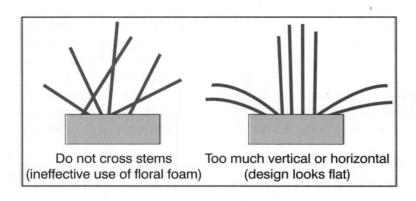

Do not cross stems
(ineffective use of floral foam)

Too much vertical or horizontal
(design looks flat)

16-23. Common radiation mistakes.

center; each leaf forms a slightly different angle to consistently fill out the circular shape.

In a floral design, allow the stems to radiate out naturally from the vase or floral foam. From a top view, stems should equally radiate out from the center like the spokes of a wheel or like a daisy's petals. Avoid crossing stems or having too many verticals or horizontals without transitional angles. Crossing stems will cause the floral design to look unprofessional and messy. Crossing stems, which is a common habit with beginners, also is a very ineffective use of the floral foam, leading to crowding and insecure mechanics. The placement of too many verticals or horizontals without the transitional angles will make a design look "flat" and unsatisfactory. A three-dimensional design is the goal.

Repetition

Repetition is achieved by the repeated use of one or more of the design elements, such as flower shape, color, space, or line throughout the floral design. Repetition unifies and strengthens the impact of an arrangement, but can be boring unless a variety of flowers or foliage types are added.

Repetition of flower shapes or colors throughout the design is an elementary, but effective method. The repetition of yellow daffodils throughout a design gives it unity and also moves the eye through the design. Generally, the color of the container is repeated within the design. Green containers are easy to use because foliage repeats their color. Some container colors that are neutral or used for dramatic effect are not necessarily repeated within the flower or foliage colors, such as glass, black, or metallic.

Several types of repetition are pleasing in producing effective rhythm.

Repetition of line is important for creating rhythm. The main line should end in one direction; a branched line will disrupt the repetitive rhythm of the

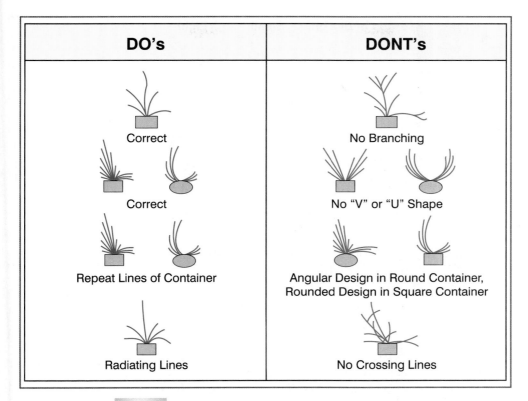

DO's	DONT's
Correct	No Branching
Correct	No "V" or "U" Shape
Repeat Lines of Container	Angular Design in Round Container, Rounded Design in Square Container
Radiating Lines	No Crossing Lines

16-24. Examples of repetition of line Do's and Don'ts

design. Also, one main rhythm should predominate with opposing lines permitted at the container to continue the line. The viewer should always be able to tell which line is the most important. Exceptions are parallel designs and naturalistic ones. Avoid V-shaped or U-shaped arrangements. The floral design rhythm should repeat the lines of the container, for example, angular lines with a square container. Place curving ovals or crescent in a rounded container. Avoid crossing lines within the design.

Transition

Transition is a smooth, gradual change from one thing to another. Rhythmic change can harmonize and unify an arrangement. The transition from lighter plant materials and placements at the outer areas of a floral design to heavier material and closer groupings near the container and focal point effectively moves the eye smoothly and rhythmically through a design. Rhythmic change in floral design refers to placing small to large flowers, light to

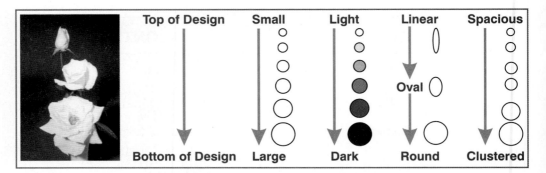

Top of Design	Small	Light	Linear	Spacious
Bottom of Design	Large	Dark	Oval / Round	Clustered

16-25. Rhythmic change through transition refers to grading flowers from small to large, light to dark, linear to oval to round, and from more spacious to more clustered.

dark colors, linear to round shapes, or spacious to more grouped flowers in sequence from the top to the bottom of the design.

A valuable floral design technique to produce rhythm through transition is to vary the flower facings within the arrangement in a systemic way. In general, flowers should face upward at the top, face to the left and right on those respective sides, face forward at the center, and face in logical intermediate placements. Varying flower facings gives a beautifully rhythmic contour to the arrangement and avoids the flat look, as if the design is drawn on a two-dimensional piece of paper.

Transition is important between the arrangement and its container. The foliage and lower flowers should partly conceal or overlap the container rim

16-26. Vary flower facings from upward at the top to outward at the bottom with transitional facings to the left and right sides also.

to provide continuity between the two. The container should not seem separated from the flowers or seem too prominent. There are exceptions to this rule depending upon the design style and the value (in dollars or sentiment) of the container.

Variation and Contrast

Variety and contrast are essential to interesting designs and pleasing rhythm. *Variety* refers to a diverse assortment or differing components. Variety focuses our attention and stimulates our interest and imagination. *Contrast* describes objects that have striking differences beyond mere variety or diversity. Contrast takes variety to a higher degree. Too much of anything is dull and boring. However, too much variety can be confusing and chaotic. In floral design, strive for variety within unity.

Try to use more like things than unlike or different things.

16-27. This container is too prominent. Transition dictates that flowers and foliage should slightly overlap the container rim to visually connect the floral design and the container.

Using too much repetition can lead to boring designs. An attractive radiating design can be monotonous if only one type of flower is used. Strive for interesting mixtures of flowers, using at least two types for variety; three or more types are even more interesting. Choose differing sizes and shapes of flowers and foliages from linear to round and everything in between. The addition of filler flowers also adds needed variety.

Contrasts that are well planned and controlled make attention-getting and striking designs. Provide contrast in texture and color by placing smooth, shiny, coarse-textured dark green leaves behind a white, spacious, frilly Fuji chrysanthemum. Team linear scotch broom with exotic bicolor lilies, or iris leaves with roses, for contrast in shape. An asymmetrical line mass provides contrast because of its opposing horizontal lines placed at the base of the arrangement.

16-28. Dominance is effectively conveyed by the bold use of peonies (plant material) in pink and rose colors (design element) designed as a vase arrangement (design style).

DOMINANCE

The effective use of dominance or emphasis lets the viewer know what is most important in the design. *Dominance* in floral design means that one design element or characteristic is more prevalent or noticeable and other elements are subordinate to the main feature. Interest and attention are captured and held if one feature dominates and others are secondary in importance.

One or more methods of developing dominance may be used, but each method should contribute to the unified effect. Dominance may be developed by using dominant plant material; an emphasized design element; a distinctive design style; an idea, theme, or holiday; or a focal point or center of interest.

For example, a vase arrangement of peonies and other flowers shows dominance because of the bold peonies, the dramatic pink and rose colors, and the style of arranging. Three methods have all contributed to the pleasing dominance of this arrangement.

Using an idea or theme is a very easy way to develop dominance. An idea such as a spring fling event would highlight spring flowers in cheerful colors

Table 16-3. Ways of Developing Dominance for Floral Events

Method	Examples
Dominant plant material	abundant garden flowers, tropicals, roses, lilies
An emphasized design element	shape, space, size, pattern, texture, color
A distinctive design style	centerpiece, asymmetrical triangle, linear bud vase
An idea, theme, or holiday	spring fling, birthday, fall, Christmas
A focal point or center of interest	large flowers, round or special form flowers, dark shades, concentration of plant material, use of framing foliage nearby, strong color contrasts, radiation of the rest of the plant material to the focal area, accessories

Circus Theme

Fall Theme

16-29. Develop dominance for floral design and events by targeting an idea, theme, or holiday.

and maybe gardening tools. A circus theme would incorporate bright colors, balloons, clowns, and circus animals. Holidays and special events dictate the types of flowers, colors, and accessories to unify the entire display.

Center of Interest (Focal Point or Focal Area)

A center of interest is an important part of many design styles. A *center of interest* (also called *focal point* or *focal area*) visually ties the entire arrangement together. The location of the center of interest is usually centered in the lower part of the arrangement just above the container rim. Some contemporary designs will actually have several focal points.

Although many design styles have a focal area, some floral designs do not. Centerpieces and vase arrangements contain equal flower placements all throughout the arrangement with no single area of focus.

Ways to Develop a Center of Interest

To create the most effective center of interest, always plan this dominant area before beginning the arrangement. In general, the greatest visual weights are concentrated at the center of interest. Consider using some of the following methods of developing a center of interest or focal area:

- Large flowers
- Round or special-form flowers

16-30. An effective center of interest may be developed by using several methods, such as concentrating the plant material, using dark, bold red colors (also a strong color contrast of white and red), using framing foliage nearby, and by letting the lines of the design radiate to the center of interest.

- Dark shades
- Concentration of plant material (greater amounts, less space)
- Use of framing foliage nearby
- Strong color contrasts
- Radiation of the rest of the plant material to the focal area
- Accessories

Several methods may be used together to create of beautiful center of interest that ties the entire design together.

Through dominance and contrast, a design gains both unity and variety. Dominance comes with repetition; contrast comes through change. Each depends on the other to make a successful floral design.

REVIEWING

MAIN IDEAS

Floral design is the art of organizing the design elements that are inherent in plant materials, containers, accessories according to the principles of design (art) to attain a floral design with the objectives of beauty, simplicity, harmony, suitability, and expression.

The principles of design are guidelines to help a floral designer create a pleasing floral design. The design principles are proportion, balance, rhythm (radiation, repetition, transition), and dominance.

Proportion is the art principle that determines the relationship in size and shape among parts of a design. Three aspects of proportion in floral design are very important, including the proper relationship of the arrangement to its surroundings, the proper relationship of the plant material to the container, and the proper proportion of the flowers and foliages to each other. Based on the Golden Mean, the height of an arrangement should be at least 1½ times the container's greatest dimension. The exceptions are centerpieces or small vase arrangements for the dining tables, which can be shorter to allow proper viewing.

Balance is the physical or visual stability of a floral design. A floral design must be balanced both physically and visually. Visual balance should be evident from side to side, top to bottom, and front to back. Symmetrical and asymmetrical balance are two forms that floral designs may take. Symmetrical balance is more traditional and formal, but very pleasing if not designed as an exact mirror image. Asymmetrical balance is informal and dynamic and is achieved through counterbalancing. It is important to understand the visual weights of plant materials to be able to use them successfully to balance arrangements, whether symmetrical or asymmetrical. In general, lighter visual weights, such as linear, light colors, are placed higher and in the outermost areas of a design while heavier visual weights, such as round, dark colors, are placed lower and closer to the center of the arrangement.

Rhythm is the orderly arrangement of design elements within a design to create a flowing visual pathway. Any design can be two types of rhythm: regular, repeated or free, variable. Radiation, repetition, and transition are three important ways of producing flowing rhythm.

Dominance indicates to the viewer the important feature(s) of an arrangement. Dominance can be developed by emphasizing plant material, a design element, a design style, an idea, theme, or holiday, or developing a dominant area or focal area.

A center of interest or focal area visually ties the entire arrangement together. Create an effective center of interest by using large, round, or special-shaped flowers, dark colors, framing foliage nearby, strong color contrasts, concentration of the plant material, and radiation of the lines of the design to the focal area.

QUESTIONS

Answer the following questions. Use correct spelling and complete sentences.

1. Why are the principles of design important to floral design?
2. What questions should a floral designer ask when designing arrangements for a specific room? List at least eight.
3. What is the general rule for arrangement height? What are two exceptions to this rule?
4. What determines an arrangement's maximum height?
5. What aspects of containers affect the floral design's height?
6. When designing, how is an arrangement checked for proper visual balance?
7. Should symmetrical balance be an exact mirror image? Why or why not?
8. What are three ways to visually balance a floral design? Be thorough.
9. Why is rhythm important to a floral arrangement?

10. What are important ways to use proper repetition within a floral design?

11. How can a floral designer develop a dominant impact for an event?

12. What is a center of interest? What are other terms for it? Where is it located?

13. What designs do not have a center of interest?

EVALUATING

Match the term with the correct definition. Write the letter by the term in the blank provided.

a. Golden Mean
b. visual weight
c. transition
d. proportion

e. asymmetrical balance
f. design principles
g. center of interest
h. radiation

i. balance
j. rhythm

_____ 1. Visually ties a floral design together.

_____ 2. A pleasing relationship in size and shape.

_____ 3. Visual and physical stability.

_____ 4. A ratio of 1 to 1.6.

_____ 5. Balanced by compensation or counterbalancing.

_____ 6. Smooth, gradual change.

_____ 7. Guidelines or rules for floral design.

_____ 8. Related, orderly flow or organization.

_____ 9. Perceived lightness or heaviness.

_____ 10. Flower stems appear to emerge from one point.

EXPLORING

1. Visit a furniture store and note the placement of the pictures on the wall in the various display areas. Determine which displays are symmetrical balance and which ones are asymmetrical. Choose your favorite type of balance.

2. Collect three of the same containers and flowers to make arrangements with varying proportion. Make design heights of 1, 2, and 3 times the container's height. Evaluate the Golden Mean for yourself.

3. Design two arrangements with similar materials. Make one a regular, repeated rhythm and the other free, variable rhythm. Which rhythm suits your personality?

17

The Design Elements

The *design elements* are the physical characteristics of the plant materials that a designer uses in a floral design. Thorough knowledge of the design elements of line and form (shape), space, texture, pattern, and color is so important because floral designers select and organize these "tools," the design elements, to create beautiful floral designs.

17-1. The beautiful shapes, colors, textures, and patterns of flowers and foliage are fascinating tools for the floral designer to use.

389

OBJECTIVES

1 Describe the importance of line and form (or shape) in floral design

2 Identify the expressive significance of the five major lines

3 Identify the major forms (shapes) used in floral work

4 Explain the concepts of space and depth as related to floral design

5 Identify and describe the importance of pattern and texture in floral work

6 Explain how colors and the properties of color influence floral work

TERMS

advancing colors
analogous
color wheel
complementary
cool hues
crescent
depth
design elements
equilateral triangle
filler flowers
form
form flowers
free form
geometric
high-visibility colors
Hogarth curve
hue
intensity
inverted T
isosceles triangle
line
line materials
lines of opposition

low-visibility colors
mass flowers
monochromatic
mottled foliage
naturalistic
pattern
polychromatic
primary colors
receding colors
right triangle
scalene triangle
secondary colors
shade
shape
split complementary
tertiary colors
texture
tint
tone
triad
value
variegated foliage
warm hues

THE SHAPE OF THINGS

The first design elements to be considered are line and form or shape. In floral design, the beauty of the design may be due to the natural, graceful, flowing lines of the plant material, or to the method of arrangement, or to a combination of both nature and the designer's skill. Good design depends upon understanding and effectively using both line and form.

LINE

Line is the prominent feature for several types of arrangements, including line, line-mass, many ikebana or Japanese-style designs, and many contemporary styles. *Line* is the visual movement between two points within a design. The four types of line are vertical, horizontal, curvilinear, and diagonal. All of these lines should appear to radiate from a central part of the design. Lines may be forceful or subtle, continuous, interrupted or implied.

Line can give a design not only structure, but also expressiveness. The emotional significance of each line can add to the expressive quality of any design. The following chart outlines the four major lines and their potential meaning in floral designs.

Type of Line		Meanings or Emotional Significance
Vertical	(like a person standing)	active, alert, aspiring, inspiring, dramatic, masculine, striking, attentive, formal, dignified
Horizontal	(like a person sleeping)	calm, restful, tranquil, peaceful
Curvilinear	(like a relaxed person)	graceful, playful, flexible, sophisticated, elegant, refined
Diagonal	(like a person running)	active, dynamic, strong, on-the-move restless, violent or changing (use sparingly)

17-2. The four main types of line are vertical, horizontal, curvilinear, and diagonal.

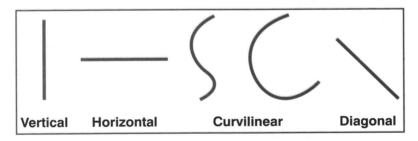

| Vertical | Horizontal | Curvilinear | Diagonal |

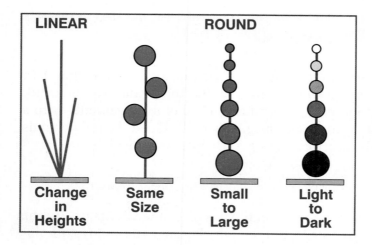

LINEAR   ROUND

Change in Heights | Same Size | Small to Large | Light to Dark

17-3. A line can be created with both linear and round plant materials.

Line can be created not only with linear plant materials, but also with round flowers. Place round plant material in a line and in a progression from upward flower facings at the top to outward flower facings near the container. The round flowers can be all the same size and color or can be varied from light to dark, small to large, or dull to bright.

FORM AND SHAPE

Line and form are closely related because appropriate lines are needed to create designs with beautiful form. **Form** is the three-dimensional shape of the outline of a floral design. **Shape** is the two-dimensional term for form. Floral design forms or shapes can be either one-sided or all-around (also called free-standing).

THREE CLASSIFICATIONS OF FORM

The three broad classifications of form or shape in floral design are geometric (the largest category), naturalistic, and free form or modern. The three forms can interact within a floral design. Seldom is an arrangement totally or stiffly geometric or completely naturalistic. Free form often incorporates parts of both geometry and nature in its composition.

Naturalistic forms suggest the natural growth of plant material through groupings of flowers and foliages. The floral designer generally uses the plant material as it would appear in nature, that is, branches (trees) placed higher than the grouped flowers with some type of moss for a "ground cover." Naturalistic designs are pleasing both as one-sided designs or all-around centerpieces. As in nature, open spaces are important.

The *free form* category is a creative, "anything goes" form that has very few rules. Free form emphasizes free-flowing lines and outlines and the artistic use of materials (unusual placement, changed color, placed upside down). Many contemporary designs can be classified as free form. It is an advanced design style that "bends" some of the design principles.

GEOMETRIC FORM

Geometric designs mirror the shapes of geometry, the circle, square, triangle, and rectangle; however, most geometric designs are based on the circle and the triangle. The three-dimensional terms for circle and triangle are sphere and pyramid. These forms are most commonly referred to as their two-dimensional shapes: circle and triangle. Even though the floral de-

17-4. Naturalistic forms suggest nature and incorporate groupings of flowers and foliages.

17-5. Free form designs are very contemporary and creative, often "bending" the rules.

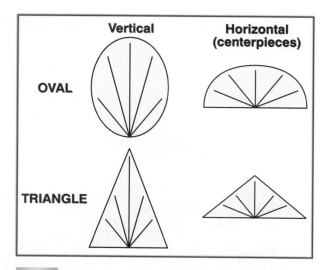

17-6. Most geometric shapes may be designed as either a vertical or a horizontal.

signer uses the two-dimensional terms for these arrangements, the goal is always a pleasing three-dimensional design.

Vertical or Horizontal

In most cases, the designer may choose whether to create any geometric shape as a vertical or a horizontal. Also, many of the geometric shapes can be designed as either one-sided arrangements or all-around designs (centerpieces). The one-sided version will exhibit more vertical orientation and the all-around version will emphasize the horizontal.

Circle

Geometric shapes displaying the spherical or circular shape may be designed as both symmetrical and asymmetrical designs. Symmetrical designs include the circle, oval, and fan or fan-shaped. These shapes are traditional favorites for many occasions and locations in the home.

Asymmetrical circular forms are the crescent and Hogarth curve or S-shaped. The **crescent** is a portion of a circle that resembles a "C" or a new moon. The **Hogarth curve** resembles an "S" and was created by William Hogarth, an English painter in the eighteenth century. His quote "A straight line is a line of duty; a curving line is a line of beauty" shows his love for the curvilinear.

17-7. Symmetrical circular shapes are the circle, oval, and fan.

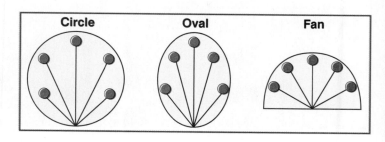

Most geometric shapes, including the circle and oval, have many variations in floral designs. These forms may be designed as upright one-sided designs or vase arrangements or they may take the form of rounded centerpieces, the "round mound." Nosegays or bouquets for weddings or proms have round, oval, or crescent shapes. Topiaries may have a circular or oval shape as well. Generally, round or curved plant material is used to create these circular shapes. Often, round or circular-shaped containers combine well with these shapes.

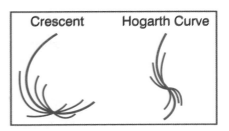

17-8. Asymmetrical circular shapes include the crescent and the Hogarth curve (or S curve).

17-9. Geometric forms, such as the circle or oval, may be designed in many variations.

Triangle

The pyramidal (a three-dimensional term) or triangular shapes may also be symmetrical or asymmetrical. Symmetrical triangles are equilateral, isosceles, and inverted "T." All sides are equal in an ***equilateral triangle***. An ***isosceles triangle*** has two equal sides with a narrower width than the equi-

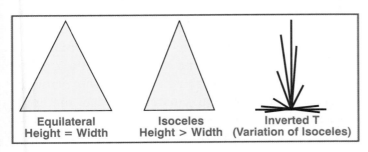

17-10. Symmetrical triangles may be equilateral or isosceles.

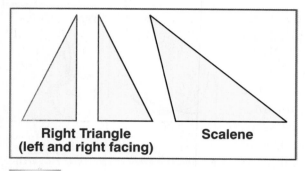

**Right Triangle
(left and right facing)**   **Scalene**

17-11. Asymmetrical triangles include right triangles (or L-shaped) and scalene triangles.

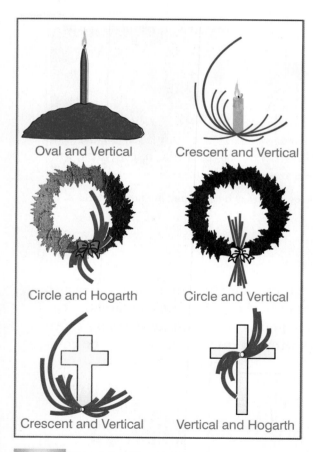

Oval and Vertical   Crescent and Vertical

Circle and Hogarth   Circle and Vertical

Crescent and Vertical   Vertical and Hogarth

17-12. Combining two lines or forms with a shared center of interest creates an eye-catching lines of opposition design.

lateral triangle. An ***inverted "T"*** is a dramatic variation of the isosceles triangle that is very vertical with more space and fewer flowers.

An asymmetrical triangle is an eye-catching shape because the tallest plant material (height placement) is placed off-center and then counterbalanced on the opposite lower side. Two examples are the right triangle and the scalene triangle. The ***right triangle*** or "L" shape forms a 90-degree angle near the container and can be left- or right-facing. The ***scalene triangle*** exhibits three sides of differing length and is dramatic and contemporary.

Combined Forms

A ***lines of opposition*** design is a high-contrast use of two different design lines or forms, sharing a center of interest to tie the design together. For example, a tradition oval centerpiece, designed with candles placed in the center, is a lines of opposition design—a vertical with a horizontal oval. A wreath with a striking vertical sheaf of wheat placed at the base of the circle beautifully combines a circle and a vertical. An asymmetrical triangle with an opposing diagonal cluster of dried materials also combines two lines or forms— a triangle with a diagonal.

GENERAL FLOWER SHAPES

Most plant materials can be divided into four general categories based upon shape—line materials, form materials, mass materials, or filler flowers or foliages. The combination of these four types of plant shapes or forms lends variety to a design.

LINE

Line materials, such as snapdragons, larkspur, liatris, gladioli, and delphinium, heather, or foliages, such as eucalyptus, Scotch broom, or horsetail (equisetum), are ideal to form the outline of an arrangement. Linear plant materials are adaptable; line foliages can be curved, tied, wired, and trimmed to suit the arrangement; line flowers can be cut into smaller sections to use as fillers or mass flowers.

FORM

Form flowers, also called special form flowers, are flowers with distinctive shapes, such alstroemerias, freesia, iris, lilies, orchids, open roses, and most tropical flowers, such as bird of paradise, anthuriums, and proteas. Form flowers and materials create a striking center of interest and add uniqueness to a design.

MASS

Mass flowers can be classified as round or solid flowers. Although mass types are usually flowers, some dried pods and cones also fit this category. Mass

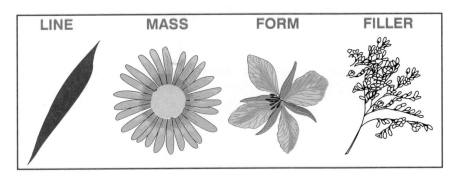

17-13. Plant materials can be classified in four main shapes or forms—line, mass, form, and filler flowers.

plant materials fill out the shape of a design. Examples of mass flowers or pods are allium, chrysanthemums, carnations, daisies, and lotus pods.

FILLER

Filler plant materials are the fourth category. **Filler flowers** (also called "fillers") are small flowers that are used to add texture, color, and depth as well as fill space between the mass and line flowers in a floral design. Examples are sea lavender, baby's breath, statice, lady's mantle, and golden aster.

FORM AND THE THIRD DIMENSION

Form is three-dimensional. Height and width are the first and second dimensions. The third dimension, **depth,** allows an arrangement to look natural and full, not flat or pressed. Flowers in a floral design should repeat nature and be full and radiating toward the front. In nature, plants do not naturally grow flat, like an espalier. An espalier is a tree or shrub that is trained to grow in a very narrow space.

Depth is gained by placing the center of interest flower(s) or focal flower(s) to extend beyond the container rim. A pleasing design has a rounded contour, not a stiff, pressed or flattened one. Achieve pleasing depth by adding flowers or filler within the design at a deeper level than the outermost contour. Depth adds interest and character to a design because the viewer is invited to look within the design. Additional methods for achieving effective depth are listed below.

Methods of Achieving Depth (the Third Dimension) in a Floral Design

1. Vary flower facings   at the top   — facing up

    left side   — angle some to the left side

    right side   — angle some to the right side

    lower front   — orient outwards

2. Radiate plant materials — avoid too many verticals or horizontals

    consider the yucca plant or

    the radiating spokes of a wheel

3. In a one-sided arrangement   1) finish the back

    2) allow some plant materials to lean back slightly and some to be extended forward

3. "Bury" some flowers so they are partially hidden by others

17-14. For depth, allow some plant material to be hidden or "buried" to provide depth and increased interest within an arrangement. Note the "buried" hydrangea, slightly hidden behind the pink ranunculus on the right side of the design and slightly showing in the back on the left side.

4. Highlight with graded use of color — place light colors (advancing) in front of dark colors (receding);

warm colors (advancing) in front of cool colors (receding);

try dull colors (receding) behind or in front of bright colors (advancing)

A floral design displaying good depth is the mark of an experienced, talented designer. Beginners tend to make flatter arrangements, seeming to fear extending any flower beyond the container or below the arrangement's basic contour.

SPACE IS GOOD TASTE

Another mark of an experienced floral designer is the generous incorporation of effective space within an arrangement. Space is an important design element in every arrangement, adding vitality and life. By creating meaningful spaces, the solids are sharply defined and important; the beauty of separate plant materials can be fully appreciated. Beautiful flowers should be seen clearly without crowding.

Space is inherent within many types of plant materials, such as ferns, iris, and clustered flowers like nerine lilies and alstroemerias. Create space

17-15. The effective use of space within a floral design gives it beauty and interest.

by incorporating branches and linear or unique shapes. Allow plenty of space near these materials for enjoyment of their interesting shapes and spaces.

Most floral designs have more spaciousness at the top with progressively less space toward the center of interest. Learn to plan for effective space at the beginning of the design. Space showcases the good taste of the floral designer!

IN TOUCH WITH TEXTURE AND PATTERN

Texture is the design element that is directly related to the sense of touch. In plant materials, **texture** is determined by both the surface quality (tactile value) and the structure or placement of the plant parts (visual value). Used wisely, interesting textures enhance and increase interest in a design.

Plant materials that have tactile value, that is, texture appealing to the sense of touch, can be described as silky, satiny, feathery, smooth, rough, hairy, furry, woolly, velvety, or prickly. Plants also have many variations in their structure. This visual value can be described as airy or dense, delicate or coarse, lacy or solid.

TIPS WITH TEXTURE

Glossy textures attract attention and should be placed carefully for proper balance. A glossy-textured flower, like an anthurium or the bird of paradise,

17-16. The textures of the flowers and the container should repeat and enhance each other.

is more eye-catching than the dull or soft textures of proteas. However, dull, matte surfaces are often easier to use in large quantities than their shiny counterparts.

Although glossy textures attract attention first, varied textures, such as rough, hairy, prickly, or other unique ones will hold the viewer's attention longer. These varied textures are more complex and keep the viewer's interest for a longer time.

The combination and the contrast of shiny with dull, smooth with rough, or polished with velvety can add heightened interest in a design because the plant textures are enhanced and highlighted by their differences. Contrast adds interest yet should be planned and controlled. Huge textural variation among a wide array of plant materials within one arrangement should be avoided.

Plant materials of medium texture can be good blending materials within a design. Foliage often provides this transition. The addition of foliage, such as leatherleaf or Boston fern, provides transition between a soft, velvety rose and lacy Queen Anne's lace.

The textures of the flowers and the container should be repeated to enhance each other. A glossy vase can be distracting if the flowers do not repeat the polished, shiny, or glossy texture. The background, fabrics, and accessories should also harmonize with the texture of the arrangement.

POINTERS ABOUT PATTERN

Pattern is determined by the physical characteristics of the plant materials. The arrangement of the leaves and petals create many structural patterns. A fern may have a repeated pattern, expressing precision. Other foliages, such as a saddleleaf philodendron, have an irregular leaf pattern and may seem informal or casual. Many plants have color patterns on their leaves. Pattern is closely tied to texture because leaves with color patterns appear textured or leathery when the surface is actually smooth.

Color patterns in both foliage and flowers add interest to an arrangement. Color patterns are often described as mottled or variegated. Plants with **mottled foliage** have leaves with flecks or areas of a different color. Examples of mottled foliage are mother-in-law's tongue (*Sansevieria*) and galax leaves. Plants with **variegated foliage** have lines, stripes, or areas of another color on the leaves. Examples of variegated leaves are Hosta, prayer plant foliage, and spider plantlets or "babies." Use plant materials with color patterns in small amounts as accents (see Figure 17-1). Overuse of color patterns can create a chaotic look.

MAKING THE MOST OF COLOR

Color is a vital part of our existence. It is all around us in nature, in fashion, and in art. Color can be a compelling entity, creating emotional responses in those who view it.

To many, color is the most noticeable and important element of a floral design. How colors are selected and positioned together will determine whether a floral design is noticed or purchased. Color choice is of the utmost importance to the bride-to-be, the party-giver, the high school student ordering prom flowers, or the interior design-conscious customer. A floral designer's knowledge of color, its properties, expressive qualities, and color schemes should be thorough. With an in-depth understanding of the use and function of color, a floral designer can be more effective and creative.

THE COLOR WHEEL

In the seventeenth century, Sir Isaac Newton illustrated the theory of color. He passed white light through a prism, causing the light to separate into a rainbow of colors—RED, ORANGE, YELLOW, GREEN, BLUE, VIOLET—all with varying wavelengths. He developed the color wheel by bending the spectrum of six colors into a circle.

In nature, the color wheel appears naturally in a rainbow or when light passes through a waterfall to create miniature rainbows. Those colors are the full spectrum colors of the color wheel. The **color wheel** that floral designers use today is a circle that divides colors into primary, secondary, and tertiary colors and includes all of the tints and shades of each color. The **primary colors** are red, yellow, and blue and are called the foundation colors since all other colors are created from these three. The **secondary colors** are orange, green, and violet and are a mixture of the two adjacent primary colors. For example, a mixture of yellow and blue creates green. The

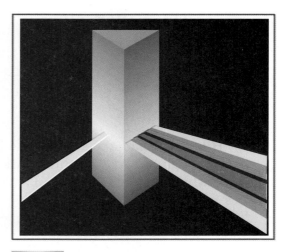

17-17. Sir Isaac Newton passed white light through a prism to discover a rainbow of colors.

six **tertiary colors** have hyphenated names such as red-orange and blue-green and are created by mixing the adjacent primary and secondary colors.

17-18. The color wheel divides colors into primary, secondary, and tertiary.

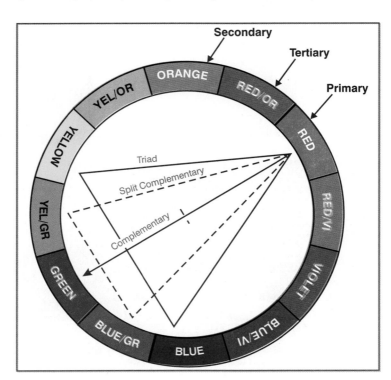

COLOR VOCABULARY

Let's learn the terminology of color. Color has three important qualities that a floral designer should know—hue, value, and intensity (or chroma).

The Qualities of Color

Hue is the name of a color. The hue or name of the color stays the same even though it may be lighter, darker, or grayer. Two major exceptions are pink, which is light red, and tan and brown, which are the light and dark values of orange.

Warm hues are red, orange, and yellow and the tints, shades, and tones of those hues. These colors evoke cheerful, warm feelings and are associated with warm or hot things like fire, heat, or the sun. These hues are considered *advancing colors*, which means that flowers, containers, and accessories in warm colors look larger and seem to advance or move toward the viewer. Warm colors are focusing and stimulating and are good choices for a design

17-19. Warm colors are red, orange, and yellow and bring thoughts of heat and sunshine. Cool colors are blue and sometimes violet, and evoke thoughts of the sky and calm, cool, icy mountain streams.

that is seen from a distance. Beware though, because some people find an excess amount of warm colors irritating.

Cool hues are blue (sometimes violet) and its tints, shades, and tones. These hues evoke thoughts of ice and cool mountain streams. These hues are considered *receding colors* and are not highly visible from a distance. These hues are great for intimate, up close arrangements or as accents in designs with warm colors or white.

White, black, and gray are considered neutral hues. Static hues are those hues between warm and cool hues, mostly green and violet. Violet is an interesting hue because it is variable, that is, it can be cool or warm depending upon its proximity with other colors, the lighting, or its background.

Value is the lightness or darkness of a hue. A *tint* is the light value of a hue, that is, the hue with white added. Think of a person tinting or lightening their hair to remember that a tint of a hue is a lighter form of the full spectrum hue. A tint of blue is light blue; a tint of red is called pink, instead of light red; light violet is usually called lavender; a tint of orange may be peach to tan. A *shade* is the dark value of a hue, that is, the hue with black added. A person pulling a shade in a room darkens the room. Adding the word *dark* to the hue or name will identify a value for most hues, such as green (dark green), blue (dark blue), violet (dark violet or purple), yellow (dark yellow), and orange (dark orange). Some values are more commonly called by other names. Dark blue may be called navy; dark orange may be called burnt orange, rust, or brown (if dark enough); dark yellow may be called gold.

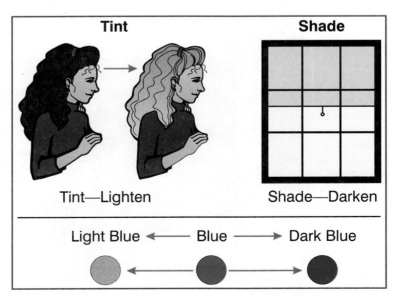

17-20. A tint is a light value, a hue with white added. A shade is a dark value, a hue with black added.

Tint   Shade

Tint—Lighten   Shade—Darken

Light Blue ← Blue → Dark Blue

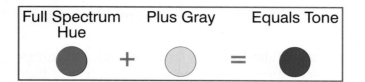

Full Spectrum Hue	Plus Gray	Equals Tone
● +	○ =	●

17-21. A tone is a grayed hue.

Intensity (or chroma) is the relative brightness or dullness of a hue. The full spectrum hues have full intensity and purity because of the absence of white, black, or gray. The colors of a rainbow after a summer rain display the bright, pure, full intensity colors. Flowers with reduced intensity (dullness) have either a mixture of gray or another color added to the full spectrum hues. A *tone* is a color that has been subdued by the addition of gray. Tone is a good word for this concept because it gives the idea of being toned down.

To determine if a flower is a full spectrum hue or a tint, shade, or tone, use the color wheel to compare it. If a color wheel is not available, think of the pure rainbow colors as a starting point.

Color Force

The combination of hue, value, and intensity all contribute to determine the visibility or color force of the flowers within an arrangement. For example, an arrangement for a large area should be designed with a majority of flowers that are highly visible and advancing. *High-visibility colors* are warm hues, light values (tints), and bright intensities. These colors are effectively used as the framework of a design for proper proportion as well as balance well throughout the interior of the design. *Low-visibility colors* are cool

17-22. Note that the yellow lilies in this centerpiece are much more eye-catching and highly visible that the light-blue sea holly (*Eryngium amethystinum*) filler. Although both colors of lilies are warm and advancing, yellow is more highly visible than orange.

hues, dark values (shades), and dull intensities. When used as the framework of a design, these colors will not be eye-catching and may make the arrangement appear too short or unimpressive. Low-visibility colors are excellent in arrangements viewed at close range or for use within an arrangement placed at a distance to provide contrast and depth.

The Expressiveness of Colors

Through the ages, color has been used to express messages and ideas. We respond emotionally to colors. Let's discover some of the qualities and emotion-producing characteristics of each color.

Red, the color of fire and blood, is a very showy, warm, advancing color and a powerful, strong hue. It conveys a wide range of contrasting emotions, such as love or hate, anger or passion, excitement or danger. Red is forceful and bold and can be placed in designs seen from a distance. Red is the most pleasing in warm color schemes, not cool ones, except in an analogous scheme with purple or with blue and white for patriotic themes. A design tip is to allow adequate space for red in a design. Red can overpower other colors so don't crowd it. Pink, a tint of red, suggests spring, lightness, and femininity. Maroon and other dark values can indicate power and maturity, but may not be as visible from a distance as standard red.

Orange is attention-getting and stimulating, but not as visually overpowering as red or as eye-catching as yellow. Orange gives warmth and radiance to a design and expresses festive, energetic, vivacious, outgoing, and friendly emotions. Generally, only small amounts of orange are used within a design, but light values (tan, peach, salmon) or dark values (rust, copper) of orange can be used in greater amounts without overwhelming the viewer. Orange is typically used in the autumn, but can be used in small amounts throughout the year to give a cheerful radiance and depth to any design. Brown, a dark value of orange (sometimes, yellow), expresses mellow, down-to-earth, tranquil feelings. It is a favorite in fall arrangements, dried arrangements, and for a container color.

Yellow is a highly visible, attention-getting, warm color that conveys cheerful, happy, vibrant feelings, or cowardly, irritating ones. Yellow reflects more light than the other colors and can be placed into a design to brighten a design and add highlights. Yellow is very versatile with many colors and can be added in small amounts to add "life" and brighten dark colors. Add yellow when designing for a dark location or for low lighting conditions.

Green is a fresh, soothing, restful hue that provides a natural background for all of the other colors. Green also conveys quietness, peace and tranquility, and "green with envy." Use green as a blending and softening effect. Green is a great choice for a container color.

Blue is a cool, receding color that is not highly visible from a distance. Blue conveys cool, calm, serene, and dignified feelings or sad, private, or boyish messages. It also expresses loyalty and truth, as in "true blue." Light blue can seem joyful, youthful, and playful. Dark blue may convey more somber or depressing emotions. Combine blue with brighter, warmer colors for visibility and highlights. Different lighting can affect its appearance.

Violet (or purple) suggests royalty, splendor, and refinement. It can be gentle, mysterious, and even sad. Violet will seem warm or cool depending upon the background, proximity of other colors, and the lighting. Violet adds depth to a design when in combination with warm colors.

Color Schemes Used in Floral Design

The study of color use in floral design is challenging, but also rewarding. Knowledge of the color schemes can help even a novice designer to design more eye-catching and pleasing arrangements. Typically, for pleasing balance and proportion, one color should be more prominent to unify the design.

Color schemes are based on either related or unrelated color schemes.

The two related color schemes are monochromatic and analogous. The unrelated color harmonies are complementary, split complementary, triad, contrast, and polychromatic.

RELATED	UNRELATED
Monochromatic	Complementary
Analogous	Split complementary
Triad	
Polychromatic	

17-23. Color schemes can be related (all yellow) or unrelated (yellow, blue, purple) color harmonies.

A **monochromatic** color scheme includes only one hue and its tints, shades, and tones. This color harmony is very pleasing to the eye and unifying. An easy-to-spot monochromatic design would include light lavender asters, medium purple mums, and deep purple delphinium. Some monochromatic designs are trickier to identify, such as one in the orange family—tan or beige gerbera daisies, bright orange safflowers, burnt orange chrysanthemums, and brown autumn leaves. Usually, green foliage and other neutral colors are considered the background of a design and not taken into consideration in determining the color harmony. Exceptions would be Christmas arrangements or other striking use of greens. To spice up a monochromatic color scheme, use varying textures and patterns.

Analogous color schemes incorporate colors of two or three adjacent hues on the color wheel, usually either warm or cool. Different values and intensities may be used. This color harmony is pleasing because of the rhythmic related color flow and the variety. A design with red tulips, orange gerbera daisies, and yellow daffodils, freesias, and forsythia is an analogous color scheme of warm colors. An analogous color scheme using cool colors is blue iris, violet-blue statice, light lavender freesia, and deep purple delphinium.

17-24. A monochromatic color scheme may have only one hue in its design, but may include tints and shades.

17-25. An analogous color harmony includes adjacent families on the color wheel, such as yellow, orange, and red. This analogous color scheme displays all warm colors.

A *complementary* color harmony (also called direct complementary) combines two colors that are directly opposite each other on the color wheel. Tints and shades are also included. Complementary colors intensify and enhance each other's color, provide very strong contrast, and make bold, eye-catching statements. The direct complements are orange and blue, red and green, and violet and yellow. One of the pair should be used in a greater amount in the design, including light, medium, and dark values.

The *split complementary* color scheme consists of one hue combined with the two hues that are on each side of its direct complement on the color wheel. This color harmony is a more subtle contrast than the direct complementary, but is still interesting and eye-catching. Examples of the split complementary color scheme are:

1. yellow with blue-violet and red-violet

2. red with blue-green and yellow-green

3. green with orange-red and red-violet.

17-26. Complementary color schemes are bold and showy.

17-27. A split complementary color scheme is eye-catching and incorporates one key hue and the two adjoining hues of its direct complement.

17-28. A triad of primary colors, red, yellow, and blue, is exciting and appeals to all ages and genders.

17-29. A polychromatic color scheme includes a wide range of colors and is very lively and festive.

A *triad* color harmony is a combination of three hues equally spaced on the color wheel. A triad may consist of the three primary colors (red, yellow, blue) or the secondary colors (violet, green, orange) as well as any tints and shades. This exciting color harmony is effective when one color dominates with the other two used in smaller amounts. The primary color triad appeals to all ages and genders.

The *polychromatic* color scheme uses a wide range of colors, both warm and cool. Generally, one color will be more prominent. This color scheme is common in spring mixtures and very festive and pleasing to the eye.

REVIEWING

*M*AIN IDEAS

A floral designer selects and organizes flowers and foliages according to their physical characteristics, the design elements. The design elements are line and form (also referred to as shape), space, pattern, texture, and color.

Line is the visual movement between two points within a design. The four types of line are vertical, horizontal, curvilinear, and diagonal. In floral design, specific lines can be chosen for the meanings and ideas that each conveys, such as alert or inspiring emotions for a vertical line or dynamic, restless feelings when using a diagonal line.

Form and line are closely related; lines are used to create the three-dimensional shape of a floral design outline. The three broad categories of form or shape are geometric, naturalistic, and free form. Naturalistic designs suggest the natural growth of plants in nature through groupings and the use of space and other aspects of nature, such as moss and branches. Free form is a creative, contemporary type of advanced design in which some of the rules are "broken."

Geometric designs mirror the shapes of geometry. Most floral design shapes are based on the circle and triangle. Geometric designs may be vertical, horizontal, circular, or triangular. Examples of symmetrical circular forms or shapes are the circle, oval, and fan; asymmetrical circular forms include the crescent and the Hogarth curve. Symmetrical triangles may be equilateral or isosceles; examples of asymmetrical triangles are right triangles (or L-shaped) and scalene triangles. Lines of opposition designs combine two high contrast design lines or forms, tied together with a strong center of interest.

The forms of plant materials can be divided into four general categories—line, form, mass, and filler.

Depth or the third dimension is a very important aspect of form. Depth creates a natural and full look, not a flat or pressed appearance. Methods for achieving depth include varying the flower facings, radiating plant materials, finishing the arrangement in the back of a one-sided design and allowing some plant materials to lean back slightly with others extending forward, "burying" some flowers (flowers are partially hidden), and highlighting with graded use of color.

Another design element is space. The effective use of space within a floral design gives an arrangement beauty and added interest.

Texture, another design element, describes the surface quality and the appearance and placement of the plant parts. Glossy textures attract attention first but do not hold the viewer's attention. Varied textures, such as rough, hairy, or woolly, hold the viewer's attention and keep it longer. Contrast in textures within a design adds variety and interest.

Pattern is a design element that is determined by the physical characteristics of the plant material. Plants have both structural and color patterns. Color patterns, used in small amounts, add interest to a design.

Color may be the most noticeable of the design elements. Colors are formed as light passes through a prism, separating into the rainbow of colors—red, orange, yellow, green, blue, and violet. Color has three important qualities, hue, value, and intensity. Hue is the name of a color; colors are warm hues (red, orange, yellow) or cool hues (blue, sometimes violet). Value is the lightness (tint) or darkness (shade) of a color. Intensity is the relative brightness or dullness of a hue. A tone is a grayed hue. Highly visible colors are warm hues, light values, and bright intensities and are effective in designs to be viewed from a distance.

A floral designer can use color to express emotions and ideas. Color schemes can be related (monochromatic and analogous) or unrelated (complementary, split complementary, triad, and polychromatic). Monochromatic schemes include only one hue and its tints, shades, and tones. Analogous color schemes incorporate two or three adjacent hues on the color wheel with varying tints and shades. Complementary color harmonies are the high-contrast use of two colors that are direct opposites on the color wheel. Split complementary schemes consist of one hue and the two hues of each side of its direct complement on the color wheel. A triad color scheme is a combination of three equally spaced hues on the color wheel. Polychromatic color schemes use a wide range of hues, both warm and cool.

QUESTIONS

Answer the following questions. Use correct spelling and complete sentences.

1. What are the six design elements?

2. What are four major lines used in floral design? List two expressive meanings for each one.

3. How are form and shape different?

4. What are the three broad categories of form?

5. Who developed the S curve and why?

6. What are typical shapes (forms) for most geometric designs? List two symmetrical and two asymmetrical examples for each shape.

7. What are the four types or shapes of plant materials? How do these shapes combine in a design to complete the composition?

8. What floral design techniques can be used to create depth within a design? Be thorough.

9. Why is space important within a design?

10. What is the value of using both glossy and varied (hairy, rough, prickly) textures within an arrangement?

11. Which hues are advancing colors and which ones are receding? Discuss the appropriate selection of colors for a large design to be displayed on a stage at graduation.

12. Name the colors of the color wheel in order and give characteristics and emotional meanings for each hue.

EVALUATING

Match the term with the correct definition. Write the letter by the term in the blank provided.

a. triad
b. tint
c. tone
d. scalene triangle
e. shade

f. complementary color scheme
g. isosceles triangle
h. texture
i. intensity
j. secondary colors

_____ 1. Relative brightness or dullness.

_____ 2. Using two hues that are directly opposite each other on the color wheel.

_____ 3. The light value of a hue.

_____ 4. The dark value of a hue.

_____ 5. An asymmetrical triangle with three unequal sides.

_____ 6. The surface quality and the placement of the plant parts.

_____ 7. Using three equally spaced hues on the color wheel.

_____ 8. A grayed hue.

_____ 9. Colors formed by mixing two primary hues.

_____ 10. A symmetrical triangle with two equal sides.

EXPLORING

1. Create two floral designs, choose one related and one unrelated color scheme. Gather flowers, foliages, containers, accessories, and fabrics in the appropriate colors, including tints, shades, and tones. Take a photograph of each one. Critique the use of color for proper proportion, balance, rhythm, and dominance (center of interest).

2. Plan, sketch, and then design an expressive arrangement with a dominant line. Identify the major line and its emotional or expressive significance. Note the evolution of the design. Did the design turn out as originally visualized or planned?

3. Visit a florist to determine which form wins the "favorite shape contest." List each featured form or shape and tally the number shown, both in the cooler and on display in the shop. Were you surprised at the results?

4. Design two arrangements using the same number and kinds of flowers. Design the first one with a flat, pressed look; create depth within the second one, using as many methods as possible. Compare.

18

Designing Corsages and Boutonnieres

For special occasions, many people add a festive touch to their attire by wearing floral accents. A woman may wear a corsage or a wrist corsage. A man may wear a boutonniere on his lapel. These special flowers show appreciation and recognition of an achievement or special happening.

Special events for wearing flowers include weddings, proms, birthdays, anniversaries, school events, like homecoming or "big games," holidays like Christmas, Valentine's Day, St. Patrick's Day (a green one, of course), Easter, Mother's Day, and many other social events.

18-1. A corsage can show recognition during a special occasion.

OBJECTIVES

1 Identify and describe supplies needed

2 Describe design mechanics and techniques

3 Identify and describe styles of corsages and boutonnieres

4 Discuss proper placement and pinning of corsages and boutonnieres

TERMS

chenille stem
combination method
daisy hook method
design mechanics
dip dyes
feathering
finishing dips or sprays
floral spray
floral tint
gauge
glamellia

hairpin method
nestled boutonniere
pierce method
staging the bow
stem dyes
stitch method
tip spraying
tulle
wrap around method
wrist corsage

CORSAGE SUPPLIES AND THEIR EFFECTIVE USE

Corsages and boutonnieres require some specialized and unique supplies compared to other aspects of floral design. Knowledge of the proper supplies and their effective design use is a good foundation for beautiful floral work.

BASIC CORSAGE SUPPLIES

The basic supplies for creating corsages and boutonnieres are floral tape, wire in several gauges, and ribbon.

Floral tape is made of paraffin-coated paper that is used to cover wires and stems in a unobtrusive way. Floral tape does not feel sticky to human hands; only when the floral tape is stretched and pulled tightly will it adhere to itself. A beginning floral designer may find that prestretching the tape will help the taping to be more secure. Floral tape comes in two widths—½ inch and 1 inch. The narrower width is commonly used for corsage work; the wider width may be used for bouquets, wreaths, or other design work. Floral tape is offered in a wide array of colors, including light and dark green, tan, white, gray, pink, yellow, and red. Generally, most corsage work is completed with light or dark green depending upon the flower stem color, but other colors can be selected depending upon the flower color and the occasion.

Florist wire is sold in 18 inch lengths by the gauge. Wires are easier to use in 9 inch lengths; wedding bouquet work may require the 18 inch lengths. The *gauge* of a wire describes its thickness or thinness. Here is a tip to remember—the smaller the gauge number, the thicker the wire. Commonly used gauges for corsage work are #26 for bows, #24 for medium-weight flow-

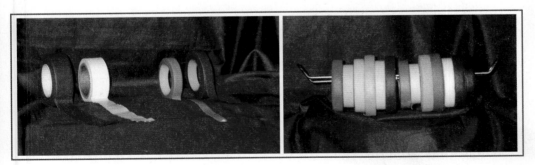

18-2. Floral tape is available in two widths and many colors.

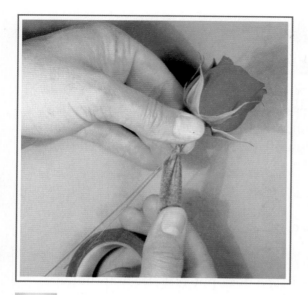

18-3. To adhere securely to itself, floral tape must be stretched and pulled tightly.

ers, such as mini carnations, spray chrysanthemums, or daisies, #22 for heavier flowers, such as standard carnations, roses, or a fully open lily. Filler flowers may be wired with #28 wire.

Ribbon also has its own terminology and differing widths. Ribbon is typically sold as #1, #1½, #3, #5, #9, #40. A thinner pixie ribbon is also offered. Thinner ribbons, including #1, #1½, and #3, are most commonly incorporated into corsage work. Ribbons #5 and #9 are used for potted plants, while #40 is used for bows on funeral sprays. Regular and wired-edge ribbon may come in satin, cotton, silk, sheer, paper, or burlap. Satin ribbon will have a shiny side and a matte or dull side. Some of the ribbons, including printed cotton, will have a definite front side and underside. Curling ribbon is another type but is usually used for tying packaged floral designs.

18-4. Remember—the smaller the wire gauge number, the thicker the wire. Use thinner gauge wire for bows and thicker gauges for flowers. Use a #24 gauge wire for mini carnations and a #22 gauge wire for a standard carnation.

COLOR CHANGING SUPPLIES

Floral sprays and tints give the designer a great tool for changing the natural color of a flower to match a fabric swatch of a special dress or shirt.

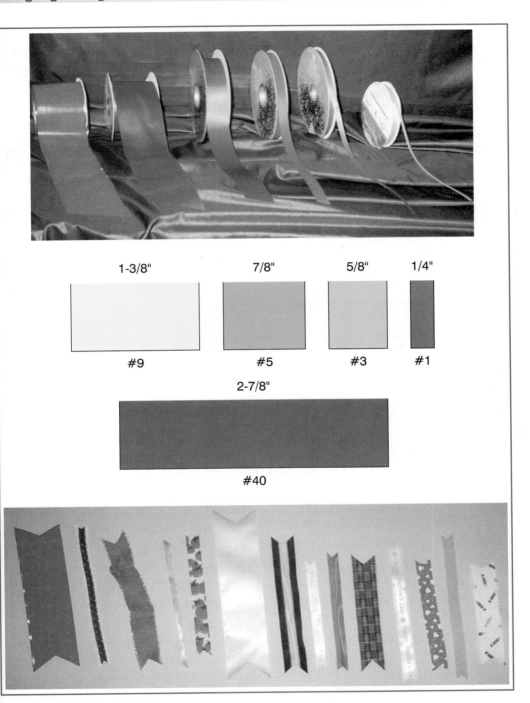

18-5. Ribbon comes in many widths and materials.

18-6. Floral sprays are great color tools for the floral designer. Color was applied to a carnation in the normal way (right side) and with the tip spraying technique (left side).

Floral sprays are opaque paints that will completely cover any flower color. *Floral tints* are translucent paints that allow some color underneath to show. Glitter sprays add a touch of glittery, metallic color.

When using floral sprays, go outdoors if possible or find a well-ventilated room. Cover adjacent areas with newspaper, or spray into a large shipping box or trash can. The methods to apply sprays, tints, or glitter are as follows:

1. Shake the can thoroughly to mix the paint.
2. Check the paint flow on a box lid or trash can first.
3. Hold the nozzle approximately 10 to 12 inches away from the flower or other item.
4. Press the nozzle down in quick bursts while moving the can side to side, starting just before the flower (or item) and going just beyond it.
5. For fresh or silk flowers, apply a single light coat. Some foliage, containers, or other accessories may benefit from several light coats for better coverage. Light sprays of glitter spray are more attractive than one heavy coat.
6. Let the sprayed material dry thoroughly. Place the just-sprayed flower upright in floral preservative solution for even drying, rather than on the counter or table. Remember, just-sprayed flowers will stain a table surface.
7. Before storing, turn the spray can upside down and press the nozzle until only air is released. Performing this practice after each use will keep the spray can from becoming plugged with dried paint.

For a varied look, try a special spray technique that applies color to only the edges of the petals, known as tipping or *tip spraying*. Tip spraying works well for carnations.

1. Wire and tape the stem.

2. Place the flower through the center of a paper towel, newspaper page, or corsage bag to protect hands from the paint.

3. Gather the paper or bag around the flower head and hold tightly, exposing just a small amount of the flower edges.

4. Spray a light coat of paint. The process can be repeated to darken it or add another color.

5. Allow flower to dry thoroughly

Stem dyes and dip dyes are also available. **Stem dyes** are color solutions that are transported through the flower's xylem in the stem to change the flower's color. Green St. Patrick's Day flowers are an obvious example of this technique. Usually, flowers are ordered and shipped directly from the wholesaler already dyed, but this method can be done as an interesting lab experiment. Flowers can be stem dyed using the following steps:

1. Mix the stem dye according to the instructions. Use warm water (90 to 100° F) for the best results.

2. Use fresh, white or light-colored flowers that have been shipped "dry" or have been set out of the cooler for 2 hours. Room temperature flowers give better and quicker results.

3. Remove the lower foliage and place the freshly recut flower stems into the stem dye solution.

4. Allow 15 to 30 minutes for the stem dye to be absorbed through the xylem. Watch the flowers carefully. Remove from the solution when the following occurs:

   a. For short-stemmed flowers—flower color is just lighter than desired

   b. For long-stemmed flowers—flower color has just appeared in the lower petals (Color will continue to darken when the dye within the xylem is absorbed.)

5. Rinse and recut the stems. Place the flowers in warm, preservative solution and let the flowers remain at room temperature until the coloring is completed (usually 1 to 2 hours).

Dip dyes are semi-transparent colors that change the flower's color by directly dipping the flower head in the color solution. Use fresh, white or light-colored flowers for the best results. After dipping the flower heads, gently shake off any excess dye. Rinse the flower in water and shake gently again to remove excess water and speed the drying process. Dry the flower thoroughly before using it to avoid staining.

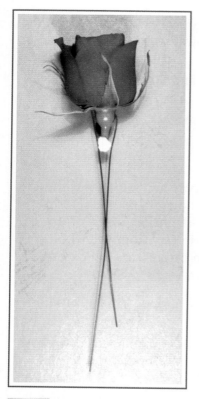

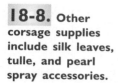

18-7. Cotton can provide extra needed moisture for some special corsage flowers.

GLUES AND ADHESIVES

Floral glue and adhesives can be used to directly attach small flowers to leaves or ribbons. Using glues can be quite a time-saver in constructing corsages and floral hairpieces. A low-temperature glue gun can be used to attach silk or fresh, durable leaves and flowers to combs or to a wired corsage with care being taken that the heat of the glue does not discolor the plant material surface. Pan melt glue is formulated as small pieces to be melted, using an electric skillet or frying pan set at 275° F. Materials or wires are placed into the pan to apply the glue. When not in use, the pan should be turned off and stored once cooled. Many companies now offer floral adhesives that are effective in attaching plant materials to many surfaces. Floral adhesives require more time to dry, compared to glue guns or pan melt glues.

OTHER SUPPLIES AND ACCESSORIES

Cotton balls can be used to extend the life of certain special flowers used in corsages and

18-8. Other corsage supplies include silk leaves, tulle, and pearl spray accessories.

boutonnieres. A small piece of moistened cotton is placed at the cut end of the flower after wiring but just before taping. This extra needed moisture is helpful for roses, orchids, lilies, and gardenias.

Silk leaves can be substituted for fresh foliage in a corsage. Silk leaves may suggest rose leaves, ferns, or simple oval shapes and are available in many tints and shades of green, white, and occasionally other colors. *Tulle* is florist netting that adds color, texture, and support for some flowers. It comes in many colors and finishes. Tulle can be wired, using #26 wire and added to corsages as needed. Other accessories for corsages include pearl sprays, rhinestones, and novelty items, such as footballs, chenille letters, butterflies, or bees. The accessories with wired stems can be taped directly to the corsage; other items can also be glued in place as needed.

PACKAGING SUPPLIES

Proper packaging is very important to keep the corsage or boutonniere in a state of high humidity. Moisture loss as well as warm temperatures will cause the rapid deterioration of a corsage. Common packaging supplies include finishing dips or sprays, a mist bottle, corsage and boutonniere bags and pins, and cardboard or clear boxes.

Finishing dips or sprays are applied to the finished corsage to seal the stomata of the flowers and minimize water loss. The stomata (or pores on the undersides of a leaf) of a flower close naturally to prevent water loss; this process is mimicked with the application of finishing solutions. Finishing sprays should always be allowed to dry thoroughly before packaging to pre-

18-9. Corsage and boutonniere packaging supplies should include bags, pins, boxes, and a mist bottle.

vent discoloration of the petals. Examples of finishing sprays include Design Master Clear Life and Floralife ™ Clear Set. Crowning Glory ™ may be used as either a dip or a spray. Read the directions carefully before using.

Corsage and boutonniere bags are available in plastic or cellophane in several sizes. A mist bottle can be used to spray a small amount of water into the fully open corsage bag before placing the corsage into it. Always avoid getting the bow wet. To close the bag, re-pleat the sides and fold two or three times, allowing air to be trapped inside the bag. Some designers blow into the bag to provide an extra air cushion (and added carbon dioxide). Seal the corsage or boutonniere bag with a single corsage or boutonniere pin. A corsage will have a second pin attached directly to it in the bag. For added protection and attractive presentation, the sealed bags may be placed into a cardboard or clear box.

DESIGN MECHANICS

18-10. Flower stems are removed to reduce bulk and allow for easy positioning. Leave a "thumb's width" (about ¾ inch) of stem.

Good design mechanics are very important to the quality of any floral design. The ***design mechanics*** are the techniques and devises that hold a corsage or an arrangement together in a secure way. Knowledge of the proper supplies and their effective design use is a good foundation for beautiful floral work and secure design mechanics.

Proper wiring, taping, and bow making techniques are crucial to making a "well-designed corsage or boutonniere". A beautiful creation that falls apart will always be remembered as a poor design. Mechanics are important!

WIRING TECHNIQUES

Flowers are wired to remove the bulky stem and allow the flower head to be easily positioned. Flowers and foliages require different wiring techniques, depending upon the structure of the plant material. The main methods are the pierce method, the daisy hook or hook method, the hairpin method, the wrap-around or clutch method, and the stitch method.

An important practice to note before wiring any flower is that the wire becomes the stem and the flower's stem must be removed except for a thumb's width, approximately ¾ inch.

Pierce Method

The *pierce method* involves inserting a wire through the calyx of a flower to wire for corsage work. It is effective for flowers that have a thick calyx just below the flower head. Flower examples are roses and carnations.

1. Pierce through the flower calyx. Use #24 or #22 wire depending upon the weight of the flower.
2. Bend the wires down parallel to the stem. Do not wrap the two wires around each other.
3. Start taping at the calyx, covering the pierced area and tape the entire length of the wire. Always cover the wires, the "mechanics" holding your corsage together.

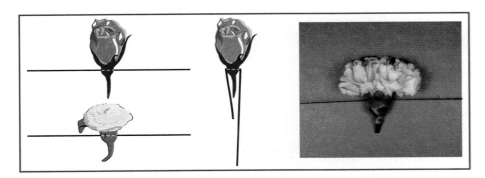

18-11. Flowers with a thick calyx, such as roses and carnations, are wired with the pierce method.

Double Pierce Method

The double piercing technique is effective to give additional support for some flowers that have a thick stem and heavy flowers, such as orchids or lilies. Other delicate flowers, such as alstroemeria or Peruvian lily, can be double pierced with two thinner gauge wires (#26) to give extra support for the flower yet not damage the delicate stem.

18-12. The double pierce method works well for alstroemeria, which is a delicate flower and stem yet has a thick calyx. This method gives added support.

1. Pierce through the calyx or stem, just below the flower head, with the first wire. Use #24 wire.

2. With the second wire, position it at a 90-degree angle and slightly lower than the first wire and pierce through the calyx or stem.

3. Cover all wires as the stem is taped.

Daisy Hook Method

The **daisy hook method** (or hook method) is a technique of inserting a wire through a flower stem and the flower itself and making a hook at the end of the wire and pulling it down into the flower. This technique will securely wire flowers that have a hard central disc without a prominent calyx, such as daisies and chrysanthemums. Other individual florets of delphinium, dendrobium orchids, and hyacinths can also be wired in this manner, using thinner gauge wire (26 gauge).

1. Place a #24 wire either through or next to the stem and push the wire through the flower head until it emerges.

2. Bend the wire into a small hook, approximately ½ inch long. For the best support within the flower, both sides of the hook should be parallel with each other; avoid bending the hook too far (almost closed) or not far enough (wide open).

3. Tape the stem, starting near the flower head, being sure to tape the end of the hook as well.

18-13. Use the daisy hook method for daisies and chrysanthemums that have a hard central disc without a prominent calyx.

Wrap Around Method

The ***wrap around method*** is effective in wiring little bunches or clusters of filler flowers, such as waxflowers or baby's breath, by encircling the stems with wire and bending the wire downward to form a new stem. Fine textured foliages, such as plumosa fern, tree fern or ming fern, can also be held together effectively with this technique.

1. Trim stems of flowers or foliage to a 1 inch length.

2. Position the middle of the #24 or #26 wire alongside the stems and wrap the other wire half around the stems and the supporting wire.

3. Bend the wire parallel to the stems and tape, always covering any wires.

18-14. The wrap around method securely holds together clusters or groups of filler flowers or foliages.

Hairpin Method

The **hairpin method** works well to wire ferns or other compound leaves and multi-flowered stems. The technique is to bend a wire in half (like a hairpin) and place it through a leaflet or frond to provide support high up the stem or to allow the plant material to be bent, curved, or positioned more easily. Boston ferns, flat ferns, and eucalyptus may be wired with this technique; freesias, larkspur, or dendrobium orchids may also be wired in this way. The hairpin method can be used to wire ribbon loops or ribbon loops with tails.

18-15. Ferns or freesias may be wired with the hairpin method for added support and ease in positioning. Ribbon loops are effectively wired with this technique also.

1. Bend a #24 wire in half to form a hairpin.

2. Place the wires through the leaflets or florets at the point where support is needed.

3. Pull the wire through until the curved part of the hairpin rests on the stem.

4. Place the wire parallel to the stem.

5. Gently wrap one wire around the stem and the other wire below the lowest leaflets or florets on the stem. Hold the top part of the hairpin firmly when wiring to avoid stripping off leaves or florets.

6. Tape the wire at the end of the stem.

Stitch Method

The **stitch method** is a foliage wiring technique, used on solid or wide leaves, such as salal (lemon leaf), Ti leaves, ivy, or individual leaflets of holly or silver dollar eucalyptus. Leaves wired with this method can be shaped and curved to fit the style and shape of corsage or boutonniere. This technique involves sewing, that is, making a small stitch or insertion through the back midrib of a leaf, pulling the wire through, bending the wires down, and wrapping one wire around the stem and other wire.

1. Cut a 1 inch stem or ½ inch petiole (if possible) on the leaf or leaflet.

2. Pierce through the center midrib with a #24 wire at or just above the halfway point of the leaf length. (If the leaf is wired too low, the leaf will not be supported. If the wire is positioned too high, the wire will show.)

3. Push the wire through until equal wire lengths appear on both sides of the stitch.

4. Bend the ends of the wire down.

5. Wrap one wire around the leaf stem and the other wire.

6. Tape the stem, covering the lower wires.

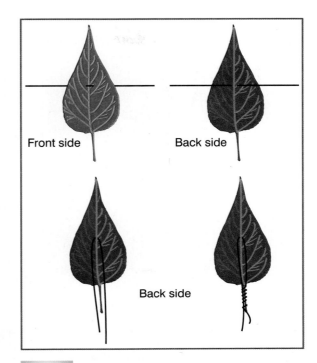

Front side   Back side

Back side

18-16. The stitch method provides good support and ease in positioning for many types of leaves or leaflets.

SPECIAL WIRING TECHNIQUES

Orchids and gardenias often require special wiring techniques because of their unusual shape and delicate nature. Manufactured stems can be effective in corsages for flowers such as stephanotis. Carnations can be made into smaller sizes by using a process known as feathering. Silk flowers also require a special technique before use in corsage work.

Combination Method

Although orchids and gardenias can be wired with the pierce method, another technique can also be used with good results. This **combination method** employs a chenille stem inserted into the 1 inch stem of the flower.

18-17. An orchid can be wired with a combination of both an inserted chenille stem and a pierced wire.

(The calyx of the gardenia is removed.) A ***chenille stem*** is a wire that is covered with soft, fuzzy chenille fibers, also known as a pipe cleaner. The stem is then pierced with a #24 wire. The stem is taped, starting at the top to cover the pierced area and continuing all the way down to cover both the wire and chenille stem.

Another combination method is wiring a football mum with a daisy hook (or simple insertion of a wire through the stem) and a pierce. The weight and type of flower may lead to the employment of a combination of wiring techniques.

Non-piercing Method

Phalaenopsis orchids are extremely delicate and should be carefully wired to give support but not damage the flower. It is important to note that the wires are positioned around and through the flower petals but are not piercing any part of the phalaenopsis orchid.

1. Tape the center of a #26 or #28 wire with white tape. A chenille stem may be substituted for the taped wire.

2. Bend the wire in half to form a U shape.

3. Place each end of the wire on either side of the narrow membrane that connects the lip to the rest of the flower.

4. Pull the wire until the taped center is resting against the membrane. The wire will extend through the flower between the petals and will not pierce any part of the orchid. The wire may need to be bent at this stage.

5. Position the wires alongside the stem.

6. Wrap the first wire around the stem and the second wire and tape completely.

18-18. A phalaenopsis orchid is wired without piercing any flower parts. The taped wire is rested against the central membrane with the wire ends taped securely to the flower stem.

Gardenia Tips

Gardenia are wonderfully fragrant and beautiful, yet fragile and easily bruised. Avoid touching the gardenia petals during the corsage-making process. Buy tailored gardenias, which have a collar of leaves already in place to keep bruising to a minimum. Another tip for working with gardenias is to cover the finished gardenia corsage with wet tissue to keep it fresh and unblemished.

Manufactured Stems

Stephanotis flowers have a lovely tubular shape that needs special treatment to prevent wilting. Special stems have been manufactured to help with this situation. Before using them, condition the flowers in cool water so each one will be firm and fully turgid.

1. Place the cotton portion of the manufactured stem upside down in water to thoroughly moisten it.

2. Gently pull the flower stem and green sepals away from the stephanotis flower.

3. With the end of the manufactured stem positioned under the flower, push out the flower parts (the ovary, etc.) through the center of the flower.

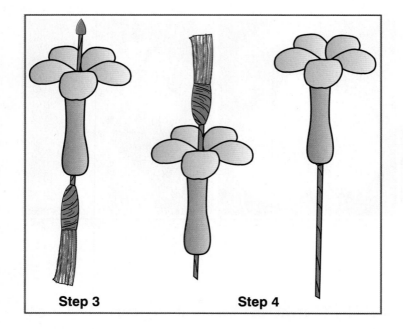

Step 3   Step 4

18-19. A moistened manufactured stem provides needed moisture and support for a stephanotis flower.

4. Insert the end of the moistened manufactured stem through the flower opening and pull it gently into the tube until it fills the tubular part of the flower. The stem can be used as is or can be taped.

*F*eathering a Carnation

Feathering is the process of making smaller flowers from a larger carnation. Depending upon the design use, a carnation can be divided into various portions to make any desired carnation size. This technique gives a designer greater flexibility in corsage work with fewer flowers in stock.

1. Remove the stem below the calyx.

2. Hold the calyx firmly and pinch (or cut apart) the carnation into halves, thirds, or quarters, depending upon the desired size of the feathered carnations.

3. Separate the carnation pieces, keeping the calyx attached.

4. Tightly tape the new smaller flower, letting the calyx enclose the petals.

5. Pierce the newly created flower with a #24 wire and tape the entire stem.

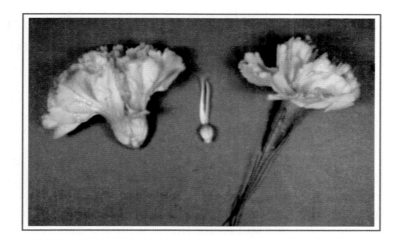

18-20. A carnation is feathered by dividing it into smaller sections, taping each part tightly, and pierce-wiring each section before taping each stem.

*R*olling Rose Petals

Outer rose petals that are removed from a rose can form a delightful little rose bud accent in a corsage or boutonniere. A single petal can be used or two or three petals to provide a fuller looking rose accent.

1. Trim a small circular area from the base of the petal.

2. Roll the petal from side to side.

3. Tape the petal to keep it rolled. Low temperature glue will also secure it.

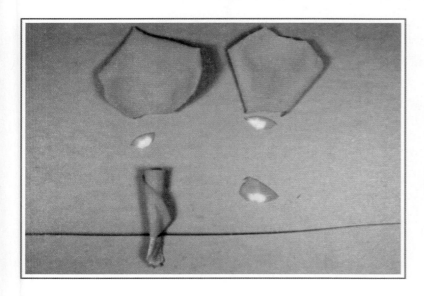

18-21. Rose petals can be rolled to make charming rose bud accents in corsages.

4. Add a second or third petal as desired. Tape or glue each petal.

5. With a #24 or #26 wire, pierce the petal(s) just above the tape and bend the ends downward.

6. Tape the entire length of the wire.

Wiring Silk Flowers and Foliages

Silk flowers and foliages can be used to create attractive corsages and boutonnieres. Silks may be added to fresh corsages to provide a needed color or an out-of-season flower or can comprise the entire corsage. Flowers with a plastic calyx may be wired with the "hot wire" method. Heat a 24 gauge wire in a candle flame and pierce through the plastic calyx. The stems of silk plant materials may be too thick or not wired at all so a simple wiring technique is useful for silks.

1. Remove all but ½ to ¾ inch of the stem.

2. Dip the end of a #24 (#22 if heavy) wire into pan melt glue, applying a fine line or bead of glue.

3. Position the glued wire along the stem of the flower or leaf.

4. Allow ample time for glue to dry.

5. Tape tightly from the base of the flower or leaf, continuing until the stem is completely covered.

18-22. Silk plant materials may be used in corsage work by gluing a wire to the shortened stem of the flower or leaf (right side). A plastic calyx may be pierced with a heated 24 gauge wire. (left side).

BOW MAKING

Bows are a fundamental part of creating corsages. On the other hand, boutonnieres should not be designed with a bow although occasionally a small ribbon treatment may be added to signify school spirit or highlight other significant colors.

Most people (customers) perceive that a corsage is not finished until a bow is added. However, some corsages can be creatively designed and not need a bow at all. Besides their addition to corsages, bows are also added to bud vases, vase arrangements, some floral designs, such as holiday ones, and on potted plants.

Basic Bow Making Tips

Take note of the following tips for the beginning bow-maker:

1. Most ribbon has two sides, shiny and matte (or dull). The finished bow should be entirely shiny or entirely matte.

2. A bow being constructed is held in place with the thumb, index finger, and middle finger. The thumb is on top, positioned inside the center loop. The index and middle fingers are underneath the bow, stabilizing and acting like a shuttle on the underneath side.

3. The opposite hand (usually the "writing hand") feeds the ribbon and makes the loops and twists.

4. The twist is an important part of bow-making success. All of the twists should be small, straight across, and aligned exactly on top of each other. A thin wire ties the bow together exactly at the point of the twists. If the twists are elongated or not made at the same spot, the bow will appear messy and crinkled in the middle with loops of differing lengths that will not position properly. "It's all in the twist!"

5. Making bows is not easy. Practice, practice, practice.

6. Avoid making bows with large, floppy loops, which are out of proportion to the design, crush easily, and flatten and lose their shape quickly.

7. Bows may be wired with chenille stems, taped wire, regular wire, or narrow, matching ribbon (listed in order of easiest to more challenging).

8. Make the bow directly off the bolt to insure the proper ribbon length.

9. Streamers or ribbon tails may be added to the bow. Sometimes, a streamer is added at the beginning of the construction; often, the streamers are created at the end. The ribbon length depends upon the

design. For example, short streamers are appropriate for corsages and longer tail lengths for bud vases or vase arrangements.

10. Streamers or ribbon tails can be trimmed as a diagonal or a bow tie finish. A blunt cut hints that the designer does not have the proper "attention to detail."

The Steps—Bow Making 101

A bow with a center loop is the most common type of bow. The center loop makes the bow appear finished and masks the area where the wire is holding the bow together.

1. Decide if the bow will be shiny or matte finish. Let's choose shiny for this explanation.

2. Hold the ribbon with the dull side touching the thumb. Loop the ribbon over the thumb, make the small center loop, and hold in place with the index and middle finger. The shiny side of the ribbon should be showing.

3. Twist the ribbon to reveal the desired finish.

4. Make a loop of modest proportions, 1½ or 2 inches long, increasing the length for larger designs. Twist the ribbon so the shiny side is visible.

5. In the opposite direction, make another loop of the same size. Twist to reveal the shiny side.

18-23. Diagonal or bow tie finishes for ribbon tails or streamers add that last finishing touch.

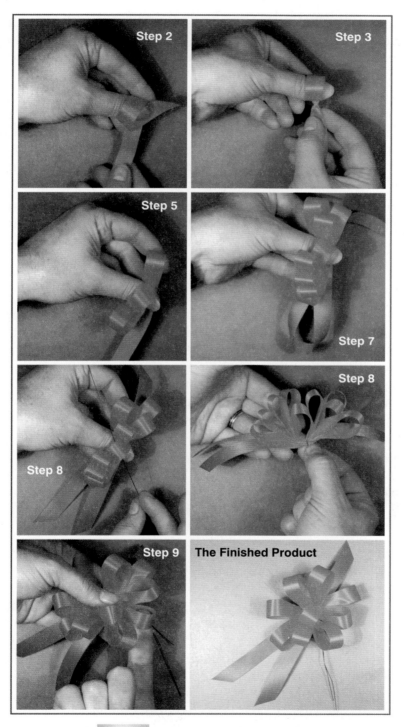

18-24. The steps for making a bow.

6. Continue making loops on each side of the center loop with an equal amount of loops on each side. A little corsage might only have six loops (three on each side); a larger one may have eight loops (four on each side) or more.

7. To make streamers, make one last twist to reveal the shiny side. Determine the desired length of ribbon tail. Grasp the shiny side of the ribbon at a point twice the ribbon streamer length (for two ribbon tails) and place the ribbon (shiny side up) directly underneath the first streamer. To add a streamer on the opposite side, determine the desired length and cut the ribbon at that spot from the bolt.

8. Place a #26 wire through the center loop with equal amounts of wire on each side. Slide the wire under the thumb and bring the ends underneath the bow between the index and middle fingers. Twist the wire, pulling tightly to gather the ribbon twists securely into place. The wire in the middle of the bow should not show. Pull the wire tighter in the center if the wire is apparent.

9. The last step—staging the bow. *Staging the bow* means to arrange the bow loops so the bow appears balanced and full or rounded. To effectively stage it, place the thumb back into the center loop and apply pressure with the thumb and index finger pinching together. With the index finger of the other hand, position the loops in an alternating fashion around the center loop, that is, pull the first loop to the left, the second loop to the right, and alternate with the remaining loops. Be sure to place the finger into the loop to move it; do not crease the loop by grabbing it by the tip.

STYLES OF FLOWERS-TO-WEAR

The styles of boutonnieres and corsages have changed over the decades and centuries. Corsages worn in the 1800s and early 1900s were much larger and more grandiose. Current styles tend to feature more petite versions.

Proportion is an important principle to remember in designing today's corsages and boutonnieres. The size of the corsage should fit the person's size; children and petite women should wear smaller corsages. The component parts of the corsages and boutonnieres should be the same relative scale to each other. The foliage should not be too long and overwhelm the flowers. Likewise, the bow should be in proportion to the flowers and foliages chosen. A beautiful corsage with an over-sized bow will be distracting and not pleasing in proportion.

Balance and focal point are also important. Choose symmetrically or asymmetrically balanced styles depending upon the occasion or attire. Often, a combination of the bow and a unique or larger flower will create an obvious and pleasing focal area.

STEM FINISHES FOR BOUTONNIERES AND CORSAGES

The stem ends for boutonnieres and corsages are usually visible and can be finished in a variety of ways. These tips will help the beginning designer.

1. At the beginning of construction, always tape the entire length of wire.

2. The stem ends should be in alignment with the top flower or foliage. A poorly aligned stem will cause a corsage to be pinned on at an angle and look poorly designed.

3. The stem finish should always allow the corsage to lay flat and should not interfere with the attachment of the corsage or boutonniere.

4. At the end of construction, another finishing touch is to pull the floral tape over any exposed wire ends after the stem finish has been completed.

The simplest finish is the straight stem. A curled stem can offer a unique variation yet it is quick and simple to do. Variations of the curled stem include a simple roll to the side, an oval loop with the end curled around the main stem as a stylized touch, or a "pig's tail" curl, fashioned by rolling the stem around a pen.

The garden finish is a natural, "gardeny" look, keeping the taped wires separate. The corsage stems are taped only at the top to secure them. The individual wires are separated and cut at slightly varying lengths.

18-25. A variety of stem finishes add uniqueness and style to both boutonnieres and corsages.

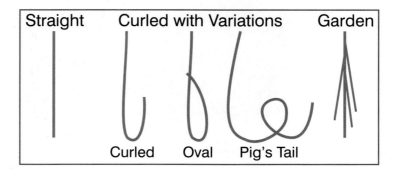

BOUTONNIERES

Boutonnieres may be designed with a single flower or several small flowers. The overall design should be attractive and tasteful and not too large or overpowering. Although roses and carnations are common boutonniere flowers, a wide variety of suitable flowers may appropriately be selected. Foliages, used individually or in combination, can add an attractive green framework to feature the flower.

Single Flower Boutonniere

A single flower boutonniere is a classic and popular boutonniere choice for weddings, proms, and many special events. A medium-sized flower is a common selection, along with filler and foliage. Avoid large flowers, such as orchids, because of the similarity to a corsage size. Mechanics, particularly smooth, tight taping, are important for a boutonniere because the stem is prominent and not covered by the bow as in a corsage.

1. Remove all but 1 inch of the stem on the chosen flower (rose, carnation, alstroemeria). Wire and tape it.

2. Adding filler, if desired—Add a sprig (or two) of baby's breath, positioned around the flower to accent it, not overshadow it. Tape the filler to the taped flower stem.

3. Adding foliage—Tape a leaflet (or two) of leatherleaf to the back of the flower (or Italian ruscus, pittosporum, or other small leaf). Fine textured, lacy foliages, such as plumosa fern, ming fern, or tree fern, may be used in combination or in substitution, depending upon the event. Some leaves may need additional support by wiring, depending upon their placement in the corsage and their size.
   * * With experience, the filler and foliage can be taped to the stem at the same time.* *

18-26. A single flower boutonniere is a classic and traditional favorite.

Table 18-1. Popular and Appropriate Boutonniere Flowers and Foliage	
Flowers	**Foliage**
Roses (all types)	Leatherleaf
Carnations (miniature and standard)	Plumosa fern
Chrysanthemums (sprays, not standards)	Tree fern
Alstroemeria	Ivy
Stephanotis	Pittosporum
Freesia	Ming fern
Asters (Matsumoto types)	Italian ruscus
Florets—Dendrobium orchids, delphinium	Evergreens (seasonal)
Linear accent flowers—grape hyacinths, lily of the valley, heather	Boxwood
Numerous filler flowers	Huckleberry

4. Stem finish—Choose the desired stem finish and cut the stem accordingly. Pull the floral tape to cover the exposed wires or add a small extra piece and tape over the ends, working from bottom to top. Add a boutonniere pin.

Multiple Flower Boutonniere

For a very special or festive touch, multiple flower boutonnieres are a nice choice. A multiple flower boutonniere is designed with smaller flowers, along with foliage (and filler—optional). If a garden look stem finish is desired, leave the stems separate during the construction steps and tape only at the top to hold the composition in place.

1. Wire and tape two or three small flowers or florets. (Be sure to remove all but ¾ inch of the stem.)

2. Adding foliage—Tape a small leaf or leaflet to the back of each taped flower.

3. Positioning—Place the smallest flower at the top, with the second flower lower and slightly to the right (zigzag pattern). A third flower is positioned lower than the middle flower and slightly to the left. Tape to hold in place.
   * * The second and third flowers are angled slightly forward. * *

18-27. A multiple flower boutonniere is comprised of smaller flowers.

18-28. A nestled boutonniere is a small flower inserted into the center of a carnation.

4. Adding filler (optional)—Add a cluster or two of filler flowers as needed.

5. Another leaf or two can be taped behind the flowers, if needed.

6. Stem finish—Complete the stem finish, cover exposed wire ends, and add a pin.

Nestled Boutonniere

A nestled boutonniere is a popular choice to showcase school colors or to add a festive touch to any event. Corsages can also be designed with nestled flowers. A **nestled boutonniere** is a boutonniere designed with a smaller flower, such as a sweetheart rose or small cluster of a filler flower, like statice or waxflower, inserted or "nestled" into the center of a carnation. The technique is the most effective when the two flowers are different colors that blend or contrast well.

1. Wire (#22 wire) but do not tape a small flower (leave only a ¼ inch stem).

2. Choose a carnation with a different color. Remove the pistil (the central female organ of a flower—ovary, style, and stigma) inside the carnation to allow the smaller flower to be nestled lower into the carnation. Remove all but ¾ inch of the stem below the calyx.

3. Insert the small flower into the carnation with the wires emerging at the base of the carnation calyx. Position the small flower in the carnation center.

4. Pierce (#24 wire) the calyx of the carnation and bend the wire ends parallel with the other wires. Tape the wires completely to the ends.

5. Add filler and foliage as desired. Tape, complete the stem finish, and add a pin.

CORSAGES

Corsages add wonderful touches of color, vibrancy, and meaning to any special event, including birthdays, weddings, anniversaries, award programs, dances, parties, and any social events. For proms and weddings, the corsage colors are very important and often swatches of fabric are needed for the designer to carefully match the color of the dress.

The flower choices for corsages are nearly limitless. Small, medium, and large flowers can be used with a variety of fillers and foliages. Wilt-prone flowers should be wired and taped with a moist piece of cotton or can be avoided altogether.

Single Flower Corsage

A single flower corsage is a showy corsage when designed with larger flowers, such as an orchid or lily. This corsage is very popular for holidays, anniversaries, and at weddings for the mothers or grandmothers of the bride or groom. This corsage can also be designed with a medium-sized flower, just

Table 18-2. Popular Corsage Flowers and Foliage	
Flowers	**Foliage**
Roses (all types)	Ivy
Carnations (miniature and standard)	Ming fern
Chrysanthemums (sprays and football)	Tree fern
Alstroemeria	Plumosa fern
Stephanotis	Pittosporum (all)
Freesia	Leatherleaf
Gladioli florets	Ruscus (all)
Gardenias	Salal or lemonleaf
Orchids—Cattleya, Cymbidium,	Evergreens (seasonal)
Dendrobium, Phalaenopsis, Vanda	Camellia leaves
Asters	Boxwood
Lilies, Lily of the Valley	Bear grass (looped)
Florets—hyacinth, delphinium, larkspur	Holly
Grape hyacinths	
Numerous fillers	

18-29. A single flower corsage can be fashioned with a larger flower that creates a showy and special look for the wearer.

like a single flower boutonniere with a bow added. This smaller single flower corsage is suitable for younger girls and for those who help at the cake table, gift table, and guest book at weddings.

1. Wire and tape an orchid with a 1 inch stem, using the double pierce method or the combination method.

2. Prepare foliage—Wire and tape three leaves.

3. Assemble the corsage—Place the foliage at the top and sides of the orchid. Tape.

4. Add the bow. Tape, covering the length of the stem ends.

5. Stem finish—Complete the stem finish. Add two corsage pins. The pins should be placed just into the stem and not through it (Ouch!).

Small Beginner's Corsage with Two Flowers

Many girls and ladies prefer a small corsage. A small, two-flower corsage is very similar to a multiple flower boutonniere except that a corsage almost always has a bow. Here are the steps for a beginner's first multiple flower corsage.

1. Select two carnations and remove all but ¾ inch of the stem. Pierce with a #24 wire and tape down the entire length of the wire.

2. Adding filler, if desired—Add a sprig (or two) of sea lavender or baby's breath, positioned around each flower to accent it, not overwhelm it. Tape the filler to each taped flower stem.

3. Adding foliage—Tape a leaflet (or two) of leatherleaf or ivy to the back of the flower. Fine textured, lacy foliages, such as plumosa fern or tree fern, can be added in combination. Additional leaves can be added at the end of construction, if needed.

*The filler and foliage can be taped to the stem at the same time to save a taping step and keep the stem thinner. * *

4. Positioning—Place the smallest flower at the top, with the second flower lower and slightly to the right (zigzag pattern). The two flowers should not form "eyes," instead, one should be higher than the other. The lower flower should angle slightly forward.

5. Stem finish—Complete the stem finish, cover exposed wire ends, and add a corsage pin.

Multiple Flower Corsage

18-30. A two-flower corsage is a simple multiple flower corsage for a beginner.

A multiple flower corsage can be quite showy and relates a sense of appreciation and recognition to the wearer. This type can be worn for numerous special occasions and holidays.

A multiple flower corsage can be designed with many types of flowers and foliage with accessories, such as tulle tufts and ribbon loops as a well as a bow. This type of corsage gives the designer much flexibility and creativity; the corsage can be symmetrical or asymmetrical with vertical, rounded, crescent, or triangular shapes.

1. Select five flowers (three to seven), ranging from buds to fully open. Wire by piercing with a #24 wire.

2. Choose foliage and fillers to add to the flowers. Position leaves and sprigs of filler of the proper proportion and tape to the flowers.

3. Placement—Place the smallest bud or flower at the top. Position a partially open or larger flower lower and to the right side. Continue the zigzag pattern by placing the third and largest flower lower and to the left. Bow loops or additional filler can also be added at this time. Tape once or twice around the stem. * * The first flower is the vertical center of the corsage and lays flat. The second and third flower are angled slightly off vertical and angle slightly forward.* *

18-31. The lower flowers in a multiple flower corsage are positioned in a downward fashion to keep the corsage a manageable size and well balanced.

4. Position the fourth and fifth flower in a downward fashion so the wire is attached at the same joining point as the other three flowers. Add bow loops or filler as needed. Trim any excess wire before taping to reduce bulk.

5. Position the bow within the flowers to form a focal area near the largest flowers.

6. Additional leaves can be added behind the corsage, if needed, to frame the flowers, complete the desired shape, or add artistic flair.

7. Determine the stem finish, tape, and trim the stems accordingly. Add two corsage pins.

8. Be sure that the corsage lays flat. "Try it on before packaging."

Wrist Corsage

A **wrist corsage** is a lightweight corsage designed to be attached to a wristband for

18-32. A lightweight corsage can be worn as a wrist corsage by using some of the pictured tricks of the trade.

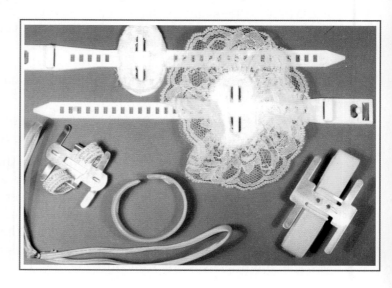

wearing on the wrist. Sometimes, a wrist corsage is preferred for dances or for attaching to strapless gowns or dresses of very lightweight material.

A well-constructed multiple flower corsage can be worn as a wrist corsage by attaching to an elasticized band, a plastic latch-type band, a plastic empty floral tape roll, or by tying on the corsage with ribbon tubing. The corsage should always be tied or taped (or both) very securely.

*F*ootball Mum Corsage

In some areas of the country, football mum corsages are traditional favorites at football games, especially homecoming events, at the high school and college level. A basic football mum corsage is designed with one mum, foliage, and a bow, but many additions can give uniqueness to the design, such as trailing ribbons, accessories—footballs, school letters and megaphones, and two or three football mums used instead of one.

1. Leave 1 inch of stem on the flower. Wire the football mum with a combination method, in this case, both a daisy hook (#22 wire) and a pierce (#22 wire).

2. Wire five salal leaves or other broad foliage with a stitch method and tape.

3. Bend the leaves to frame the football mum in a symmetrical fashion. Tape.

18-33. A football mum corsage is a great way to show school spirit.

4. Add a bow. Accessories may also be added.

5. Finish the stem and add pins.

*G*lamellia Corsage

A variation of the single flower corsage is the unique glamellia corsage. A **glamellia** is a composite flower that is comprised of gladiolus florets, made to resemble a camellia, that is, a gladiolus camellia (gla + mellia =

18-34. A glamellia is created by using gladiolus buds and partially to fully open florets.

glamellia). Many parts of the gladiolus in various stages of opening are used, including buds and partially to fully open florets.

Key tips for making a glamellia:

- Selection of buds and florets—Select gladiolus buds and florets in various sizes.

- Preparation of florets—Each floret chosen is cut at the base of the floret. The central flower parts will fall out (or can be pulled out), but the petals will remain together.

- Placement of florets—Each floret is placed to form a rounded composite flower. The added floret is trimmed on the appropriate side to fill in the round shape.

- Floral adhesives—Floral adhesives can also be used to attach additional florets instead of or in addition to wiring.

- Size—Glamellias may be created from only three or four buds and florets or may be much larger and showier, using five or six buds and florets with a collar of gladiolus petals underneath it.

The steps in designing a glamellia are as follows:

1. Select a bud, removing the green sepals and all but 1 inch of stem. Wire by piercing and tape.

2. Slip the wired and taped bud into a partially open bud until the bases of the florets meet. Pierce with a #26 wire and bend the wire ends down. Tape.

3. Slip the two wired buds into a partially open floret and pierce with a #26 wire. Bend the wire ends down. Tape.

4. Cut open a nearly open floret on the appropriate side and position it around the three wired florets. Wire as before and tape. Use glue if necessary.

5. Continue adding florets, making a rounded, symmetrical shape until the desired size is reached.

6. Add salal or other bold foliage to support the delicate new flower. Add other foliage as desired.

7. Add filler, if desired, complete the stem finish, and insert two corsage pins just into the stem.

18-35. Gladiolus florets are wired and taped together to form a showy composite flower called a glamellia.

PROPER PLACEMENT AND ATTACHMENT OF FLOWERS TO WEAR

Corsages and boutonnieres are worn on the left shoulder because of the Victorian practice of placing them "over the heart." Place flowers "over the heart" on the left side; place name tags on the right side as an extension of the hand-shaking arm.

Boutonnieres are worn near the buttonhole of a jacket lapel. One pin should be sufficient to provide secure placement. Boutonniere pins are shorter than corsage pins and have a smaller head in black, gray, or white colors. An effective technique is the "hidden pin method." Pin the flower so the pin is hidden underneath the lapel. From underneath, pin through a small amount of the fabric, pierce through the stem, and pin another small amount a fabric on the other side. With this technique, only the flower and stem will show. If pinning from the front side, match the boutonniere pin to the jacket color.

Corsages should be placed higher on the shoulder and pinned securely with two pins. One pin is placed through the corsage stems with another one positioned higher, through the flowers, to keep the corsage from shifting or falling forward. The hidden pin method works well for jackets and vests. When pinning corsages on dresses or blouses made of delicate materials, added support is needed to support the weight of the corsage. Position a small folded tissue or lightweight piece of fabric underneath the area to be pinned. Pinning through a bra strap will also give security to the attachment. Most corsage pins are white or pearl-headed.

Wrist corsages are worn on the left wrist although some left-handed persons may prefer to wear them on the other side. A wrist corsage should be small enough to be comfortable wearing and should not be worn too high on the forearm away from the wrist.

A corsage or boutonniere should always be constructed in a secure way so the person wearing it enjoys the experience. Mechanics and other details of design should not be apparent; the beauty and suitability of the design should be the most obvious features.

REVIEWING

MAIN IDEAS

Corsages and boutonnieres are special designs worn by ladies and gentlemen for holidays, weddings, and numerous special occasions. Knowledge of the necessary supplies and their use, proper design mechanics, appropriate styles of boutonnieres and corsages, and their proper placement are all important factors to know to be a good designer of flowers-to-wear.

The basic corsage and boutonniere supplies are floral tape, wire, and ribbon. Floral tape is a paraffin-coated paper that is self-adhering when stretched. Wire is available in different gauges or thickness and is used to replace the natural stem of flowers or foliages. Ribbon is available in many widths and finishes. Other important supplies are floral sprays, tints, stem dyes, and dip dyes for changing the color of flowers or foliage. Floral glue and adhesives are great time-saving tools for the designer in creating corsages and boutonnieres. Small pieces of a cotton ball can be a device to add moisture to the cut stem of a flower before wiring and taping. Other supplies include silk leaves, tulle, and accessories, such as pearl sprays, footballs, or school letters. Packaging supplies are finishing dips or sprays, corsage and boutonniere bags, boxes, pins, and a mist bottle.

Basic design mechanics are vital to a well-constructed corsage or boutonniere. Design mechanics are the techniques and tools that hold a design together securely. Proper wiring, taping, and bow making techniques are important design mechanics. Important wiring techniques for corsage and boutonniere making are the pierce, double pierce, daisy hook, wrap around, hairpin, stitch, and other special techniques, such as combination wiring, the non-piercing method, and using manufactured stems. Tips for working with gardenias, feathering a carnation, rolling rose petals, and wiring silk plant materials are also included in the design mechanics section.

Bows are a fundamental part for creating most corsages. The steps for creating a bow include making a twist after each loop, beginning with the center loop and each succeeding loop on either side of the center loop. Streamers or ribbon tails can be added at the completion of the bow loops. The bow is then wired securely and staged (or positioned).

The stem ends of corsages and boutonnieres may finished in several ways, including the straight stem, the curled stem with a very curly "pig's tail" variation, and the garden look with separate taped wires, cut at varying lengths.

The common boutonniere styles are the single flower and multiple flower types. A nestled boutonniere is a specialty type that has a small flower (sweetheart rose, for example) inserted into a carnation of a different color.

Popular corsage styles are the showy single flower type, a beginner's two-flower corsage, and the multiple flower style. A wrist corsage can be adapted from a small corsage, which is attached by a variety of bands or other techniques to be worn at the wrist. Stylized corsages include the football mum corsage and the glamellia corsage.

Proper placement and attachment of the flowers to be worn is also important. A boutonniere is worn slightly lower than a corsage's placement. Both types should be pinned on securely on the left side. Wrist corsages should be worn at the wrist and not on the forearm.

QUESTIONS

Answer the following questions. Use correct spelling and complete sentences.

1. Why does a person wear flowers?
2. What does it mean to "cover your mechanics"? Give two examples.
3. What are some basic supplies needed to design a corsage? Be thorough.
4. Why are stems removed when making boutonnieres and corsages?
5. How is a boutonniere different from a corsage? How does the placement of a boutonniere differ from that of a corsage?
6. What are the different ways to wire foliages? List and give examples for each method.
7. What is a chenille stem and how is it used in corsage work?
8. How have corsage styles changed over the years?
9. What are different methods for wiring flowers? List the methods and specific flower types.
10. What are three important tips for successful bow making? What are the steps of making a bow with a center loop?

EVALUATING

Match the term with the correct definition. Write the letter by the term in the blank provided.

a. nestled boutonniere
b. hairpin method
c. glamellia
d. stitch method
e. stomata

f. pistil
g. finishing dips and sprays
h. dip dyes
i. gauge
j. feathering

_____ 1. The thickness or thinness of a wire.

_____ 2. Adding florets to make a bigger composite flower.

_____ 3. Dividing a flower to make smaller sizes.

_____ 4. Adding a smaller flower within a larger one.

_____ 5. A sealant to prevent water loss.

_____ 6. Ovary, style, and stigma—the female parts of a flower.

_____ 7. To change color by immersing the flower head in a color solution.

_____ 8. The pores on the undersides of a leaf.

_____ 9. Inserting a wire through the midrib of the underside of a leaf, bending the wires down, wrapping around the petiole.

_____ 10. Bending a wire in half and inserting through leaflets or parts of a flower to give support or modify the shape, then wrapping the wire around the stem and other wire.

EXPLORING

1. When attending a dance, prom, or wedding, make note of the styles of flowers that are worn or carried. Determine which style is the most popular. If possible, casually interview a few people to find out why that style was chosen.

2. Feather a standard carnation. Make a range of sizes and incorporate five to seven flowers within a corsage.

3. Make a multiple flower corsage and a multiple flower boutonniere to match. Use five different wiring techniques. Complete each design with a garden stem finish.

4. Experiment with color. Try all of the color changing methods, using white carnations. Compare the colors produced and the time involved for each method.

19

Designing Basic Floral Work

Floral designers may choose many types of designs to create. Before creating more difficult floral work, a designer must master the basic designs and styles. Knowing and using the correct tools and supplies is essential for a floral designer. The effective use of floral foam, as well as other foundation mechanics, makes a floral designer more flexible and artistic.

Learning and mastering many styles, such as vase arrangements, geometric, and naturalistic designs, is an exciting challenge for the beginning designer. The proper choice of a design style will depend upon the place, the occasion, and the designer's skill.

19-1. Learning basic design skills is a good framework for the beginning floral designer.

453

OBJECTIVES

1 Identify and describe supplies and tools needed

2 Explain how to design bud vases and vase arrangements

3 Explain how to construct basic geometric designs

4 Define naturalistic and contemporary freestyle

5 Describe how to foil a potted plant

TERMS

anchor pin
brick
contour
floral foam
florist shears
foliage grid
greening pin
grid

grouping
hyacinth stake
needlepoint holder
poly foil
pruning shears
rosette
tape grid
water tube

DESIGN TOOLS AND SUPPLIES

Knowing and using the correct tools and supplies is very important to the floral designer. Since new products and supplies are constantly being developed, a designer needs to stay current and look for new items that may make the job even easier.

CUTTING TOOLS

Knives

With experience, a floral designer will learn that a knife is the fastest and most efficient cutting tool to use. Any type of knife can be chosen depending upon the designer's preference. Pockets knives are convenient because they can be folded; knives that resemble paring knives are another option. Always keep the knife sharp for the best results.

In the beginning, using a knife may result in an injured thumb or fingers. Hold the stem in one hand and the knife in the other. Cut the stem with a diagonal cut while pulling the stem upward with the other hand. Avoid placing any fingers or a thumb in the way. Using a knife may be awkward at first but will become quite natural with practice.

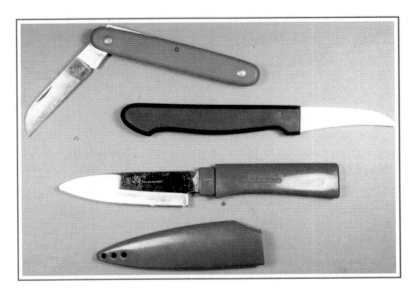

19-2. A knife is an efficient tool for any floral designer. Folding or paring-type knives are chosen depending upon the designer's preference.

Shears and Pruning Shears

Florist shears are a cutting tool with short, serrated blades for cutting thick or woody stems. Some tropical flowers and small branches can be easily cut with shears rather that a knife or scissors. Florist shears are preferable over ordinary scissors for cutting plant material because the blades will not pinch the stem.

Pruning shears will cut very thick or tough branches with a smooth cut. Often, florist shears may not be able to cleanly cut through a big branch. When selecting pruning shears, be sure to select a type with a sharp cutting blade; always avoid the anvil-type, which cuts the stem by pinching it.

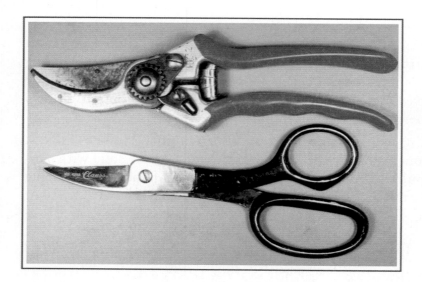

19-3. Florist shears and pruning shears are indispensable for cutting thick and woody stems.

Scissors

Both ribbon scissors and utility scissors will be useful for a designer. Ribbon scissors are cutting tools with long, sharp blades designed for cutting ribbon, netting, or fabric. To maintain their sharpness, these scissors should not be used to cut anything else, including plant materials. Utility scissors are scissors that can be used for trimming leaves, paper, or other materials. Having a pair of utility scissors will allow the ribbon scissors to be used only for their intended purpose.

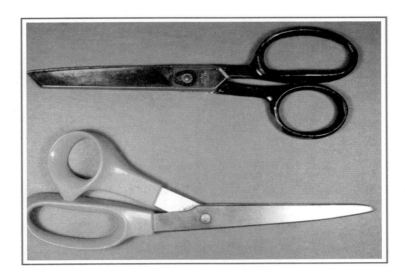

19-4. Ribbon scissors should be used only for ribbon, netting, or fabric. Utility scissors can be used for trimming foliage or cutting paper or other materials.

Supplies and Their Use

Floral Foam

Floral foam is a porous material designed to hold water and provide stability for stems within a floral design. Flower stems can be held at any angle when inserted into a block of floral foam. Floral foam comes in two formulations for both fresh and dry plant materials. The dry foam will be discussed

19-5. Floral foam is porous and easy to cut with a knife. Floral foam is available as a brick.

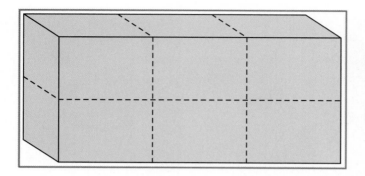

19-6. To avoid waste, cut the foam brick into the fraction of the brick needed. For a one-sixth brick, cut into thirds and then in half lengthwise.

in Chapter 23. The fresh foam is green and commonly available as a brick or a block. A **brick** of foam is approximately the size of a fireplace brick.

Because of its porous nature, floral foam can be easily cut to any size or shape, depending on the container size. A simple butter knife, florist knife, or a heavy-gauge wire can be used to cut the foam.

To avoid waste, cut the foam into the fraction of a brick needed. For example, green plastic design bowls can be fitted with either a quarter (small to medium centerpiece) or a third (larger centerpiece) of a brick. Turn the foam to the side and cut the brick into thirds or quarters. For a smaller container, one-sixth of a brick may be needed. In this case, the foam is first cut into thirds and then half lengthwise. The foam may be cut before or after saturating with water.

The floral foam should be properly and thoroughly soaked with water before using. The correct method is to place the foam into warm preservative

19-7. To insure proper soaking, let the floral foam naturally take up water at its own rate. Never hold dry foam under water because air pockets will form inside the foam.

water and let it sink into the water at its own rate. Never quickly force a block of foam under water. Air pockets may be trapped in the foam. When properly and fully saturated with water, the foam provides adequate moisture to the flowers and foliage. Do not reuse floral foam because rewetted foam is not an efficient water-holder.

Placing Foam in the Container

The foam should be placed into the container with some of the foam extending above the rim of the container. Some stems may be placed into this

19-8. Position the foam with a portion of it above the container rim.

top area of the foam. If the foam is too short, stem placements will look awkward and too upward; if the foam is too tall, the top portion will dry out too quickly. For small arrangements, leave a ½-inch foam area; for larger designs, one or two inches of foam can extend above the container.

For foam placed into glass containers, the green foam can be camouflaged with silver foil or the appropriate color of cellophane. Corsage bags or other plastic can also be used to downplay the green color showing through the crystal vase.

Always provide a small area to add water to the arrangement. For round

19-9. Foil or colorful cellophane can camouflage green foam placed into glass containers.

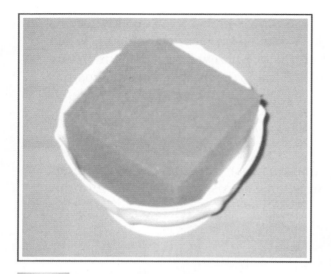

19-10. The foam should not completely fill the container. Always allow an area for watering the arrangement.

containers, the square or rectangular foam will not totally fill the space so that makes watering the arrangement easy. In square or rectangular containers, the foam may completely fill the container so a triangular piece of the foam should be trimmed out from the back of the foam to provide a spot to water the arrangement without excessive spilling.

Attaching the Foam to the Container

Foam can be secured to a container with waterproof tape, an anchor pin, or pan melt glue.

The moistened foam should be attached to the container. The foam should fit snugly into the container, but can be further secured with tape. Foam can be taped to the container with waterproof tape. The tape is available in two widths, ¼ and ½ inch, and also in three colors—white, green, and clear.

An anchor pin is an effective way to secure foam in a low bowl. An **anchor pin** is a plastic, four-pronged design mechanic that is attached to a container with floral clay (and sometimes, glue). The anchor pin allows the designer to use a smaller piece of foam positioned anywhere within the

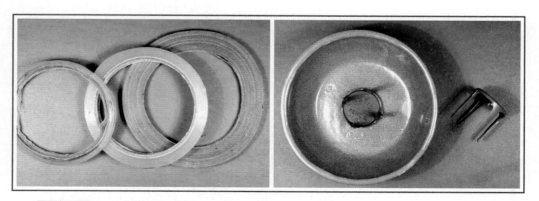

19-11. Foam can be secured to a container with tape (left) or an anchor pin (right)

container. However, if a large piece of foam is used, several anchor pins may be needed to secure it.

Glue can be used to attach foam to a plastic container or liner. The foam must be dry for this technique to work. The foam is dipped into the pan melt glue, covered with a thin layer of glue, and then immediately placed into the plastic container or liner. The glue should be allowed to cool and then the foam and container are both placed in the preservative water to wet the foam. Tip the container slightly to the side to allow the foam to take up water gradually. The advantage of this method is being able to prepare the container and foam ahead of time for a large event or party.

Other Foundations

Needlepoint holders are also useful in creating designs. A *needlepoint holder* is a design mechanic that has a heavy metal base with many sharp, closely spaced, upright metal pins. These holders, also called pin holders or frogs, are available in different shapes (round, oval) and sizes and are attached to a container with floral clay. Needlepoints are used for line designs or designs with just a few flowers. Except for designs created for the shop or an exhibition, florists do not use this mechanic because of the expense of each needlepoint and the difficulty in delivering the design.

Wire mesh, also called chicken wire or poultry netting, can also provide a support mechanic for designs. Chicken wire can be used both in vases as the only foundation or in combination with foam. The wire mesh covering the foam gives added support, especially for designs with thick or heavy stems.

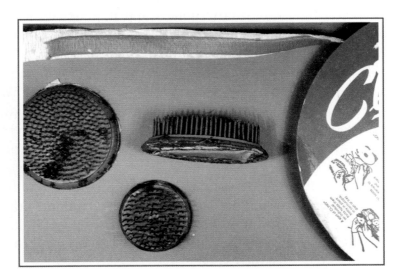

19-12. Designs can be created using the needlepoint holder as a design mechanic. The needlepoint holder is attached with floral clay.

19-13. Wire mesh or chicken wire can provide support in vases and as a covering over foam.

Other Supplies

Other supplies that may be needed in design work are greening pins, water tubes, and wooden picks or hyacinth stakes. *Greening pins* look like hairpins with an "S" or flat top and are used to secure moss or foliage in a design. Short pieces of wire can also be bent in half to secure moss if greening pins are not available.

Water tubes are small, rubber-capped, plastic tubes used for holding water and a single flower or a small cluster of filler flowers. A flower stem is placed through the small opening in the rubber cap and into the small reservoir of the water tube. Since the water tube holds only a small amount of water, the water level should be frequently checked. Water tubes come in various sizes, in green or clear colors, and are rounded or pointed. The rounded tubes may be used for boxed or packaged flowers that may be out of water for a while; the pointed water tubes are ideal for placing into floral foam. To extend the stem length of a flower in a design, a pointed water tube may be used alone to add a small amount of additional stem length. For greater stem length needs in a tall arrangement, the water tube can be wired to a wooden pick or attached to a hyacinth stake. Some water tubes are made to fit over a hyacinth stake; other water tubes can be wired, taped, or both to a hyacinth stake.

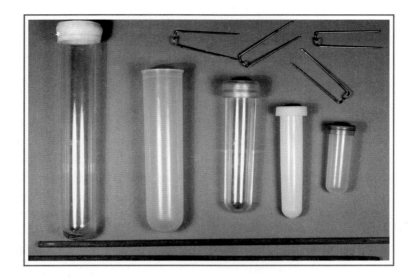

19-14. Water tubes, hyacinth stakes, and greening pins are common supplies that a floral designer may use.

A *hyacinth stake* is a long green wooden stick that is commonly used to support heavy flowers, such as hyacinths, in a flowering pot. Hyacinth stakes can also add height and give support to accessories in an arrangement.

BEGINNING WITH THE BASICS

Learning the basic design styles will help build the skill and confidence for a floral designer to tackle more difficult styles. Some of the basic design styles include bud vases, vase arrangements, basic geometric shapes, and wrapping a potted plant. A variety of vases and containers can be used to create basic designs. Glass, pottery, plastic, ceramic, metals, and baskets can all provide an interesting foundation for basic designs. Bud vases are quite slen-

19-15. A variety of vases and containers are suitable for basic design styles.

der; vases for vase arrangements are taller and wider; basic geometric designs can be created in a multitude of sizes and shapes.

BUD VASES

A bud vase design is a simple and versatile design style of one or several flowers as well as foliage. A bud vase arrangement is usually one-sided, but can also be designed as an all-around arrangement for a small dining table. Bud vases can brighten a spot on a desk, table, counter, or other small area.

Containers for a bud vase design are typically called bud vases and are commonly available in 6- and 9-inch heights. Other smaller vases make quite intimate and charming designs; taller bud vases make dramatic statements. Be sure to check if the bud vase opening is large enough to insert more than one or two stems. The vase itself may be quite beautiful but can be totally impractical for flower arranging. Bud vases can be made of glass, crystal, plastic, or metal in straight and flared shapes.

The flowers for a bud vase should be at least one and a half times the vase height. For a dining situation, the flowers can be slightly shorter to allow viewing over the flowers. Choose a shorter vase for a table centerpiece.

Suitable flowers for bud vases are small to medium-sized flowers that would be in proportion with the thin vase. Examples are roses, carnations, irises, tulips, daffodils, alstroemerias, chrysanthemums, tropical flowers, such as small anthuriums and heliconias, and all filler flowers. Foliage that is suitable for a bud vase would be all types of ferns, galax leaves, myrtle, ivy, pittosporum, ruscus (all types), small-leaved eucalyptus, euonymus, and evergreens. Large leaves, such as palms, tropical foliages, and even salal, may be too overwhelming for a small bud vase.

Bud vases may have one to three flowers or multiple smaller flowers. Most bud vases have a bow added for color, but may be designed without one depending upon the flowers used and the skill of the floral designer. The bow should be designed with green enameled wire, which resists rusting.

The bow is located in the lower part of the design, sometimes slightly overlapping the rim of the bud vase. The bow can shorten the visual height of a bud vase if the flowers are slightly short for the vase. Once the location of the bow is determined, the bow wires may be merely placed into the vase. For a more secure attachment, gently wrap the wire around the stems and twist them together in the back. The loose wire ends can be trimmed or positioned to overlap the stems a second time. For a very finished look, cover the wire with matching ribbon and tie in a knot. These secure bud vase flowers can be easily delivered or can be given away at the end of a banquet or other event. This tying technique is one way to make a small presentation bouquet.

A Bud Vase with a Single Flower

A bud vase with a single flower can be a simple yet elegant expression of love or appreciation. Any flower that is proportionate to the bud vase can be chosen.

1. Select the bud vase and fill it to within an inch of the top with floral preservative solution.

2. Select and position the foliage to form a framework for the flowers. The foliage should be approximately one and a half times the vase height. Remove any leaves that will be in the vase solution.

3. Place the single flower in the center and just slightly lower than the tip by ½ inch. If designing with a rose, be sure to remove any bruised or irregularly colored outer petals.

4. Add additional foliage near the bud vase rim to give stability to the flower.

5. Add filler flowers if desired.

6. Make a bow and place it in the center beneath the flowers near the vase rim.

7. Check the vase solution for debris or leaves. Hold the flowers firmly and lift them out of the vase. Flush out any debris by adding more preservative solution. Remove any leaves in the vase solution.

19-16. A single flower bud vase can be a simple yet elegant way to express appreciation or love.

A Bud Vase with Three Flowers

A bud vase with three flowers is a traditional favorite. The three flowers are usually all the same kind of flower, but can also be a tasteful mixture. The three flowers should have varied heights and placements, forming a zigzag pattern. A linear arrangement of flowers will also work if filler flowers are used to add variety.

1. Select a bud vase and fill it with floral preservative solution. Leave an inch space at the top.

2. Choose three flowers. Start with the tallest one and place it at the necessary height for proper proportion. Center it in the vase.

3. Vary the height by cutting the second flower shorter. Place it to the left or right of the first flower. This second flower should "zig" compared to the first one.

4. Place the third flower lower and on the opposite side of the second flower. The third flower should "zag". The lower two flowers will zigzag compared to the top flower.

5. Add linear foliage to accent the flowers. Place foliage at the container rim to add texture and stabilize the flowers. (Note: The foliage can be added at the beginning also.)

6. Add filler and a bow if desired. The bow may be placed off-center if the design warrants it.

19-17. Vary the heights and placement of three flowers designed in a bud vase.

Multiple Flowers in a Bud Vase

For a showy bud vase that expresses emotions, such as the joy of spring or the beauty of the Christmas season, several flowers and foliages can be arranged in a bud vase. The bud vase should be carefully selected with a wide enough opening to allow space for multiple flowers. The technique is similar

19-18. Multiple flowers in a bud vase are colorful, cheerful designs. Note: The lavender and pink bud vase has a double bow made with both lavender and pink ribbon. The red and white bud vase does not have a bow at all.

to the three flower bud vase with varied heights and placements of flower. A bow may be included or deemed unnecessary depending upon the design.

VASE ARRANGEMENTS

The Italians were the first to arrange flowers from the garden in a vase. Vase arrangements are a classic way for gardeners to display and feature their garden flowers indoors. Vase arrangements may be one-sided or all-around designs. The containers for this style can be various shapes and sizes, available in ceramic, glass, pottery, or plastic. Avoid extremely wide openings on some vases (some low bubble bowls) because the flowers tend to fall out easily. Vase arrangements can be designed as one-sided arrangements or to be viewed from all sides (all-around).

Tips and Techniques

Many beginning designers become frustrated when designing in vases because the flowers all fall to the outside edge. There are tips and techniques to help avoid the dilemma of the "doughnut arrangement" (a circle of flowers with a big hole in the center). Grids can be used to give some support to the

19-19. Vase arrangements can be designed to be viewed from one side only (left) or from all sides (right).

flowers. A **grid** is a framework of materials at the top of a vase that provide support for flowers in a vase arrangement. Grids may be formed with foliage, tape, or wire mesh.

The most natural type of grid that does not require additional materials is the **foliage grid**. The designer places the foliage, such as leatherleaf or Italian ruscus, into the top of the vase in a radiating pattern. The overlap of the stems forms a natural framework that will allow some control in the placement of the flowers.

The **tape grid** is achieved by placing tape across the opening of the vase at 90-degree angles to form a support grid. The ends of the tape are secured with additional piece of tape around the outside rim of the vase. The tape color should be chosen to match the vase if possible, for example, clear tape with glass vases, green tape for dark-green or black vases, and white tape for white or light-colored vases. The clear tape can be used for any other vase colors.

Marbles and gemstones (somewhat flattened, rounded glass pieces) can also be used in both bud vases and vases to provide color, texture, and weight, if necessary. Match the color of the marbles and gemstones to the color of the flowers or foliage.

19-20. Grids, made with either foliage (left) or tape (right), form a framework to provide some control in placing flowers in a vase arrangement. (Note that a glass vase would be taped with clear tape. The green tape allows the technique to be clearly seen.)

Traditional Vase Arrangement of a Dozen Roses

Who wouldn't want to receive a beautiful vase of a dozen roses? A dozen roses symbolizes love and romance and is a very important design style to learn.

Both the one-sided and all-around styles are appropriate for a dozen roses.

Designing a One-sided Design with Twelve Roses

A traditional one-sided arrangement of a dozen roses looks very full and colorful. A one-sided design of twelve roses may be triangular or rounded in outline.

1. Select an appropriate vase.

2. Create a taped grid over the opening of the vase, using clear tape.

3. Position 8 to 10 stems of leatherleaf in a radiating pattern.

4. Remove all thorns on the roses and any leaves that will be below the water line. Remove damaged or discolored "guard" petals on the roses.

5. Position the tallest rose in the center of the back of the vase. Additional foliage may be needed to lend support. The height of the rose should be approximately 1½ times the container's height.

6. The next roses are cut slightly shorter (½ inch) and positioned to the left and right of the first rose. Add the next slightly shorter pair of roses to the left and right sides of the previous pair. The third pair of roses is cut ½ inch shorter and placed as the outermost roses on both the left and right.

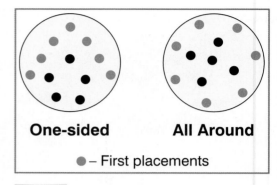

One-sided   All Around

● – First placements

19-21. The comparison of stem placements for arranging a dozen roses in a one-sided versus an all-around arrangement

7. Position the last five roses in front of the back row or "V". Center one of the roses in front of and shorter than the first rose placement. Space the last four roses to fill the remaining area, leaving room for a #9 bow, if desired.

19-22. A dozen roses can be designed as a one-sided arrangement (left) or as an all-around arrangement (right).

8. Make a #9 bow in an appropriate color, attach the wire to a hyacinth stake or unused stem, and insert the stake or stem into the design.

9. Check the vase solution for debris, flushing it out if found. Fill (don't over-fill) the vase with preservative solution.

Designing an All-around Arrangement with Twelve Roses

An all-around arrangement may be the preferred choice for arranging a dozen roses depending upon the site, perhaps in the center of a room or in the center of a table. The outline of the arrangement may appear triangular or rounded.

1. Select an appropriate vase. Fill with preservative solution to within an inch of the vase rim.

2. Create a foliage grid by positioning 8 to 10 stems of leatherleaf (or other foliage).

3. Remove all thorns and any foliage that will be in the vase solution. Remove any damaged or discolored "guard" petals from the roses.

4. Determine the height of the design, using the tallest, prettiest, or straightest rose as the guide. Trim the rose to the correct height, but do not place it into the vase yet. Trim four roses ½-inch shorter and seven roses approximately 1-inch shorter than the tallest one. Lengths will vary depending upon the shape of the vase.

5. Start by positioning the seven shortest roses to form the outer ring of flowers. Place the stems into the vase in an angled manner, not vertically. The angled placement will allow the rose to extend outward.

6. Continue by adding four roses in the inner ring. These roses should be taller than the first ones and placed more vertically.

7. Place the tallest rose in the center, forming a 1½:1 ratio of flowers to vase. The rose length may dictate a slightly shorter arrangement height.

8. Add additional foliage, filler, and a bow as desired. Check the vase solution for debris, flush any debris, and fill with preservative solution.

The traditional arrangement of a dozen roses can be varied by cutting the stems at slightly differing lengths to create a casual bouquet. One-sided or all-around vase arrangements can be designed with many different kinds and

19-23. Vase arrangements can be so versatile! The smaller one-sided design mirrors the larger design of lilies, roses, and alstroemeria. A lemonade pitcher has a colorful burst of lilies and crocosmia with a few slices of lemons and oranges in the vase solution to add to the theme. (The citrus slices contribute additional citric acid, but should be changed frequently.)

mixtures of flowers and foliages. Vase arrangements are versatile designs, adapting to a variety of locations, occasions, colors, and flowers.

DESIGNING BASIC GEOMETRIC SHAPES USING FLORAL FOAM

The most common geometric shapes are based upon the vertical, triangle, and circle. These shapes may be symmetrical or asymmetrical, traditional or casual, formal or informal depending on the occasion, the flowers chosen, and the designer's preference. This part of the chapter will discuss the one-sided basic geometric shapes that are designed in floral foam; chapter 20 will cover all-around designs, or centerpieces, in the different geometric shapes.

A beginning designer should visualize the shape before and during the design process, making adjustments if the actual shape does not match the desired goal. A simple guideline for designing is to start with the height placement, then add the width placement(s), and next determine the outermost contour. In other words, design with a plan in mind—height, width, and con-

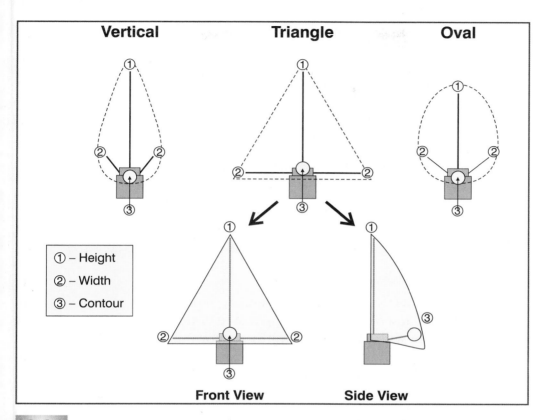

Vertical **Triangle** **Oval**

① – Height
② – Width
③ – Contour

Front View **Side View**

19-24. Beginning designers can follow a pattern of placement—height, width, and contour. The framework, created with foliage or flowers (or both), helps novices to visualize the appropriate design shape.

tour. *Contour* is the three-dimensional radiation in a gradual way from the vertical height placement to horizontal, as viewed from the side. The contour of an arrangement, viewed from the side, should be gently rounded, not steep or flat nor puffed out or pregnant-looking. These placements, in foliage or flowers, or both, create the basic shape or framework. Once the designer is more experienced, the steps become automatic and can be varied without losing track of the desired design results.

The floral foam is a great tool and should be utilized in a wise manner. Position the initial foliage and flowers, establishing the arrangement height, in the back one-third of the foam to allow proper support and to facilitate additional placements, if necessary. Symmetrical designs should have centered placements; asymmetrical designs will be placed to the left or right of the exact center. Adequate stem length should be placed into the foam to give proper support. Do not cross stems; use the left side of the foam for flowers

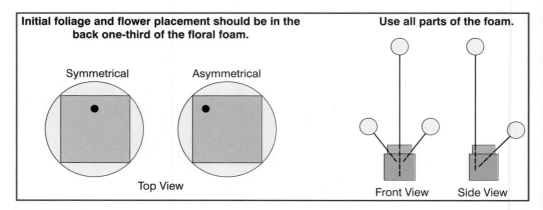

19-25. Use the floral foam wisely when designing. Strategic placements will enable the designer to finish an arrangement without the foam self-destructing (the Swiss cheese syndrome).

appearing in the left side of the arrangement and the right side of the foam for those flowers to be placed in the right side of the design. Equally spacing stem placements will allow the foam to support all of the flowers without falling apart. Beginning designers often experience the Swiss cheese syndrome—lots of holes and not much support.

VERTICAL DESIGNS

Vertical designs are very eye-catching and bold. Branches, line flowers, or form flowers placed in a linear fashion form a strong vertical statement. The width placements should be secondary to the height. Vertical designs are suitable for desks, tables, or counters with a small amount of space. Bud vases are typically vertical designs. Tall, rounded containers, as well as low bowls, can be used to create vertical arrangements.

1. Select a container and place the floral foam securely within it. The floral foam should be ½-inch above the rim of the container.

2. Place two snapdragons or three roses or bird of paradise in a vertical fashion into the foam. These flowers should be vertical or slightly leaning backward.

3. Add corkscrew willow to emphasize the height.

4. Green up the design with linear myrtle and leatherleaf.

5. Create a center of interest.

19-26. Vertical designs are eye-catching and great for limited table space or for placing on the floor.

6. Add mass flowers, if needed or desired, to fill in the shape. Do not widen the arrangement too much.

7. Add framing foliage, if desired.

8. Cover foam with moss or foliage. Green up the back of the design. Add floral preservative solution to the vase.

TRIANGULAR DESIGNS

The triangular design is a popular one for all types of occasions. It is a distinctive shape for small hospital designs, as well as large altar pieces for weddings, church services, or funerals. Triangles can be symmetrical designs (equilateral or isosceles) or asymmetrical designs (right triangle or scalene triangle). The inverted T, which can be either symmetrical or asymmetrical, is a type of isosceles triangle with a strong vertical emphasis.

Symmetrical Triangles—Equilateral and Isosceles

The equilateral triangle is a symmetrical triangle with three equal sides. The symmetrical isosceles triangle has two equal sides with greater height than width. The choice of either the equilateral or the isosceles triangle would be the designer's preference.

The steps in designing the two types of symmetrical triangles are similar.

1. Select a container and position moistened floral foam with at least ½-inch above the rim. Tape the foam to secure it.

2. Green up the triangular shape.

3. Position the height flower at least 1½ to 2 times the height of the container.

4. Add the width placements. Position the width placements in the side of the foam near the back with the stems angling slightly forward.

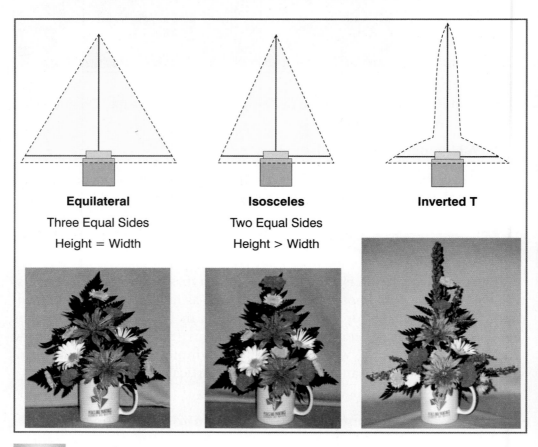

Equilateral
Three Equal Sides
Height = Width

Isosceles
Two Equal Sides
Height > Width

Inverted T

19-27. Outline of the equilateral triangle, the isosceles triangle, and the inverted T. Equilateral and isosceles triangles are two variations of a symmetrical triangle. An inverted T is a type of isosceles triangle.

a. For an equilateral triangle, each width placement should be just less than one-half the height. For an isosceles triangle, each width placement is approximately one-third the height.

b. For an inverted T, the width varies from one-third to one-half the height.

5. The contour flower may be added now (also later). From the side, determine a gentle curved contour for this arrangement. Curve the hand slightly to help in the visualization. Position this outermost flower in the front of the foam. The focal area can be completed now.

6. Next, add mass flowers to fill in the shape of the triangle. Strive for smoothly transitional flower facings. For the inverted T, the outline is not filled in. The vertical and horizontal placements are featured along with the focal area. The arrangement looks like an upside down T.

7. Add filler and additional foliage for texture as desired.

8. Green up the back of the arrangement and add floral preservative solution to the container.

Asymmetrical Triangles—Right Triangle and Scalene Triangle

A right triangle and a scalene triangle are both asymmetrical designs. Another name for a right triangle is an L-form or L pattern arrangement. Asymmetrical triangles may be created with the vertical height on the right or the left side. Asymmetrical triangles may be displayed in a more formal setting by creating one left-sided design and one right-sided design. The complementary pairs can be placed to face toward or away from a painting or other important feature.

The asymmetrical triangles have unequal materials, yet equal visual weight on each side of the vertical axis. It is important to visually balance the materials used in these designs. Begin by counterbalancing the height and width placements. The width placement of an asymmetrical triangle is approximately one-half the height. If the width placement is positioned at a 90-degree angle, this triangle is called a right triangle or L pattern. If the width placement is positioned diagonally, the triangle is an asymmetrical scalene triangle.

A right triangle may be designed in a low or tall container depending upon the occasion and location. Because of a width placement that angles

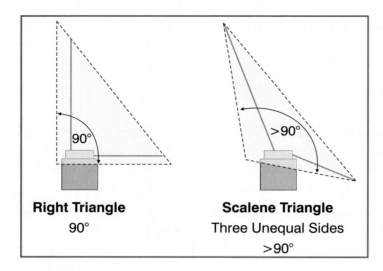

19-28. The width placement is positioned differently for a right triangle and a scalene triangle.

Right Triangle
90°

Scalene Triangle
Three Unequal Sides
>90°

downward, a scalene triangle should be designed in a tall container. If designed in a lower container, it should be placed on a base or pedestal that allows room for the width placement to flow downward.

The designing steps are similar for both asymmetrical triangles. A right-sided triangle (high on the left and low on the right) will be described.

1. Select the appropriate container and tape moistened floral foam into it in a secure way. Foam should extend above the container rim.
2. Place the linear flower in the back left side of the foam. The height should be two times the height or width of the container.
   a. For a right triangle—vertical
   b. For a scalene triangle—slightly leaning left (or right)
3. Establish the width (one-half the height) with a linear flower or filler or foliage.
   a. For a right triangle—straight out from the side at a 90-degree angle
   b. For a scalene triangle—angled downward
4. Green up the outline with foliage.
5. Add the contour flowers to form a center of interest or focal point.
6. Add the mass flowers to fill in the outline of the shape.
7. Place filler and additional foliage to cover the floral foam.
8. Green up the back of the design. Add floral preservative solution to the container.

19-29. A right triangle (left) and a scalene triangle (right) are two types of asymmetrical triangles.

CIRCULAR DESIGNS

An oval design, a crescent, and a Hogarth (or S-curve) are all one-sided circular designs. Circular designs are a diverse group of arrangements that may be one-sided or all-around. The circular centerpieces will be covered in the next chapter.

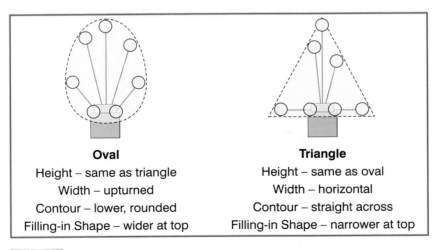

Oval	**Triangle**
Height – same as triangle	Height – same as oval
Width – upturned	Width – horizontal
Contour – lower, rounded	Contour – straight across
Filling-in Shape – wider at top	Filling-in Shape – narrower at top

19-30. Take note of the differences in width and contour placements for the oval and the triangle. An oval also has wider flower placements at the top of the design.

Oval Designs

Oval or egg-shaped designs are appropriate as small informal designs or large formal designs. An arrangement may also be designed as a round shape, although the oval shape is the more common style. The symmetrical oval and triangle should be constructed in differing ways so that they do not resemble each other. For example, the width placements vary in that the triangle has horizontal placements and the oval has an upturned, rounded placement instead of the width placements. The front contour varies also because the triangle forms a straight line across the front and the oval has a rounded shape.

19-31. An oval design can be a cheerful arrangement, suitable for formal or informal occasions depending upon the flowers selected.

Designing a Symmetrical One-sided Oval Arrangement

1. Select a container and position moistened floral foam in a secure way. Allow floral foam to extend above the container rim. Tape it in.

2. Green up the outline, judging the proper proportion for the container. Add height, width, and contour foliage. Fill in the center of the foam with foliage as desired.

3. Place the tallest flower centered in the back of the floral foam. The height should be 1½ to 2 times the vase height. The flower should be positioned vertically or slightly leaning backward.

4. Position the width flowers in an upward fashion extending from the center of the side of the foam. There should be no horizontal placements in an oval design.

5. Add the outermost contour flowers to form the rounded outline at the bottom of the design.

6. Fill in the outline starting from the top. Add flowers, such as round shapes like daisies or carnations, to widen the top of the arrangement to make it round.

7. Add round mass flowers and fillers to complete the oval design. Look at the arrangement from the side to check for a smooth curved contour.

8. Add foliage to mask the floral foam and green up the back of the design.

9. Fill the container with floral preservative solution.

Crescent Design

A crescent design is a curving C-shaped line mass that can be a cheerful expression of spring with daffodils and pussy willow or a dignified arrangement for the Christmas holidays with evergreens and holly. This design can be informal or formal and can be successfully combined with accessories like candles or hurricane lanterns. Some wedding bouquets are designed as an inverted crescent shape. A crescent arrangement is usually designed in a low container or bowl.

Finding curving material to use for a crescent arrangement can be challenging. Some branches or other foliages may curve naturally and can be easily used. Other materials, such as eucalyptus, scotch broom, ferns, Italian ruscus, and myrtle can be curved by shaping with the hands or wiring. The wiring should be inconspicuous. Flowers may also be wired to follow the curved lines within a crescent.

Designing a Crescent Arrangement

1. Select a low bowl and add foam that extends slightly above the rim. Tape to secure the floral foam.

2. Position a curving branch in the upper left side of the design. The height should be at least 1½ times the width of the container.

3. Counterbalance the height with a curving width placement in the lower right side. The width placement should be one-half the height.

19-32. A crescent design is a flowing C-shaped arrangement.

4. Add foliage as a framework for the flowers. Do not widen the arrangement beyond the C shape.
5. Position the flowers in the height, width, and contour placements.
6. Fill in with flowers and fillers to finish the C shape.
7. Add foliage and moss to cover the floral foam.
8. Finish the back of the design with foliage. Add floral preservative solution to the container.

Hogarth Curve

A Hogarth curve is an S-shaped line mass design. This geometric shape is named for William Hogarth, an 18th century painter, who said "a straight line—a line of duty, a curving line—a line of beauty." The S curve is a serpentine or gently undulating S, not a bold rounded S. The Hogarth curve is an elegant design style that can be used for formal occasions. The upright Hogarth is much more common that the horizontal style.

Designing a Hogarth Curve

1. Select a tall container and position moistened floral foam with at least an inch extending above the rim. Tape the foam to the container.
2. Select Scotch broom, sea lavender, or a leptospermum branch and work it into a gentle curve. The material can be carefully massaged into a curved shape while blowing hot air on it with your breath.
3. Position the curving material in the center of the back of the floral foam. The line should curve just like an S.
4. Counterbalance the height placement with a downward placement of the same material, placed in the center and front of the foam.

19-33. A Hogarth curve is a line mass design that is shaped like a slim S.

5. Use ferns and galax leaves to green up the serpentine shape of the S curve. Place additional sea lavender, Scotch broom, or leptospermum throughout the outer framework.

6. Position roses or carnations—first the height placement, then the repeating downward placement.

7. Add a fully open rose or large carnation at the center of interest. Group other mass flowers nearby to emphasize the focal area.

8. Position others flowers in a transitional way from the height and downward placement toward the center of interest.

9. Add foliage and filler as needed to fill and to cover the foam.

10. Finish the back of the design. Fill container with floral preservative solution.

NATURALISTIC DESIGN

A naturalistic design draws on nature and the garden for its inspiration and incorporates the grouping of flower and foliages and the use of natural materials, such as branches, stones, moss, bulbs, fruit, or seedpods. *Grouping* means to place flowers and foliages in units or sections of just one type as if they were growing that way in nature. A designer who understands how plants grow and knows the plants' relative heights to each other can add a realistic touch to the design. Think of this design as a "little niche of nature" or a miniature landscape. The possibilities and combinations are endless. A design could represent the spring woodland, the summer garden, or the autumn roadside. The designs can be designed with all fresh-cut flowers, fresh and dried materials, or a combination of fresh flowers and potted plants.

The containers used to design naturalistic arrangements vary from low baskets and bowls to saucers and trays. Moistened green sheet moss masks the floral foam and is allowed to show, giving a realistic landscape look to the arrangement. Foliages can be placed into the designs in *rosettes* with the stems all emerging from one place as if it were growing in the woodland. The rosette technique mimics the growth of ferns and other plants and is very natural looking. Use longer leaflets on the outer ring and progressively shorter leaflets toward the middle of the rosette.

Accessories, such as realistic purchased birds, nests, butterflies, and even insects, can add interest and realism to the design. Do not over-do the accessories, rather, let the plant materials be the most important part of the design.

Designing a Naturalistic Design

1. Select a basket or appropriate low container. Use a liner or make one from poly foil.

2. Position moistened floral foam in the container with just a small amount extending above the rim. For some designs, the foam can be even with the top of the container.

3. Gather sheet moss and slightly moisten for ease in using it. (Before using it, place the sheet moss in a plastic bag and spray with water or furniture dusting spray to make it pliable and less dusty.)

4. Fill in the edges of the container with moss to cover the liner. Additional moss will be used after the flowers are positioned.

5. Place line flowers, such as snapdragons or liatris, in a grouping with varied heights and angles.

6. Position a second grouping of lilies, sunflowers, or other interesting flowers. Use varied heights. One grouping is usually taller and more dominant than the other grouping.

19-34. Floral designers can use nature and the garden for their inspiration when creating naturalistic designs. A naturalistic design is a miniature landscape with grouped flowers and foliages.

7. Position additional mass flowers in groupings as needed. Place ferns in rosettes with all of the stems emerging from one "growing point".

8. Add fruit, seedpods, birds, nests, or other accessories in appropriate amounts. Accessories can be placed at the base of the container for repetition.

9. Cover the floral foam with sheet moss. Add floral preservative solution.

Wrapping a Potted Plant

Learning to decorate a potted plant is an important basic skill for a floral designer. A beautifully decorated plant can be a welcome gift or display feature. There are several ways to decorate blooming plants and foliage plants. The pot can be hidden by inserting it into baskets, containers, and preformed pot covers that look like upside-down hats and by wrapping the pot with foil or cellophane or both. Decorated pots can be adorned with ribbons, birds and nests, branches, or seasonal items, such as hearts or shamrock accessories.

Foil is available as two types—lightweight foil and poly foil. The lightweight foil is colorful on one side and silver on the other. *Poly foil* is a thicker foil with a thin plastic covering on the silver side. In addition to wrapping potted plants, poly foil is useful as a liner in baskets or containers with drainage holes or as a protective liner for containers that need be protected from moisture (metal containers). Foil is available in many colors and patterns. The designer may choose which colorful side to display.

Steps in Wrapping Potted Plants

1. Cut a square of poly foil to fit the size of the pot. Smaller pots will need a smaller square with some of the foil trimmed away. Fold one corner of the foil across to the opposing side to determine a smaller square. The sides of the foil should extend beyond the rim of a centered pot. If not, the piece of foil is too small and should be re-cut.

2. Fold the cut edges over to present a more attractive look.

3. Place the plant in the center of the foil.

4. Holding the foil in the center of the opposing sides, bring the foil up to the pot rim and tuck a small portion into the rim of the pot.

5. Bring the other two sides up to tuck into the pot rim. The points of the foil should project smoothly upward and slightly outward from the pot.

6. Smooth the foil gently around the potted plant.

7. Determine the front and most attractive side of the plant. Near the edge of the pot, insert a wooden pick (or half of a hyacinth stake) through the foil and into the pot.

8. Wrap a length of #9 ribbon (#5 for smaller pots) around the pot to hold the foil in place. Tie the ribbon with a knot around the wooden pick (or stake).

9. Attach the bow to the pick (or stake).

19-35. The steps of wrapping potted plants.

REVIEWING

MAIN IDEAS

A floral designer should learn the proper tools, supplies, and basic design styles to provide a strong framework of knowledge in flower arranging. The tools that a floral designer will use include a knife, florist shears, pruning shears, ribbon scissors, and utility scissors. With practice and experience, a sharp knife can help the designer to become an efficient and fast designer. Shears are useful for thicker stems; pruning shears provide needed strength for cutting thick branches or tough stems. Ribbon scissors should not be used to cut plant materials but should be reserved for only ribbon, netting, or fabric. Utility scissors find many uses in trimming leaves, paper, or other materials.

Floral foam is an important design mechanic for the floral designer. Floral foam is a porous material, designed to hold water and give support to stems in design work. It is available in bricks and can be trimmed any size to fit any container. To avoid waste, cut the foam brick into the fraction needed. Floral foam should be soaked thoroughly before using. Always allow it to take up water at its own rate. The foam should be placed into the container with some of the foam extending above the rim of the container and with a small open area in the back for watering the arrangement. To provide stability, the foam can be secured to a container with waterproof tape, anchor pins, or pan melt glue.

Other foundations for arranging flowers are needlepoint holders and wire mesh. Other supplies that floral designers may use include greening pins, water tubes, wooden picks, and hyacinth stakes.

Learning the basic design styles will help a floral designer to build skill and confidence to be able to tackle more difficult styles. The basics of floral arranging includes learning to design flowers in vases from small designs, such as bud vases, to larger ones called vase arrangements. Bud vases may have one to three flowers or multiple smaller flowers.

Vase arrangements can be designed with the help of a few tips and techniques, such as using a grid to avoid the "doughnut arrangement" (a circle of flowers with a big hole in the center). Grids give some support to the flowers. The types of grids are the foliage grid or a tape grid. Marbles and gemstones can be used in the vases to provide color, texture, and weight. The traditional vase arrangement is a dozen flowers, such as roses, designed in either a one-sided or all-around arrangement. Vase arrangements are very versatile and can be designed with many types of flowers and foliages.

The basic geometric shapes designed using floral foam are vertical, triangle, and circle. These shapes may be symmetrical or asymmetrical. Beginning designers should keep the shape in mind while placing the starting framework of height, width, and contour placements, in foliage and flowers.

A vertical design has greatly reduced width placements and is a dramatic design for limited table area or to place on the floor. The symmetrical triangles are equilateral and isosceles triangles. An inverted T is a type of isosceles triangle. The height should equal the width for an equilateral triangle. The height is greater than the width for both the isosceles triangle and the inverted T. Two types of asymmetrical triangles are the right triangle and the scalene triangle. The height placements for all asymmetrical triangles are placed to the left or right of center. A right triangle has a 90-degree angle width placement compared to the height; a scalene triangle has a downward width placement, and therefore, forms a larger than 90-degree angle.

One-sided circular designs include the oval, crescent, and the Hogarth curve. The width placements of the oval design are placed in an upward fashion to create a rounded shape. A crescent is a C-shaped design that employs curving materials (naturally or wired) to successfully design it. A Hogarth curve is a slim S shape (serpentine shape) that is an elegant type of design.

Naturalistic designs are a little niche of nature or a miniature landscape. Plant materials are placed in groupings and rosettes and accessories, such as stones, nests, branches, birds, and moss, are welcome additions to create the naturalistic look.

Knowing how to attractively wrap a potted plant is an important skill for a beginning designer. Potted plants may be placed in baskets or containers or wrapped with cellophane or foil or both.

QUESTIONS

Answer the following questions. Use correct spelling and complete sentences.

1. What are five basic cutting tools needed for the floral designer and what function do they each serve?

2. What is the proper way to size, position, and secure floral foam into a container?

3. Why is it important to learn the basic design styles?

4. What is a doughnut arrangement and how do you avoid making one?

5. How do you position a dozen flowers to create a) a one-sided vase arrangement and b) an all-around vase arrangement?

6. What are the guidelines or steps when designing any basic geometric shape?

7. What are the differences in designing an equilateral triangle, an isosceles triangle, and an inverted T?

8. How are the scalene triangle and right triangle different? What container choices would you make for each type?

9. Which circular design is your favorite? Discuss its construction.

10. What is a naturalistic design? What are some design techniques used in this style that are not used in geometric designs?

EVALUATING

Match the term with the correct definition. Write the letter by the term in the blank provided.

a. poly foil
b. anchor pin
c. contour
d. needlepoint holder

e. foliage grid
f. floral foam
g. water tube
h. hyacinth stake

i. florist shears
j. pruning shears

_____ 1. Small, plastic, rubber-capped container for holding a single flower in a floral preservative solution.

_____ 2. A cutting tool with short, serrated blades for cutting thicker stems.

_____ 3. Positioning leaves in an overlapping, radiating fashion to provide support of flowers.

_____ 4. Wrapping material with a thin plastic covering on the silver side to hold water.

_____ 5. Cutting tool with a sharp cutting blade for cutting very tough or extremely thick stems.

_____ 6. Side view of an arrangement showing a gradual, gently rounded, three-dimensional radiation from vertical to horizontal.

_____ 7. Porous material that provides support for stems and holds water.

_____ 8. A long green wooden stick that supports flowers and adds height to the accessories in an arrangement.

_____ 9. A weighted, metallic base with upright metal pins for supporting flowers.

_____ 10. A four-pronged plastic holder attached to a container to secure floral foam.

EXPLORING

1. Obtain three potted plants of different pot sizes (4-inch, 6-inch, etc.). Select appropriate foil and ribbons and gather wooden picks or hyacinth stakes and seasonal accessories, such as birds or holiday picks. Decorate each potted plant in an attractive and different way.

2. Gather the materials to design three asymmetrical triangles—a right triangle, a scalene triangle, and an inverted T with branches or other asymmetrically placed materials. Determine occasions and locations where each design would be appropriate. Which design is your favorite and why?

3. Create two vase arrangements of garden flowers. Try making one vase arrangement without using any grids. Was a doughnut arrangement the result? Then, use the foliage grid for one vase and a tape grid for the other one. Decide which grid was the most successful for you.

4. Gather moss, branches, and stones, as well as some flowers, leaves, and a low container for designing a naturalistic arrangement. Determine if you will design a woodland walk or spring garden or fall landscape and create a little niche of nature.

20

Designing Centerpieces and Holiday Arrangements

Flowers make a beautiful impression at a social event. Designing floral arrangements for parties, holidays, and other events is a creative challenge for a floral designer. The flowers should convey the theme and the formality or informality of the event as well as be attractive and suitable for the location. Both centerpieces and one-sided designs are appropriate for social events, depending on where the design is placed.

For an event with a definite theme, suitable accessories can add to the expression of the design. Many holidays and events, such as birthdays, anniversaries, and going-away parties, can rely on the clever use of accessories to enhance the flowers and design styles.

20-1. Centerpieces and floral arrangements can add a beautiful and festive flair when entertaining.

491

OBJECTIVES

1   Identify types of centerpieces

2   Explain how to properly design a centerpiece

3   Learn how to take a centerpiece order

4   Describe floral arrangements for holidays and themes

TERMS

binding
candleholders
conical centerpiece
contemporary design
cornucopia
novelty design
paddle wire

plush animals
pavé
pillowing
plush animals
raffia
terracing
votive candles

DESIGNING CENTERPIECES

Centerpieces have been a traditional favorite for entertaining since the English first developed them in the 18th century. Centerpieces add a colorful splash in the center of a dining table, coffee table, or banquet table. They may be formal or informal styles, traditional or contemporary, vase arrangements or arrangements designed in floral foam. Centerpieces are also called all-around arrangements because the design is colorful and attractive on every side.

Traditional centerpieces are designed to allow people to see each other across the dining table. The centerpiece should not obstruct the view at eye level. Contemporary centerpieces are designed to allow viewing over the centerpiece as well as through or under it. Topiaries and other contemporary designs may have splashes of color below and above eye level.

Centerpieces and one-sided designs can be created for the same event. For instance, centerpieces would be used to beautify the tables and a one-sided arrangement would be suitable for the buffet table that is along one side of the room. The two styles would be designed to coordinate in color, flowers, and feeling.

20-2. Centerpieces add color and interest to a table. Centerpieces are designed to allow viewing over, under, and through the flowers or accessories. Note the two diverse styles—traditional (left) and contemporary or high style (right).

TYPES OF CENTERPIECES

The shape and style of the centerpiece will depend on the dining area where the centerpiece will be placed. Round or rectangular tables are the most common choices for a dining room or banquet room. In general, round centerpieces are placed on round tables and oval centerpieces are designed for rectangular or oval tables. Centerpieces may be simple bud vases, small vase arrangements, or round or oval designs created with floral foam as the design mechanic.

Bud Vases

Bud vase designs are well suited for use on a small dining table or for placing several along a rectangular table. The designs should be fashioned in an all-around style. For an informal teacher's reception, small asymmetrical bud vases were positioned equally along the rows of three rectangular tables. Curling ribbon was used in each bud vase to create the bow and provide long streamers. Some streamers were curled and arranged on the table and some long streamers were tied to apples. The apples were placed in one's and two's informally along the tables.

Small clusters of bud vases of different types of flowers in each vase can make a unique centerpiece. Tie the grouping together with a round mirror placed underneath them. Small individual vases could also be placed at each person's place at the table.

Small Vase Arrangements

Small vase arrangements can replace the traditional round centerpieces designed in floral foam. The vase arrangements should be designed in short vases with a 1:1 proportion to allow people to see each other across the table.

20-3. Small vase arrangements are great for table centerpieces.

Vase arrangements are very colorful and emphasize flowers more than bud vase designs. Symmetrical or asymmetrical styles may be chosen according to the theme and formality of the event.

Round Centerpieces

A round centerpiece is perfectly suited to a round table. It is a popular style and can be designed with one type of flower or a colorful mixture. The size of the centerpiece should be appropriate to the table size, amount of people, and table furnishings. The round centerpiece has a similar appearance when viewed from any direction in a room.

Choose a low rounded container that suits the theme. The choices include low plastic utility containers, small wicker baskets (lined) with or without a handle, low pottery bowls, or metal containers with liners. For some centerpieces, the container may not be noticeable when the arrangement is completed.

A round centerpiece is round when viewed from above, however, from a side view, a round centerpiece may be either rounded or triangular in contour. The type of plant material and designer's preference will determine which outline is chosen.

20-4. A round centerpiece is round when viewed from above. A round centerpiece may be either rounded or triangular in outline when viewed from the side.

Designing a Round Centerpiece

1. Select a low container with a large diameter opening to allow an adequate piece of floral foam.

2. Position a moistened piece of floral foam into the container with ½ to 1 inch of foam extending above the container rim. Trim off the corners of the foam at a 45-degree angle. The angled corner allows easier stem placements into the foam and is easier to mask with foliage (covering the mechanics). Secure the foam to the container.

3. Green up the container by placing leatherleaf (or other thin-stemmed foliage) around the rim of the container. Place the leaves so the tips angle slightly downward. (Do not over-do it or there will no room for flowers.) The foliage should extend an equal distance away from the container to form the round shape. The size of the finished arrangement will dictate the length of the first leaf placements.

4. Add more leatherleaf in the center of the foam to give a rounded or triangular outline and to mask the floral foam.

5. Place the tallest flower (daisy or cushion chrysanthemums) to establish the height. This placement should not extend above eye level when a person is seated at a table (under 12 inches).

6. Position additional chrysanthemums (5 to 6) to form the width of the centerpiece. Place these flowers equally around the container rim and the same distance from the center of the arrangement. Stop and look at the design from above to check for the round shape.

7. Position three to five additional chrysanthemums to begin filling in the shape. Watch for appropriate flower facings.

8. Using mini carnations, begin filling the width and contour of the design. Do not crowd the flowers. Allow space between each flower. Place a few

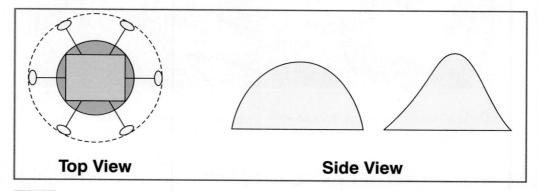

Top View   **Side View**

20-5. The top view reveals equal width placements around the container rim and equidistant placements from the center of the design (and from the container, too). The side view reveals the effect of varied width and height placements—rounded or triangular outlines.

carnations deeper within the arrangement to add depth and fullness of color without crowding.

9. Look for gaps in the outline and fill in with a third type of flower or a filler flower.

10. Cover any noticeable floral foam with foliage, if necessary. Add more foliage, if needed, in the center of the design. A second type of foliage can be added also.

20-6. The steps of making a centerpiece.

Oval Centerpieces

An oval centerpiece is an attractive horizontal style to adorn oval and triangular tables. Oval centerpieces may be created as a garden mixture, a traditional, formal design with candles, or an asymmetrical, informal design.

Appropriate containers to use are low containers that are round, oval, square, or rectangular. The container should match the theme and formality of the event although the foliage tends to mask the container in most cases.

The oval centerpiece is oval in shape when viewed from above. A low centerpiece may also be diamond-shaped from the top view. Linear plant materials are positioned at the width and outermost contour placements to create the diamond shape.

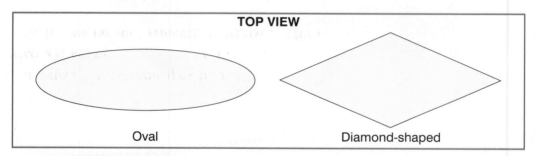

TOP VIEW

Oval   Diamond-shaped

20-7. Low horizontal centerpieces may be oval or diamond-shaped from the top view.

Like the round centerpiece, an oval centerpiece may also be rounded or triangular in outline. When viewed from the side, the contour can be either rounded or triangular due to the designer's preference or the types of plant materials.

20-8. An oval centerpiece was designed with a triangular outline. The heather was removed from the top and sides to create a rounded outline.

Designing an Oval Centerpiece

1. Choose a low plastic utility design bowl, add 1/3 brick of moistened floral foam, sculpt the foam edges by cutting at an angle, and tape the foam to the bowl with 1/8-inch green waterproof tape.

2. Green up the centerpiece by inserting two matching longer pieces of leatherleaf on each side. Green up the narrow sides of the oval by placing shorter pieces of leatherleaf and sprengeri fern. Check the shape from above before adding any flowers.

3. Add ming fern, leatherleaf, and sprengeri fern in the center to form the oval framework and to mask the floral foam.

4. Insert purple statice for the height placement, keeping the height under 12 inches.

5. Add lily buds for the elongated width placements, one on each end.

6. Place alstroemeria to form the contour on the narrow side of the oval.

7. Position a lily and bud and two peonies on each side and fill in the shape with alstroemeria and purple statice.

8. Insert ming fern and sprengeri fern to cover the foam.

20-9. An oval centerpiece can add beauty and color to the center of an oval or rectangular table.

Conical Centerpieces

Conical centerpieces are cone-shaped or three-dimensional isosceles triangles. Cone-shaped designs originated after the historical period of the

Greeks and Romans and before the Middle Ages during a period called the Byzantine period. Designs were symmetrical, conical, and formal. Although this style is not highly prevalent, the cone design is a perfect shape for a tabletop Christmas tree centerpiece or a Colonial Williamsburg design with fruit, foliage, and flowers.

Conical centerpieces are too tall to be placed in the center of a dining table, but make an attractive centerpiece for a buffet table or corner table. A pair of conical centerpieces would effectively enhance each end of a large serving table or fireplace mantle.

The mechanics of a cone-shaped design should be carefully constructed. There are two ways to make the floral foam foundation.

1. One method is to sculpt a brick of floral foam by trimming the top corners away at an angle. (The floral foam does not have to be cone-shaped because the plant materials can be trimmed to appropriate lengths to create the cone shape.) The moistened foam is placed upright in a plastic design bowl, ceramic container, or basket and secured by placing a hyacinth stake horizontally through the foam at the level of the container rim and taping or wiring (or both) that stake to the container. The excess length of hyacinth stake is removed.

2. Another method is to wrap chicken wire or wire mesh around moistened pieces of floral foam to form a cone or pyramidal shape. Waxed string or paddle wire can be used to hold the form together. The framework is securely positioned into a container and then covered with a thin layer of moss, held in place with a few greening pins. This mechanic works well for inserting heavy placements, such as fruit.

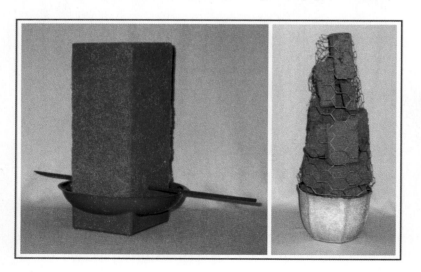

20-10. Conical designs can be created using either a floral foam foundation or a chicken wire base.

For Christmas tree designs, use evergreens that are available in the area or your yard or purchase "trimmed off" branches from a Christmas tree grower. Outstanding choices are boxwood, yew, spruce, pine, cedar, and arborvitae used singly or mixed. Color schemes should enhance the setting, ranging from traditional red and green; red, white, and green; red and gold; burgundy and pink; silver and blue; to mixed colors. The style may be formal with elegant accessories and containers of gold or silver, child-oriented with toys and lots of bright mixed primary colors, or contemporary with unusual colors and accessories.

For a charming conical buffet piece for any time of the year, form the foliage framework with salal, huckleberry, ruscus, Italian ruscus, philodendron leaves, and ivy. Moss may be used to cover any foam that shows. Add whole fruits, such as grapes, apples, oranges, lemons, limes, and kiwis, as well as cutting some of the long-lasting citrus and kiwis in halves. The original Byzantine designs, shown in paintings, used a pineapple at the top of the design. Vegetables can be added if the theme is suitable.

Designing a Conical Centerpiece

1. Gather evergreens, pinecones, flowers, ribbon or netting, accessories, and the container prepared with a moistened brick of sculpted floral foam.

2. Begin with the framework of evergreen foliages, adding 6- to 8-inch height placement and 3- to 4-inch width placements. Smaller or longer pieces can be used depending on the desired size of the finished tabletop tree. Optional, a string of lights (50 or 75 lights) can be wound loosely around the foam at this stage.

3. Continue adding evergreens to fill in the shape. Step back from the design to evaluate the shape, adjusting as necessary.

20-11. Conical designs make an eye-catching tabletop Christmas tree.

4. When the greens are 2/3 finished, add wired pinecones, appropriate accessories, and flowers, such as carnations, roses, star of Bethlehem, lilies, or fillers, such as sea lavender (to give a frosty or snowy appearance) or white Monte Casino asters (for a more casual look).

5. Fill in with additional greens if needed. Moss may be added, if desired and appropriate to the theme.

6. Adorn with ribbon, bows, or tulle, if desired.

7. Place in the chosen setting with fabrics draped underneath or behind as needed. Position suitable accessories at the base of the tree.

8. Fill the container with floral preservative solution.

ADDING ACCESSORIES

Accessories can add flair and an expressive touch to centerpieces and holiday designs. However, the accessories should be in harmony, necessary, and properly placed to be effective. Do not overdo the addition of accessories. Always ask yourself these simple questions before using any accessories.

- Does the accessory go with the theme? Is it in harmony with the style and feelings of the design?

- Is the accessory necessary? Does it form a center of interest, convey an idea, or provide a needed color or texture?

- Is the accessory properly placed?
  For symmetrical designs—centered or placed on either side
  For asymmetrical designs—off center or something tall on one side with a counterbalancing smaller object on the other side

- Have I used too many accessories? Could the design be improved with fewer items near it?

What are some typical accessories? Let's explore the choices and the methods of placing each one into an arrangement.

Candles Add Class to a Design

Taper candles are lovely additions to centerpieces. Taper candles come in many colors and sizes from 5 to 18 inches long. The 10-, 12-, 15- and 18-inch lengths are most often used in centerpieces. Choose candle lengths that will keep the flame above or below eye level. Pillar candles also come in many colors and in 2- and 3-inch diameters in lengths of 6, 9, and 12 inches.

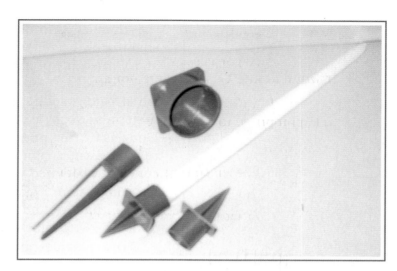

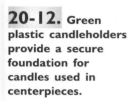

20-12. Green plastic candleholders provide a secure foundation for candles used in centerpieces.

The mechanic used to securely insert candles into a design is called a candleholder. ***Candleholders*** are green plastic devices with a round fitted top to secure a candle and a pronged base to insert into the floral foam. Candleholders come in varying sizes to fit the candle diameter being used. When designing with candleholders, hot glue moss or position leaves to cover the mechanics of the candleholder.

When using more than one taper candle in a design, be sure to place them two finger widths apart, approximately 1 inch. Candles placed closer than this will heat up and burn very fast. Candles that are chilled in the cooler or refrigerator for several hours will burn more slowly.

If candleholders are not available, tapers candles may be slightly carved to form a taper at the bottom and deeply inserted into the foam. This method leaves less foam for the flower placements. If the taper is not securely positioned in the foam, it may result in a wobbly candle. Pillar candles may be firmly placed into a design without candleholders by attaching five or six wood picks taped to the bottom of the candle with waterproof tape. Securely tape the tops of the 4-inch wood picks to the candle base. The wood picks are inserted into the foam and the pillar candle rests on top of the foam. The picks can be trimmed to a shorter length if needed.

*O**ther Accessories**

Wholesale florists and craft stores offer a wide array of seasonal and holiday accessories to place into a design. These accessories are usually attached to a wire stem for ease in adding to a design. Choose accessories that add to

20-13. Make a stem to insert a cone by slipping a heavy gauge around the base of the cone. Twist the wires tightly to form a stem. The cone may be added to centerpieces and wreaths.

the theme. Examples are birds, hearts, shamrocks, Easter eggs and bunnies, flags, and Christmas presents and other novelties. Some accessories will need to be wired before adding to a design. Natural materials, such as the cones of spruce, Douglas fir, and pine, are perfect additions to a Christmas centerpiece. Each of these cones can be wired with heavy gauge wire to form a stem. Take a 22-gauge wire and bend in half around the base of the cone. Twist the wire tightly to form a stem for it.

Fruit provides an interesting addition to suitable designs. A variety of choices are colorful and unique for adding mass, providing a center of interest, adding to a topiary or conical design, and attracting attention in a design. Fruit can be added to a design by placing the sharp end of a wood pick or hyacinth stake into the fruit and inserting the other end into the design. For heavy fruit, add a second pick and a bead of hot glue where the pick and the fruit join. For grapes, use greening pins and/or 22-gauge hairpin wire placed between the stems. Oranges, lemons, limes, pineap-

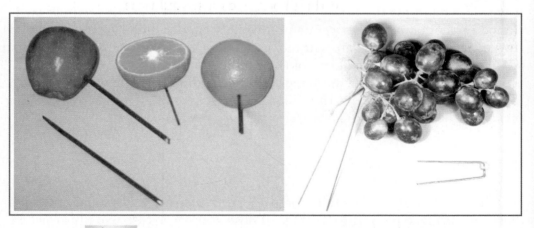

20-14. Use wood picks or a hairpin wire to add fruit to a design.

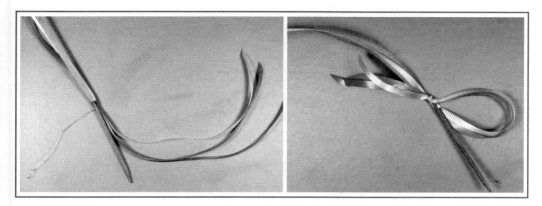

20-15. Attach balloons to a design using a wood pick and a double wiring method.

ples, or kiwis can be cut in half and placed into a design with the wood pick method. Position fruit near the container as was common for Dutch Flemish designs. Check the fruit frequently and replace as needed.

Balloons add a festive and eye-catching excitement to an arrangement. The balloon color and message should coordinate with the flowers and the theme. Balloons may be filled with air or helium but should always be securely attached to a flower arrangement. One, two, three, or several balloons can be added to a design. Add balloons to a design using the following steps:

1. Wrap the wire of a wood pick around the ribbon ends of the balloons.

2. Loop the ribbon ends back around to the wood pick.

3. Wrap the wire around the ribbon ends a second time.

4. Insert the wood pick completely into the floral foam. The wood pick will swell slightly in the moist floral foam and securely hold the balloon ribbons in place.

TAKING AN ORDER FOR AN EVENT

If someone asks you to design the flowers for an event, do not take this responsibility lightly. Much information should be gathered to insure the appropriate flower designs are provided. Remember, a beginning designer can always say "No" until more experience and skills are gained.

The following checklist is helpful to learn as much about the event as possible.

- WHEN is the event? Date? Time of day? How much time to set up?
- WHERE is the location of the event? Size of room? Ceiling height?
- WHAT is the style of the room?
- What is the color scheme of the room?
- What is the preferred style of the event? Formal or informal? Traditional, elegant, casual, or contemporary?
- What is the color scheme? Theme? (Avoid specifying flowers, if possible.)
- HOW MANY tables will need centerpieces? Table shape? Size of table? (Ask how many people will be seated at each table.)
- What is the color of the tablecloths and napkins?
- How many additional centerpieces or one-sided designs will be needed? (Centerpieces could also be used on serving tables and head tables. One-sided designs could adorn an entryway, a buffet table near a wall, or a head table with a tabletop lectern.)
- What is the budget?

The location should be visited in person if it is an unfamiliar one. Sketch the room shape and general placement of the tables, including the head table, if any. Sometimes, large hotels and banquet halls have mirrors and votive candles available for patrons to use. Ask about reserving these items, if it is appropriate to the theme.

DESIGNING SEASONAL AND HOLIDAY ARRANGEMENTS

Flowers can play a pleasing, integral part of every season and many major holidays.

- Spring — Some of the spring holidays include Valentine's Day, St. Patrick's Day, Easter, Professional Secretaries' Week (last week in April), and Mother's Day.
- Summer floral holidays include Memorial Day, Father's Day, Independence Day (4th of July), and many local festivals and fairs.

▨ Fall holidays include Grandparents Day (1st Sunday in September after Labor Day), Sweetest Day (3rd Saturday in October), Halloween, and Thanksgiving.

▨ Winter brings the Christmas season and New Year's Eve celebrations.

VALENTINE'S DAY

Valentine's Day and flowers are inseparable. Nothing conveys love and romance like flowers. Red, pink, and white are the traditional colors, but mixed colors of flowers can also convey a springy mood as well as a romantic feeling. Typical design styles are the ever-popular dozen roses in a vase, other vase arrangements, bud vases, and mixed bouquets designed in floral foam. Popular containers are bud vases, crystal vases, ceramic or metallic containers, baskets, mugs, and anything red or heart-shaped. Hearts, ribbons, candy, and balloons are all typical Valentine's Day accessories.

Designing a Sweetheart Bouquet

1. Select a red or hot pink basket with a handle. Fit it with a liner or line it with a double thickness of poly foil.

2. Cut a piece of foam to extend 1 inch above the container rim. Moisten the foam and securely position it in the basket. With a preformed liner, tape the foam securely to it. Use moss to cover the liner edges. With a foil liner, add a small amount of moss along the edges to cover the foil and wire the foam to the basket. The wire is inserted through a small amount of the woven material on the basket edge. Twist-tie the wire. Bring the other end of the wire across the moss and foam (the moss keeps the wire from cutting through the floral foam) to the other side and repeat the process. Remove any excess wire. Trim off the pointed corners of the foam.

20-16. Hearts and flowers make a great duo for a Valentine's Day celebration.

3. Green up the basket with red huckleberry, galax leaves, and leatherleaf to form a triangular (isosceles) design.

4. Position the three red roses, the top one forms the height of the design along with the tallest red huckleberry branch. Place the other two roses in a vertical line below the tallest roses in a slightly zigzag fashion.

5. Fill in the width and contour placements with genistra and mini carnations in pink and light-pink colors.

6. Position four tulips, two on each side of the handle. Do not position them as a mirror image, rather counterbalance them. Note: Tulips will continue to elongate after being added to a design. (Note, the tulip in the center of the right side—it has realigned itself upward, moving away from its original spot, which is now open just below it and to the right.)

20-17. A sweetheart bouquet speaks of love in red and pink colors.

7. Add hot pink carnations lower in the design and on the opposite side of the roses.

8. Fill out the design with genistra and carnations, using the carnation buds also.

9. Cover any floral foam that shows with leatherleaf, moss, or red huckleberry.

10. Green up the back of the design. Add floral preservative solution.

11. A heart accessory and a card with a message can be added before delivery.

EASTER AND SPRING THEMES

Easter and springtime themes go together so well. Easter designs can be 1) whimsical with Easter bunny themes or 2) spiritual with Resurrection

Sunday themes. Typical color schemes would be mixed spring colors, both pastel and bright colors. Appropriate designs and styles would be decorated Easter lilies or other spring plants, mixed flowers in vase arrangements, geometric shapes in baskets, pots or vases, and novelty designs. Suitable Easter containers would be baskets, ceramic containers of all shapes, crystal or ceramic vases, terra cotta pots (lined), novelty containers shaped like bunnies or including a cross in the design. For whimsical designs, accessories include plush animals, such as bunnies, chicks, lambs, Easter bonnets, silk carrots, radishes, or cabbages, eggs, birds, and nests. ***Plush animals*** are stuffed figures, animals, or other items that can be added as accessories (use small ones) to floral arrangements. For religious themes, the cross, a stone (the stone was rolled away), a crown of thorns, an open bible, and symbolic flowers, such as white lilies and calla lilies are all meaningful and appropriate accessories.

A ***novelty design*** is a unique whimsical, imaginative arrangement of flowers to resemble kittens, bunnies, clowns, birthday cakes, or ice cream sodas, just to name a few. A novelty design is appropriate for children, holidays,

20-18. Easter themes can be nostalgic, such as an Easter bonnet design, or religious with lilies and a cross. In the Easter bonnet design, the flowers were designed in a floral cage attached to the hat. In the lilies and cross design, the cross was fashioned from rustic fence posts and secured within a container with quick-setting concrete.

special occasions or anniversaries, birthdays, and hospital designs. Special construction techniques are needed to design these cute arrangements.

Designing an Easter Novelty—an Easter Bunny

1. Select a white 9-inch bud vase and fill it with floral preservative solution.

2. Wire a white standard chrysanthemum (football mum) with 22-gauge wire and bend the flower head slightly forward.

3. Cut out Styrofoam™ hands and feet. The feet have three toes and the hands resemble mittens. Be sure to make both a left and a right hand. (Refer to Figure 20-17) Spray the cutouts hot pink. And let dry.

4. And now—the ears. Take two white chenille stems and bend in half, shaping each one to resemble a slightly curving bunny ear. Trace each ear's shape on pink springy fabric or #9 or #40 ribbon. Fold the front sides of the fabric inward and cut out two for each ear. For the ribbon, place two lengths of ribbon together with the front sides touching and cut out two for each ear. Glue the fabric or ribbon to the front and back of the chenille stem ears. (Optional: just the front side can be covered.) Lay aside until ready to assemble.

20-19. A cute bunny is a great novelty design for Easter.

5. Position the hot pink feet in front of the bud vase. Cut out slightly to match the rounded shape of the bud vase. Hot glue or use a floral adhesive to attach the feet to the bud vase. Be sure that the feet are firmly attached before proceeding.

6. To make the tail, use quilt filling, called polyester cotton, to form a round ball. Spray it hot pink, let it dry, and glue to the back of the bud vase.

7. Place the white mum in the vase with the slightly angled stem facing forward. Wedge a small piece of Styrofoam on each side of the stem to support it. (The Styrofoam should be hidden by the bow.)

8. Using either a white or pink chenille stem, wrap it around the stem two times to form the arms. Cut the "arms" to the same length and insert each end into a hand.

9. Slide the ears in between the petals of the mum to determine the best location. Hot glue the ears to the mum, placing the ears deeply within the petals to give support. The ears should stand upright.

10. Next, the face—Use eyes purchased from a craft shop or wholesale florist or cover two corsage pins with pink floral tape. For the nose, spray a small white pompon mum a hot pink color; remove the stem when dry. For the mouth, fashion a 3-inch piece of pink chenille stem (spray it hot pink). Lay each part on the face of the mum. Adjust as needed and hot glue in place.

11. Add a bow with streamers to make a festive bow tie.

Designing an Easter Basket with a Plush Bunny

1. Select a pastel basket with a handle and a liner. Position the moistened floral foam securely into the basket and tape it to the liner.

2. Green up the design to form a one-sided equilateral triangle suitable for an Easter buffet table.

3. Add the yellow foxtail lily (snapdragons or other line materials can be substituted) to form the height (1½ times the width of the basket).

4. Insert the width placements, both carnations and alstroemerias.

5. Place mini carnations to form the outermost contour in front of the handle.

20-20. A plush bunny can be added to an Easter basket or other special arrangement.

6. Cover the back (or lower part) of the Easter bunny (plush animal) with a corsage bag (to keep the toy dry). Wrap the plush animal two or three times with paddle wire, twist the wires and cut them shorter to form a stem, and insert into the design on the right side.

7. Add four or five roses to form the top part of the triangle. Add two more line materials to form the shape on the left side.

8. Fill out the right side of the triangle with alstroemeria and the left side with statice. Add some deeper statice placements. Add carnations to complete the triangle.

9. Add more foliage, as needed, to cover the foam.

10. Cover the back of the design and fill the container with floral preservative solution.

MOTHER'S DAY

Mother's Day was first celebrated on the second Sunday in May in Lincoln, Nebraska, in 1908 and quickly caught on as a wide spread holiday in other states. What better way to honor Mother than with a beautiful bouquet of flowers? Spring colors as well as monochromatic schemes are good choices. Corsages and many types of designs are excellent gifts for Mother on her day. Suitable containers include teapots, teacups, mugs, ceramic and pottery containers, watering cans, pots, or other containers with a gardening theme, and baskets. Birds and nests, soaps and sachets, picture frames, garden tools or novelty items, and jewelry are accessories to add to Mother's Day designs.

Designing a Spring Basket with Plants

Potted plants and cut flowers are a welcome springtime combination a for Mother's Day design. Designs of all sizes can incorporate plants. The pot is covered with a corsage bag or larger plastic bag to keep the floral preservative solution in the floral arrangement from mixing with the soil that may drain from the potted plant. The plastic bag also keeps the plant from becoming over-watered.

1. Select a low basket with a liner. Add saturated floral foam to the basket, leaving adequate space for adding two pansy plants.

2. Cover the containers of the two pansy plants with corsage bags and place both plants in the basket. Place one in the front on the left side and one in the center of the right side.

20-21. Add plants to a floral design to increase the enjoyment. Cover the container of the potted plant with plastic.

3. Green up the basket with huckleberry, salal, and leatherleaf in an informal rounded shape.

4. Add pussy willow to give height on the upper left side. Add a stem or two on the lower right side.

5. Add heather in a radiating manner to define the rounded shape.

6. Position white daisy chrysanthemums and yellow freesias to fill the round shape.

7. Insert some purple statice to add color and depth. Tuck a few sprigs deeper into the design.

8. Cover the foam with foliage and moss. Green up the back of the design.

9. Fill the container with floral preservative solution. **Do not water the plants with this solution.** Check the plants' soil for dryness before watering.

A Spring Contemporary Design

A new and creative design style, called contemporary design or free style, may be a pleasing change for a Mother's Day arrangement. *Contemporary design* is a term that describes an arrangement that is designed using the latest trends in floral design. Contemporary design is imaginative and bends some of the principles of design. It may be one-sided or all-around. Some of the techniques used in contemporary design are grouping, binding, pillowing, pavé, and terracing. Grouping plant materials together is also used in naturalistic designs. *Binding* is a technique of physically tying stems together for physical support and beauty. *Pillowing* describes the technique of placing flowers very low and close together within a design. These clusters form peaks and valleys like a landscape. *Pavé* is a technique of positioning plant materials very close together to cover the foam in organized lines or areas. Pavé is a jeweler's term that refers to jewelry with stones placed so close together that no metal shows. *Terracing* means to place plant materials in a series of different levels, one above another. For example, galax leaves can be placed horizontally on the side of a design with five or six leaves placed in a stair-step fashion.

1. Select a low bowl and place saturated floral foam with an inch extending above the container rim.

2. Insert a calla lily on the upper left side, using a 3:1 proportion to the container width. Place a second calla low and on the right side. Use the

binding technique to tie the removed stem of the second calla in a diagonal way between the two calla lilies. Use natural raffia. ***Raffia*** is the fiber of a palm tree (*Raphia ruffia*) used like string or ribbon to tie things together. It is available in many colors.

3. Insert three pussy willow stems for an interesting line.

4. Use the pillowing technique to place four roses in the center and close to the floral foam.

5. Group sweet peas on the left side and low in the back. Use groupings of seeded eucalyptus on both sides of the roses and in the back.

6. Add salal leaves on the lower right side and to the back left side to cover foam and continue the line of the calla stem.

7. Cover any foam that shows with moss.

20-22. A spring contemporary design is creative, imaginative, and may bend some of the principles of design. Grouping, binding, and pillowing are techniques used in this design.

AUTUMN HOLIDAYS AND THEMES

Autumn is a time of rich, beautiful colors, combined with the grains and fruits of the harvest. Halloween, Thanksgiving, and many harvest themes are all inspiring for the floral designer. Warm colors predominate, as well as rustic or pottery containers and baskets. Containers fashioned from pumpkins and cornucopias are quite common for this time of year. Accessories center around trick or treating (Halloween) or the harvest season (Thanksgiving).

Designing a Halloween Centerpiece in a Pumpkin

1. Select a small to medium-size pumpkin. Cut a large opening and clean out inside. Save the pumpkin "cap" with stem to add as an accessory later. Carve a Jack-o-lantern face, if desired.

20-23. A lined pumpkin is a fun and appropriate container at Halloween.

2. To absorb excess moisture, add a small amount of silica sand inside the pumpkin. Line the pumpkin with a plastic bag, overlapping the rim slightly with the plastic. Cut the moistened foam to fit snugly, leaving 1 inch above the rim and an area to water the arrangement.

3. Green up the design to create a round centerpiece.

4. Using fall mums in bronze and gold colors and orange safflower, fill in the round centerpiece shape. The outline may be triangular or round.

5. Add fall leaves, acorns (hot glued to a 22-gauge wire), and a branch (optional).

6. Add foliage to cover the foam. Fill the plastic liner with floral preservative solution without watering the pumpkin.

7. Check the pumpkin frequently for signs of softness or decay. The pumpkin should last a week and should then be discarded. Transfer the centerpiece to a clay pot or basket with a liner.

Thanksgiving Centerpiece

A cornucopia is the traditional Thanksgiving centerpiece container. A *cornucopia* is a cone or horn-shaped container; it is also called a horn of plenty. The finished arrangement should look as if an abundance of the harvest is flowing out of the container. The cornucopia arrangement shape re-

20-24. A cornucopia centerpiece is traditional for Thanksgiving. The centerpiece is one half of an oval shape with the container forming the other half.

sembles one half of an oval centerpiece. Add accessories to enhance the harvest theme, such as grains, leaves, gourds, pumpkins, and decorative corn.

1. To design in a wicker cornucopia or horn of plenty, place a low saucer with a moistened piece of floral foam on the lip of the horn. Hot glue and/or wire the saucer securely to the cornucopia.

2. Green up the oval shape.

3. Add wheat to elongate the oval. Add colorful fall mums and golden alstroemeria to fill out the oval shape.

4. Insert wheat throughout the centerpiece to unify the design.

5. Add floral preservative solution by placing the arrangement near a sink and carefully watering it. Allow time to drain or dry any spills with a towel.

CHRISTMAS

The Christmas season is a glorious time of lights, tinsel, and pine. Red and green are the traditional colors but color schemes may vary depending upon the décor of the person's home. Burgundy and gold, silver and red, green and white, and even maroon and pink can be Christmas color schemes. The poinsettia makes it debut as a centerpiece flower. Be sure to condition

20-25. Count the days until Christmas while enjoying a seasonal arrangement, complete with accessories.

the cut stem with very warm water. Holly and evergreens are beautiful, seasonal additions to any Christmas arrangement.

Centerpieces, wreaths, garlands, vase arrangements, and geometric shapes all have their place for this festive season. Containers include all types of vases, metallic and ceramic containers, baskets, or containers may be fashioned from toys. Suitable accessories include ornaments, a nutcracker, a nativity scene, toys, stockings, Santa Claus, elves, reindeer, angels, snowflakes, and even cookie cutters. Candles are especially popular at Christmas, including votive candles. **Votive candles** are short, stocky candles that are placed in holders (votive candleholders). Ribbon loops are another festive way to add ribbon to a Christmas centerpiece without adding a bow. Make one ribbon loop and a streamer; place a hairpin over the ribbon ends, wrapping one wire around the other. The wire becomes the stem to insert into the centerpiece.

20-26. An oval Christmas centerpiece features pinecones, ribbon loops, variegated holly, and evergreens with votive candles as accessories.

Christmas Wreath

A Christmas wreath adds a festive touch to any Christmas décor. Wreaths are also quite charming as a centerpiece placed on a table with candles or other accessories. Typical wreath decorations are a bow, ribbon flourishes, cones, and seasonal accessories. Wreaths may be designed for any season or time of the year with a variety of plant materials, including evergreens, silver king artemisia, or a variety of herbs or everlasting flowers.

Wired wreaths are designed in the same basic way with overlapping placements of plant materials that are attached to a wire frame. Mixed evergreens or other materials are bunched into small groups (3 to 5 inches in length) and wired onto the frame. The next bunch should be approximately the same length and thickness and wired with the tip ends covering the cut ends of the previous bunch. Each bunch should slightly overlap with a smooth transition in shape among all of the bunches on the ring.

Round metal wreath frames may be purchased in various diameters. A small wreath may also be fashioned from a metal hanger that is bent into a round shape. Do not untie the hanger; just bend it into a round shape. For a single ring frame, the frame should be wrapped with paddle wire at ½-inch intervals to provide friction for holding each bunch in place. *Paddle wire* is wire wound on a piece of wood; it is available in most gauge sizes. Using paddle wire makes wrapping the plant material onto the frame very efficient and fast. The paddle allows the designer to pull the wire tight to insure a snug attachment.

Christmas wreaths may be designed as circular or two-sided wreaths.

The circular wreaths are designed in a continuous overlapping fashion until the wreath is completed. The last grouping of evergreens needs to fit under the very first group and then be wired onto the frame. The advantage of the circular wreath is the wreath may be decorated as either a symmetrical or asymmetrical design. The bow may be placed anywhere according to the chosen style. The disadvantage of the circular wreath is that although the needles lay flat on one side, they may project forward on the other side. To compensate for this, attach accessories or pinecones to hold the evergreens flat.

Two-sided wreaths are designed in two parts, starting at the base of the wreath. When one side is completed, the next side is also designed from the bottom up. A bow is positioned where the two sides meet. The two-sided wreath has a design style limitation because the bow always needs to be placed at the top to cover where the two sides meet. The advantage is that the needles on both sides lay nicely due to gravity.

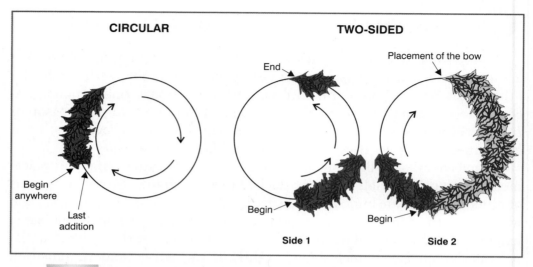

20-27. Wreaths may be designed in two different ways—circular or two-sided.

OTHER THEMES

Designs celebrating life's happy occasions may be designed around a myriad of themes and ideas. The possibilities are endless, limited only by the planner's and floral designer's creativity. The most common themes and parties revolve around birthdays and anniversaries. The birth of a baby is a popular floral theme.

Parties and social events should reflect the personality of the honored guest(s). For children, the party may center on themes like the circus, cowboys, race cars, being a princess, magic, farm or zoo animals, or favorite hobbies.

Themes based upon movies, songs, or plays could be the basis for an event. Other social events may focus on travel, ad-

20-28. A baby's birth is often celebrated with flowers (and toys).

venture, or a particular country or region. Bon voyage or going-away parties may use these themes.

Summer themes could be Garden Party, Backyard Fun, Baseball Days, Wet and Wild, or The Good 'ole Summer Time. A nostalgic theme can be challenging and unique. Near the 4th of July or election-time, patriotic themes can be quite popular. The color scheme is obvious—red, white, and blue, yet accessories and draping add uniqueness to a design.

Use your imagination to dream up ideas for parties and social events. The colors schemes, flowers chosen, design styles, and accessories help create the expression necessary to carry out the chosen theme. Be creative!

20-29. Bon voyage themes may emphasize tropical flowers, coconuts, and colorful and appropriate accessories.

20-30. A patriotic theme is a great one for the 4th of July or election-time.

REVIEWING

MAIN IDEAS

Centerpieces were developed by the English in the 18th century and have become a traditional favorite when entertaining guests. It is important that guests be able to see over the centerpiece. Typical centerpieces include bud vases, small vase arrangements, and round or oval centerpieces designed with floral foam.

A round centerpiece is round when viewed from above, but can be rounded or triangular in outline when viewed from the side. An elongated centerpiece can be oval or diamond-shaped when viewed from above, but can be rounded or triangular in outline when viewed from the side (like the round centerpiece).

The steps of making a centerpiece include securely positioning the floral foam, greening up the width of the design in a radiating fashion, and then positioning additional foliage to form the outline. Flowers are added to establish the height and then the width. The width flowers are placed in an equidistant way from the center of the design. Additional flowers are added to fill out the shape. Flower facings should be varied, showing radiating angles with no two flowers alike. Fillers and foliage are then added as needed to add color and cover the foam.

A conical centerpiece is cone-shaped or three-dimensional isosceles triangle. It can be a terrific tabletop Christmas tree or a striking design with fruit or vegetables combined with flowers and foliage. A conical centerpiece needs either a floral foam base or a chicken wire base.

Accessories can add to the expression of the centerpiece, holiday design, or theme. Be sure that the accessories are in harmony with the theme or style, necessary, properly placed, and not over-done in kinds or amounts. Suitable accessories may include candles, wired seasonal items, natural cones, fruit, balloons, or plush animals.

Before agreeing to design flowers for an event, be sure to carefully consider the responsibility and find out as much information as possible. Ask many questions about the location, theme, colors, and designs needed.

Flowers can play a pleasing, integral part of every season and many major holidays. Some of the major holidays are Valentine's Day, Easter, Mother's Day, Halloween, Thanksgiving, and Christmas. Novelty arrangements can be a fun design to create at the holidays. Novelty designs are whimsical, creative arrangements of flowers, designed to resemble an animal, a birthday cake, a clown, a person, or any other imaginative theme.

Contemporary designs may be an option for a holiday arrangement. Contemporary design is a style that incorporates the latest floral design techniques. Some techniques include binding, pillowing, pavé, and terracing.

Wreaths may be designed at Christmas and many other times of the year. Although many types of plant materials may be used, the technique for designing a wreath is basically the same. Plant materials are bunched into small groups on 3 to 5-inch lengths and wired onto the frame. The bunches should slightly overlap with a smooth transition in shape among all of the bunches on the ring. Wreaths may be designed as circular or two-sided wreaths.

Other centerpiece or design themes for parties or social events are limited only by the designer's creativity. Themes may be child-oriented, bon voyage, summer themes, or nostalgic ones. Be creative!

QUESTIONS

Answer the following questions. Use correct spelling and complete sentences.

1. What purpose does the centerpiece serve? What are some general guidelines for centerpiece design?

2. How is the top view shape of a centerpiece determined? What shapes may the outline (side view) of a centerpiece be?

3. What are the steps in designing a centerpiece?

4. What are conical centerpieces? What are some locations or ways that they may be displayed or used?

5. How do you determine if accessories should be used?

6. When designing the flowers for an event, what questions should you ask? List five.

7. How do you make a liner for a basket or container that does not hold water?

8. What is a novelty design? How do you make one?

9. What are three techniques used to create a contemporary design?

10. What are two techniques to make a wired wreath?

EVALUATING

Match the term with the correct definition. Write the letter by the term in the blank provided.

a. raffia   e. cornucopia   i. conical centerpiece
b. pavé   f. contemporary design j. pillowing
c. novelty design   g. binding
d. candle holders   h. votive candles

_____ 1. A plastic design mechanic for securing candles in arrangements.

_____ 2. Placing flowers low and close together in a design to form undulating heights.

_____ 3. A traditional container resembling a horn.

_____ 4. Physically tying stems together for artistic beauty and support.

_____ 5. Short and stocky candles that provide small pinpoints of lighting near a centerpiece.

_____ 6. An arrangement style designed using the latest trends in floral design.

_____ 7. A three-dimensional isosceles triangle.

_____ 8. Placing plant materials very close and low in a design forming patterns or lines.

_____ 9. A unique, whimsical arrangement that uses flowers to create other objects, animals, or ideas.

_____ 10. The fiber of a palm used like string or ribbon for tying things together.

EXPLORING

1. Choose a theme that is not listed in the chapter. Gather the plant materials, container and mechanics, and accessories to create that theme. Choose the appropriate design style and color scheme. Give the display a title.

2. Create a centerpiece for a family holiday. Add candles and two other types of accessories (ribbon loops, fruit, cones, unique figurine, etc.).

3. Make a novelty design of your own creation. Gather the container, flowers, and supplies. Use your imagination to create the details of the face, body, clothing, and/or shape. Gauge the reaction of a wide range of people and ages.

21

Designing Wedding Work

A wedding is a big day in the life of a bride and groom. A floral designer needs to be knowledgeable about planning and designing a wedding. A wedding consultation appointment should be a time to learn about the bride and groom and their ideas for their wedding, but also a time to help them with wedding hints and suggestions.

There are many kinds of designs that are unique to a wedding, such as bouquets, pew decorations, and other specialized floral pieces. Designing the specific flowers needed for the ceremony and the reception will make a floral designer more knowledgeable and experienced.

21-1. Flowers add to the beauty of a wedding.

OBJECTIVES

1 Describe typical wedding needs

2 Explain the process of designing a wedding

3 Identify and describe types of wedding bouquets

4 Explain how to service a wedding

TERMS

aisle runner
aisle runner tape
altar arrangements
arm bouquet
candelabra designs
cascade bouquet
chuppah
colonial bouquet

crescent bouquet
floral foam holder
hand-tied bouquet
joining point
kneeling bench
pew decorations
toss bouquet
unity candle arrangement

THE PLANNING PROCESS

The wedding planning process is an important time for the prospective bride and groom. Many decisions need to be made about the wedding ceremony and reception. An experienced floral designer can help guide the couple through the planning process of selecting the wedding flowers.

THE CONSULTATION

Once the date of the wedding is set, the bride-to-be will call for an appointment with the florist. The site of the wedding consultation should be in an area where the conversation will be undisturbed by telephones or other people. Provide a table and enough chairs to accommodate three or four people. The bride-to-be may bring the groom, or a friend, or her mother.

At the first meeting, the floral wedding consultant will find out all of the dates and times and information about the dresses and colors. It is helpful to have a wire service selection guide or book on wedding flowers to allow the bride-to-be to see specific bouquet styles or flowers. Some florists provide a portfolio of other outstanding weddings or examples of wedding bouquets designed in silk. The consultant should have a wedding order form and extra paper for sketching.

21-2. The wedding consultation area of a floral shop should have all the necessary wedding planning tools—order forms, bouquet examples, candelabra or unity candle design ideas, selection guides, and other wedding books.

The Wedding Order Form

The wedding order form is the most helpful tool for the floral designer in planning weddings. A complete order form (purchased or composed by the designer) reminds the consultant of all of the possible wedding flower needs. The bride-to-be can decide which floral pieces fit her wedding and budget. It is noted on the order sheets the person who traditionally pays for each floral part of the wedding. However, each couple may decide for themselves the payment arrangements and convey them to the floral designer.

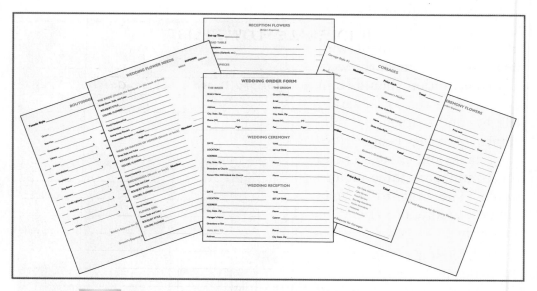

21-3. A wedding order form is an invaluable wedding planning tool.

TYPICAL FLORAL NEEDS

The order form outlines typical floral needs for a wedding ceremony and reception. Flower needs for the wedding ceremony are church decorations, the bouquets for the bride, maid or matron of honor, bridesmaids, and flower girl, and boutonnieres for the groom and groomsmen, ring bearer, and ushers. The parents and grandparents of the bride and groom receive flowers to wear; the parents may also receive a presentation bouquet from the bride and groom during the ceremony. Many other special people who are involved in the ceremony, such as a minister, musicians or soloist, attendants at the guest book or gift table, and special friends or relatives, may also be given a corsage (or boutonniere) to wear. For the reception, typical floral needs include the centerpieces, the head table decorations, cake table decorations, and other decorations as needed. Other flower needs would be the rehearsal dinner decorations.

ORDERING THE FLOWERS

Be aware of the bunch sizes when taking a wedding order. If the bride-to-be orders roses only in the parents' presentation bouquets, then just six of a

WHOLESALE FLOWER LIST

Wedding of _____   Date _____

Flowers/Foliages	Color/Cultivar	# Needed	Bunch #	Source	Cost/Bu	Total

Total Wholesale Flower Cost: $_____

21-4. A list of flowers needed for each wedding helps the floral designer to be organized and efficient when ordering from the wholesale florist.

bunch of 25 will be sold. Take orders so almost all of the roses in a bunch will be utilized. A few extra flowers may be necessary to allow for unforeseen needs, such as an extra boutonniere or a damaged flower in shipping.

For each type of design, make a list of the flowers needed. Some floral designers make a sketch of each bouquet or major design to help visualize the design and flower amounts needed. Tabulate the totals needed for each type of flower. Then, the bunch amounts can be calculated. Call the wholesaler well in advance to insure that the flowers will be available. Depending upon flower needs and availability, two or three sources (wholesale florists) may be necessary to completely fill the flower order

DESIGNING THE WEDDING FLOWERS

Once the planning and ordering has been successfully completed, the designing process begins. A few aspects of the wedding can be started well ahead of the wedding week. Pew bows can be created and supplies can be ordered and gathered. Most of the design work will, however, be done during the last day or two before the wedding.

*B*OUQUET TYPES

The bouquet that the bride-to-be carries should reflect the personality of the bride and the style of the gown and wedding. Bridal bouquet choices are the colonial, the cascade, variations of the cascade, an arm bouquet, a hand-tied bouquet, and other special bouquet designs. The flower selections will also help to define the formality and style of the event. Classic styles may feature roses and calla lilies; contemporary, high-style designs may incorporate tropical flowers or alstroemeria; traditional styles may feature carnations or daisies; elegant styles may combine rubrum lilies and lisianthus.

Bouquets may be designed in a floral foam holder or wired and taped. A **floral foam holder** has floral foam encased in a plastic cage with a handle. The holder allows a designer to position flowers and foliages into a saturated piece of floral foam, which helps the flowers to last longer. Another advantage is that the bouquets may be designed a day or two before the wedding. One word of caution is that a bouquet designed in a floral foam holder should not be thrown because of the weight and the wet mess that it will make when caught.

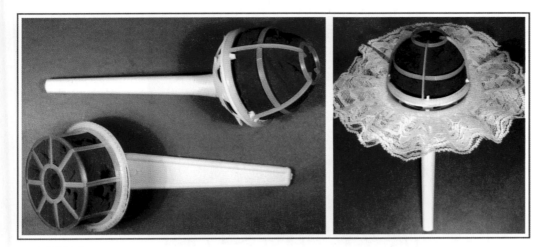

21-5. A saturated floral foam holder allows flowers to last longer in bridal bouquets.

Finishing sprays and dips may be used on the finished bouquets. These products minimize water loss and reduce transpiration for bouquets in floral foam holders or for ones that are wired and taped. Stems can be secured into the floral foam with a product that forms a tacky or sticky glue-like bond between the foam and the stems. An example is Flora-Lock™. Completed bouquets should be allowed to dry for a short time after application of any sprays or dips and then placed in a sealed plastic delivery bag in the cooler. Bouquets can be placed upright in a bud vase or bouquet stand or laid down on cushions of colorful waxed tissue before being sealed in the plastic bag. Add a mist of water to the flowers, avoiding the ribbons or bows.

Colonial Bouquets

The ***colonial bouquet*** is a round bouquet that is based on the English nosegay of the Georgian and Victorian eras. This style is popular for both brides and bridesmaids.

1. Place the entire floral foam holder into a floral preservative solution to saturate it. Allow it to drain for a few minutes before designing in it. Use a stand or a bud vase filled with water to support the holder upright to design in.

2. Add a collar of foliage around the back outside edges. Mix two or three types of foliages for variety.

21-6. The colonial bouquet is a round bouquet that is popular for both brides and bridesmaids. Colonial bouquets can be designed with a variety of flower sizes as well as ribbons.

Steps 1 and 2

Step 3

Step 4

Step 5

The Finished Product

21-7. The steps of making a colonial bouquet include greening up the floral foam holder (1 & 2), adding centered showy flowers (3), filling in the round shape with flowers (4), and adding filler flowers (5) and any foliage to cover the floral foam.

3. Green up the center of the bouquet with foliage.

4. Add a few showy or bright flowers (or the most expensive flowers—roses) in the center of the round shape.

5. Position the flowers along the outside edge to form the round shape.

6. Fill in the center with additional flowers and filler flowers.

7. Check to see if any floral foam shows and add foliage as needed. Add foliage in the back of the holder to cover the foam. A bow or lace collar can also be added in the back to cover the foam.

8. Mist, seal in plastic, and store in a cooler or cool place.

Cascade Bouquets

A *cascade bouquet* has a full, rounded central area with an eye-catching trailing line(s) of flowers and foliage. The cascade bouquet shape has many

21-8. The cascade bouquet is a trailing bouquet style that can be designed with many variations.

21-9. The longer stems of the trailing section of the cascade bouquet are wired together and inserted into the floral foam holder. The wire is hooked around the plastic cage in the back of the holder to insure that the stems do not fall out of the bouquet.

variations, including the crescent. The *crescent bouquet* is one variation of the cascade bouquet that is designed in a C shape. The cascade style is a beautiful design for elegant or formal weddings.

The cascade bouquet is basically designed the same way as the colonial bouquet with the exception of the beginning placement of the trailing foliage and flowers. The foliage and flowers are placed in a pleasing trailing manner and then wired together. The wire and the stem ends are inserted into the floral foam holder; the wire is brought out the back of the holder and fashioned around one of the supports of the plastic cage. This wiring technique insures that the heavy, longer stems will not fall out of the bouquet.

Chains or strands of florets, such as hyacinths or stephanotis, may be added to cascade bouquets

21-10. Chains or strands of florets, such as hyacinths, add a lovely touch to a cascade bouquet.

Arm Bouquets

An arm bouquet is a classic and time-honored style of bouquet. An *arm bouquet* is a grouping of flowers that is tied together and cradled in the bride's left arm as she walks down the aisle with her father.

The arm bouquet is a versatile design because it may be carried during the wedding ceremony and then placed in a vase to adorn the head table during the reception. Presentation bouquets (to the parents), or the Virgin Mary bouquet, are designed using the same technique as the arm bouquet.

1. Gather three calla lilies, three blue iris, Italian ruscus, salal leaves, corkscrew willow, a roll of floral tape, and a long, taped 24-gauge wire . Remove the lower leaves on the foliages.

2. With the left arm bent, lay two stems each of Italian ruscus and salal along the forearm, holding the grouping where the bow will eventually tie it together.

3. Position the three calla lilies in a vertical arrangement. Nestle the corkscrew willow in and around the callas.

4. Place the three iris in a triangular manner around the callas. One—in the upper right, one—in the center left, and one below the calla lilies near the bow.

21-11. The arm bouquet is a classic bouquet style. These two brides carried arm bouquets in ceremonies that were 70 years apart.

5. Add greens to form a framework around the flowers as needed.

6. Using the green floral tape, tape several times around the stems where the bow will be tied on. The floral tape will protect the calla lily stem from being cut by the wire. Adding leaves around the calla lily stems will also give protection.

7. Wire the stems securely together. The loose wire ends can be wrapped around the stems additional times or trimmed off.

8. Make a #9 bow with streamers and wire it on. Use a foot of matching ribbon to wrap around the wires once and then tie it in a knot. Trim off excess ribbon.

9. Trim the cut ends of the flowers and foliages shorter, if necessary, and at varying lengths.

10. The arm bouquet may be placed in a vase with floral preservative solution until carried. Before handing to the bride, dry the stems thoroughly with a towel.

21-12. An arm bouquet requires very few flowers to make a distinctive bridal bouquet.

Hand-tied Bouquets

A **hand-tied bouquet** is a natural-looking gathering of flowers and foliages with the stems tied together. Hand-tied bouquets may be adorned with ribbon, cording, or tulle. Any combination of flowers and foliages may be incorporated into a hand-tied bouquet. Once considered informal, this style may be designed for any type of wedding with the flower selection determining the informality or formality.

1. Gather the desired flowers and foliages. Have a taped 24-gauge wire or chenille stem ready to use. Remove any leaves on the lower part of the stems.

2. The floral designer may start with a foliage base of a few greens grouped together, such as plumosa fern, leatherleaf, or sprengeri fern. Group the

21-13. A hand-tied bouquet is a lovely style of bouquet for any type of wedding—formal or informal.

stems in a radiating fashion. (Or, the designer may start with the flower groupings.)

3. Starting in the center, begin adding flowers through the foliage framework. Vary flower sizes and look for pleasing color combinations.

4. Add flowers in a slightly angled placement as the shape is filled out.

5. Add foliage and filler as desired.

6. When the rounded shape is completed, wire the stems with a taped 24-gauge wire or chenille stem. Add ribbon to cover the wires or chenille stem. Add a bow, streamers, or tulle as the design dictates.

7. Trim the stems at even or slightly varied lengths and place into a vase with floral preservative solution. Dry the stems before handing to the bride-to-be or bridesmaid.

Other Bouquet Styles

Wedding bouquets can be designed on a fan, a muff (winter weddings), or parasols. These styles can be designed like a corsage and wired or pinned to the accessory. Brides may choose to carry a bible of their mother's or grandmother's. Bridesmaids may carry bouquets designed in a basket. A flower girl typically carries a basket of flowers with loose petals easily accessible for her to drop along the bridal aisle.

Toss Bouquet

A ***toss bouquet*** is a small, wired and taped bouquet that is tossed by the bride to one of her unmarried female friends or relatives during a traditional part of the wedding reception activities. The bride turns around and throws this small bouquet over her shoulder. The lady who catches the bouquet is then thought to be the next one to get married. A bouquet designed in a floral foam holder should **never** be used as a toss bouquet. A floral foam bouquet is too heavy and would make a wet mess when caught. The experienced floral designer will recommend this small bouquet to prevent the bride from throwing her own bouquet. The bride often wants to keep her bouquet to have it preserved (by pressing or silica sand covering), whether it is designed in a floral foam bouquet holder or wired and taped.

1. Gather small to medium flowers in suitable colors, foliage, floral tape, long 24- or 22-gauge wires, and ribbon.

2. Wire by the appropriate method 10 to 12 flowers, 8 to 10 foliage pieces, and 7 to 8 filler flowers placements.

3. Starting in the bouquet center, position wired flowers and foliage pieces together. **Do not wrap the wires around each other**, just press them together. A 28-gauge wire can be wrapped occasionally around the ***joining point*** (place where the stems converge) to keep the stems together, if needed.

21-14. A toss bouquet is a small wired and taped bouquet used during a traditional part of the wedding reception. The bride with her back turned tosses this small bouquet over her shoulder to an unmarried female friend or relative. That lady will be the next to wed, as the saying goes.

4. Continue adding flowers and foliage to form the rounded shape. The toss bouquet should have a rounded shape and contour. Add some small flowers or buds deeper within the bouquet.

5. Finish the toss bouquet by adding a collar of lace or foliage (salal wired with the stitch method).

6. Store the toss bouquet in a sealed plastic bag in the cooler.

*F*LOWERS FOR THE HAIR

The bride may choose to wear flowers on her veil. Flowers that are designed like a corsage can be attached on or near the veil. A small chaplet may be attached to the back of certain types of veils. The flowers are designed using a wreath or garland technique. The bride may also choose to have the bridesmaids and flower girl to wear flowers in their hair. These flowers may be just a simple sprig or two of baby's breath placed in the hair, flowers hot-glued to a floral comb, or a chaplet or halo of flowers. The flower girl might also wear a halo or chaplet of flowers. These flowers are designed as a garland or wreath onto a wire that is formed into a circle and pinned on with bobby pins.

21-15. At weddings, flowers are often worn in the hair or attached to the veil.

*F*LOWERS FOR THE CEREMONY

The flowers for the wedding ceremony may be as simple or elaborate as the bride wishes. Typical floral pieces include altar arrangements, candelabra designs, unity candle flowers, and pew bows or decorations. Other floral decorations might include floral designs for an arch, a chuppah, or a kneeling bench, aisle decorations, and blooming or foliage plants. A **chuppah** is a canopy under which the Jewish bride and groom stand to be married. A **kneeling bench** is requested for some weddings for the bride and groom to kneel for prayer during the ceremony. Both the chuppah and the kneeling bench may be adorned with flowers by designing in foam cages attached to them.

The floral designer usually positions the aisle runner, a traditional part of the ceremony. An **aisle runner** is a fabric or cloth-like paper covering for the center aisle during the wedding ceremony; the aisle runner is pulled down the aisle by the ushers after all of the guests are seated to create a clean surface for the bridal party to walk upon. The floral designer typically purchases it and pins or tapes it at the front of the church before the ceremony. **Aisle runner tape** is double-sided tape that can secure the aisle runner to the tile without the tape showing. If the aisle runner is placed on stairs, it should be pinned or taped to each step to avoid tripping someone.

21-16. A single altar arrangement can be centered between two candelabras for a lovely setting for the wedding ceremony.

Altar Arrangements and Candelabras

Altar arrangements are floral designs placed near the altar of the church to provide a lovely floral framework for the bride and groom during the wedding ceremony. Altar arrangements should be highly visible, large designs, including vase arrangements or designs arranged in floral foam. The colors should harmonize and blend with the overall color scheme of the wedding as well as the colors of the church. Two altar arrangements are usually symmetrically placed at the front of the church. For some church settings, a single altar arrangement may be more appropriate; a single altar piece is very appropriate when placed between two candelabra designs.

Some churches practice the lighting of candles at weddings as a traditional part of the ceremony. An evening wedding is

21-17. The floral mechanic for a candelabra design is a spray bar wired to the candelabra frame.

also enhanced by the presence of candlelight. Candelabra designs may supplement or substitute for the altar arrangements as a framing and focal area for the bride and groom. *Candelabra designs* are formal, dignified arrangements of flowers attached to candelabras, which hold seven or more candles. The flowers are designed in floral foam cages or floral foam spray bars that are attached to the candelabra. The design is similar to a sympathy easel design.

Another traditional arrangement placed on or near the altar is the unity candle arrangement. A *unity candle arrangement* is usually a low, horizontal centerpiece with a centered candle that the couple light during the wedding ceremony to symbolize their union in marriage. Several types of special pillar candles are available to purchase for placing in unity candle arrangements.

21-18. A unity candle arrangement is a low, horizontal centerpiece with a centered candle that the bride and groom light during the wedding ceremony to symbolize their union in marriage. This unique arrangement also has the bride and groom's candles within the design.

Pew Decorations

Another unique feature of a wedding is the decoration of pews. ***Pew decorations*** are bows, flowers, or floral designs that are attached to the end of the pews in the aisle where the bridal party walks. Some pew decorations are more elaborate to denote the family pews. Bows do not have to be placed on every pew. In fact, adding decorations on every other or every third pew can be just as decorative and effective. Some brides may wish to decorate only the family pews.

21-19. Typical pew decorations are bows with long streamers. Floral pew decorations can be designed in a floral foam holder specifically for pews.

Bows may be designed with #9 or #40 or a combination of widths and colors to match the wedding colors. The bows should have long streamers. Tulle adds a soft romantic look. The bows should look uniform and should be designed by the same person or two persons with the same style. Attach the bows carefully to the pews with tape or a rubber band. The rubber band (subtle, blending color to the pew) is placed horizontally around the pew end with the bow attached to the rubber band. Flowers may be attached to the bow for a more floral effect. For a larger floral effect, use a floral foam mechanic designed to create pew decorations. Floral pew decorations are usually one-sided with an upright or rounded shape, as well as some trailing or cascading foliage, such as ivy or ferns.

Guest Book

The guest book is a standard feature at every wedding. Sometimes, the table upon which the guest book is placed is too small for any flowers so a bow is the only decoration. If the table is large enough, a basket of flowers or other suitable centerpiece design can be placed on it to attract the guests' attention. The attendant can then ask each guest to sign the register.

RECEPTION FLOWERS

The floral decorations for the reception can be as varied as each bride's personality. The location also dictates many of the floral features. Common reception decorations are centerpieces at the guests' tables, the head table decorations, the cake table decorations, and possibly an entryway feature, such as an arch.

21-20. A colorful basket of flowers can adorn a guest book table.

Head Table Decorations

The head table is a place of honor for the bridal party. Head table decorations enhance the setting for the bride and groom. Typical head table decorations are centerpieces often featuring the bride's and bridesmaids' bouquets and floral garlands. Garlands of similax or sprengeri fern can be purchased from the wholesale florist, which is a time-saver for the floral designer. The garlands are draped across the front of the head table. Flowers and ribbons may be hot-glued into the garland for touches of matching wedding colors.

21-21. A head table or cake table can be adorned with garland and flowers.

Small bouquets or clusters of flowers are attractive adorning the table and garland. The garlands are securely pinned to the table skirting. Manufactured table clips can be purchased to attach the garland.

Cake Table Decorations

The wedding cake is a focal point at the reception. The cake table decorations should all revolve around the wedding cake to emphasize it, not distract from it. The wedding cake can be enhanced with flowers placed on top and with foliage and loose flowers at the base. Cakes with tiers might have flowers on each tier. The flowers can be designed like corsages or in a floral foam base. Do not place the flowers directly on the cake; place the flowers on a doily or a plastic separator, which can be provided by the baker.

Depending upon the style of the wedding, garland is also appropriate to decorate the cake table. Small flowers can be hot-glued into the garland. Sometimes, the toasting glasses and the cake knife are decorated with a small bow or small floral accent. If a punch bowl is placed on the cake table, the base of the bowl can be decorated with flowers that coordinate with the cake base flowers.

21-22. The flowers for the cake top can be designed in a special container designed for that purpose or in a small floral foam foundation.

Other Reception Decorations

An entryway arch into the reception might be included in the reception area decorations. Flowers for an arch can be designed as presentation bouquets (like the arm bouquet) and attached by tying with ribbon. Hidden water tubes will extend the lasting qualities of the flowers. Flowers may also be added to an arch by inserting them into a moistened floral foam cage or spray bar that is securely attached to the top or sides of the arch.

Potted plants are a nice feature when grouped around a small stage area, near the arch, or an entryway. The containers should be foil or fabric wrapped with bows in appropriate colors.

SERVICING A WEDDING

The florist is responsible for delivering the wedding flowers to the ceremony and to the reception site. The reception site requires more set-up time because of the cake flowers and garlands. Many florists and wedding consultants offer additional services for a fee, that is, servicing a wedding. Servicing a wedding includes helping with the details of distributing the flowers, pinning on corsages and boutonnieres, lighting the candles as needed, positioning the aisle runner, working with the bridal party on the proper holding of the bouquets, and possibly transporting wedding ceremony flowers to the reception.

The floral wedding consultant should direct the bridal party to hold the bouquets in a relaxed manner with the arms slightly bent at the elbows and near the waistline. The flowers should face outward, not downward. If the bouquet is designed in a foam bouquet holder, the holder should be held angling downward (never to the side).

A servicing kit is a recommended item for the wedding consultant who services weddings. The kit allows a floral designer to have extra items that might be needed by the bridal party before the wedding. Items can be carried in an unobtrusive carry-all, tackle box, or other type of box or basket with a handle.

Items to Include in a Wedding Servicing Kit
Extra pins (corsage, boutonniere, straight, and safety)
Bobby pins, floral combs, comb, hair spray
Florist knife, shears
Scissors, extra ribbon
Floral tape, wires, chenille stems
Small glue gun and extra glue sticks
Matches or lighter
Needle and thread, extra buttons
Anti-static spray
Tissues, moist toilettes, anti-stain toilettes
Aspirin, antacid tables, chewing gum, breath mints
Small first aid kit
Fingernail polish or extra pair of nylons

Other Items to Bring When Servicing a Wedding
Small rechargeable hand vacuum
Dust pan and hand broom
Drop cloth (for easy clean-up when designing on-site)
A small vase for extra flowers

21-23. Items to include in a Wedding Servicing Kit

REVIEWING

MAIN IDEAS

A wedding is an important day for the bride and groom. Planning is vital to the success of a beautiful wedding. The floral designer becomes a wedding consultant to help the couple choose the flowers for the big day. The wedding consultation site should be in an area where conversation will be undisturbed by telephones. Selection guide and books of wedding flowers are helpful to guide the bride-to-be's decisions.

The wedding order form is the most helpful tool for the floral designer in planning weddings. Typical floral needs for the wedding ceremony are church decorations, the bouquets for the bride and her bridal party, boutonnieres for the groom and his party, and corsages and boutonnieres for family and special people or attendants during the ceremony. For the reception, typical floral needs include the centerpieces, the head table decorations, cake table decorations, and other decorations as needed. The rehearsal dinner will also warrant some floral decorations.

The efficient floral designer will make a detailed list of flowers needed for each design, tabulate the totals, calculate the number of bunches, and call the wholesale florists in advance.

The bouquets, which the bride-to-be may choose for her and her bridal party are a colonial bouquet, a cascade bouquet with many variations, including a crescent bouquet, an arm bouquet, and a hand-tied bouquet. Bouquets may be wired and taped or designed in a floral foam holder.

The colonial bouquet is a round bouquet, suitable for both the bride and her bridesmaids. The cascade bouquet has a full, rounded central area with a trailing line(s) of flowers and foliage. The cascade bouquet can be designed with many variations, including the crescent bouquet. An arm bouquet is a classic style with a grouping of flowers that are tied together; the bouquet is cradled in the bride's left arm. A hand-tied bouquet is a natural-looking gathering of flowers and foliages with the stems tied together. Other bouquet styles include bouquets designed on a fan, a muff, a parasol, a bible, or in a basket.

A flower girl may carry a basket or small bouquet with loose petals easily accessible to her to drop along the bridal aisle. A toss bouquet is a small wired and taped bouquet that is tossed by the bride to one of her unmarried female friends or relatives during a traditional part of the wedding reception activities.

The bride or bridesmaids may wear flowers in the hair. A chaplet, a small floral comb, or just a few sprigs of baby's breath in the hair add to the beauty of the bridal party.

The flowers for the ceremony include altar arrangements, candelabra designs, unity candle flowers, and pew bows or decorations. Other floral decorations might include adorning an arch or a chuppah, a traditional canopy under which a Jewish bride and groom stand to be married. An aisle runner is also a traditional part of many wedding ceremonies.

The reception flowers include decorating the head table with centerpieces (often, the bride's and bridesmaids' bouquets) and garlands. Garlands are gracefully draped along the front of the table. Flowers and ribbons can be added by hot-gluing them.

The cake table decorations are another part of the reception flowers. A cake top of flowers and a base of greens and loose flowers add color and beauty to the reception. Other reception decorations may include placing flowers on an entryway arch and positioning green and blooming plants.

Servicing a wedding means to help with the details of distributing and pinning on personal flowers, positioning the aisle runner, lighting candles, and helping the bridal party with the proper way to hold the bouquets. Bouquets should be held with the arms slightly bent and near the waist; the bouquet should be held with the flowers facing outward (not downward). A servicing kit is a recommended item for the floral designer who services weddings.

QUESTIONS

Answer the following questions. Use correct spelling and complete sentences.

1. What takes place during a wedding consultation? What supplies or items are helpful when consulting on weddings?
2. Why is a complete wedding order form indispensable?
3. Before calling the wholesale florist, what is the process of determining wedding flower needs?
4. Why are finishing sprays and dips used?
5. What is a cascade bouquet? What are some variations of this style? Use sketches when needed.
6. How is an arm bouquet different from a hand-tied bouquet?
7. What are two advantages and two disadvantages of designing a bouquet in a foam bouquet holder?
8. What are some typical wedding ceremony flowers? Be thorough.
9. What are some typical reception flowers?
10. Why is servicing a wedding necessary?

EVALUATING

Match the term with the correct definition. Write the letter by the term in the blank provided.

a. cascade bouquet
b. toss bouquet
c. joining point
d. pew decorations

e. arm bouquet
f. hand-tied bouquet
g. candelabra designs
h. aisle runner

i. foam bouquet holder
j. colonial bouquet

_____ 1. A plastic cage filled with floral foam with a handle.

_____ 2. A trailing bouquet from a full, rounded center.

_____ 3. A round bouquet.

_____ 4. A floral arrangement attached to a candle-holding framework, used to enhance the wedding ceremony and feature the bride and groom.

_____ 5. A small, wired and taped bouquet designed for use at the reception during a traditional activity with the bride and her single female friends and relatives.

_____ 6. The place where the stems converge.

_____ 7. A natural-looking gathering of flowers and foliage, tied together with ribbon or string.

_____ 8. Bows, flowers, or floral designs placed along the aisle where the bride and groom walk into the ceremony.

_____ 9. Fabric or covering for the center aisle during the wedding ceremony.

_____ 10. A vertical placement of flowers and foliage tied together physically and visually with a bow.

EXPLORING

1. Go to your church and sketch the floor plan of the sanctuary. Sketch the location of two candelabra designs, an altar arrangement, a unity candle design, and pew decorations.

2. Purchase two foam bouquet holders. Gather flowers and foliage to design a colonial and a cascade bouquet. Moisten the bouquet holder and create both styles of bouquets. Note the amount of flowers and foliage used. Which design do you prefer?

3. Sketch a three-tier wedding cake centered on a round table with skirting. Design a cake table. List the colors, chosen flowers, and supplies needed. Sketch your idea.

4. Create a timeline of activities that the floral designer must complete from the time the bride-to-be has her initial wedding consultation with you until the wedding flowers are delivered and set up. Refer to other chapters if necessary.

22

Designing Sympathy Flowers

Flowers play an important part in the grieving process. Their beauty and colors can symbolize love, respect, and thoughts of sympathy and concern. Sympathy flowers give a comforting presence to the bereaved person's family at the visitation and funeral services. Typical sympathy pieces come in many styles and types, such as casket sprays, baskets of flowers, sprays, set pieces, and wreaths. A floral designer should be knowledgeable about design types and construction when designing flowers for funerals.

22-1. Sympathy flowers are important to honor the deceased and comfort the living.

OBJECTIVES

1 Explain the importance of sympathy flowers

2 Identify and describe typical sympathy pieces

TERMS

casket saddle
casket inset piece
casket spray
dish garden
easel
easel spray
fireside basket
flat spray
full couch

full-couch casket spray
full-couch lid spray
half couch
half-couch casket spray
papier-mâché
set piece
standing spray
sympathy flowers

IMPORTANCE OF SYMPATHY FLOWERS

Sympathy flowers are flowers that are sent to a funeral home or a funeral service to honor the deceased or to comfort the bereaved. Flowers add warmth, vitality, and a softening garden-like presence to the uncomfortable atmosphere before and during the funeral service. Research by the American Floral Endowment and the Society of American Florists Information Committee concluded that flowers at the funeral home and funeral service serve the important roles of honoring the life of the deceased and giving comfort and some relief or softening of sorrow for the living.

TYPICAL SYMPATHY FLOWER DESIGNS

Typical sympathy flowers include the family flowers, which are ordered by the family to honor their loved one. The family flowers typically include the casket spray, a casket inset piece (usually from younger family members), and sometimes a matching arrangement. A particularly attractive setting occurs when the family orders two matching arrangements for either side of the casket.

When the family comes to the floral shop to order family flowers, the tactful florist will find a quiet or private area for the family to make their decisions. Treat the family in a tactful, compassionate, business-like fashion to guide them through their decisions. Provide books and selection guides to make the process an easier one.

Other sympathy flowers include arrangements, basket designs, easel and flat sprays, and set pieces, such as wreaths, organization symbols, hearts, or crosses. Blooming and foliage plants as well as dish gardens are also typical sympathy expressions. A *dish garden* is a grouping of different types of plants potted in the same container. Flowers in water tubes, accessories, and bows are often added to decorate plants. The most popular expressions of sympathy vary from region to region. When sending sympathy flowers as a wire order to another area, check the selection guide to choose the most appropriate type.

CASKET SPRAYS

A ***casket spray*** is a floral arrangement that is placed on the top of a casket during a funeral service. A casket spray is ordered and sent by the immediate

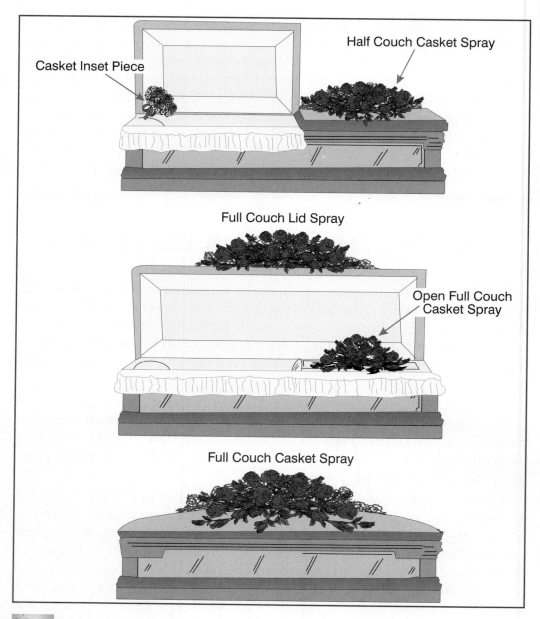

22-2. The types of casket sprays ... A half-couch casket spray has the most widespread usage throughout the country. The full-couch casket spray has two variations for flower placements.

family members. The type of casket determines the size of the casket spray. Caskets are available as half couch and full couch.

A *full couch* is a casket with a one-piece lid, which may be closed or open. An open full couch has an inner lid on the right side. A *full-couch casket spray* is a large casket piece that is placed in the center of a closed full couch. A *full-couch lid spray* is a large casket piece placed in the center of the open lid of a full couch. The full-couch lid design is placed in a stand (hidden by the lid) that displays the spray sideways or is attached to the wall by a bracket on the wall. A smaller casket spray may be placed on the inner lid. Full-couch casket sprays range from 4 to 5 feet wide or wider. (The typical casket is slightly longer than 6 feet.)

A *half couch* is a casket with a two-piece lid; the head (left side) of the half couch is open during the visitation services. A *half-couch casket spray* is a floral piece that is placed on the right side of a half couch. A half-couch casket spray should be at least a yard wide (3 to 3.5 feet).

Half-Couch Casket Spray

The foundation for a casket spray is a *casket saddle*, a container with a rounded base, which fits the curving contours of a casket lid. Casket saddles are molded plastic and available in many sizes and shapes. The flowers and foliage should completely cover the saddle.

The shapes of a half-couch casket spray may be an oval (or fan), crescent, or triangular (or T-shaped). These designs should be low (12 to 14 inches) to allow transporting by the funeral director. Script denoting the relationship of the deceased (such as, Loving Wife, Dear Husband) is often attached to the long streamer on the bow.

22-3. A casket saddle has a rounded base to fit the contour of a casket lid.

1.	Position the brick(s) of floral foam to fit the casket saddle, moisten, and securely attach to saddle (by accompanying supports or by taping).

2.	Green up the outline of the design—oval (or fan), crescent, or triangular (or T-shaped). Use a combination of greens, such as salal, leatherleaf, flat fern, or huckleberry, to form the basic framework. Finer textured foliages, such as sprengeri fern, tree fern, and ming fern, can add softness and interest.

3.	Add flowers to form the width and contour placements. Some flowers should angle toward the back of the design. Some casket sprays will be viewed from the back.

4.	Add the center of interest flowers, such as fully open or unique ones.

5.	Place the bow in a central or slightly off-centered position. Some designers make a bow from individual loops and streamers wired to wood picks that are placed in a composite way to form the look of a bow.

22-4. Half-couch casket sprays may be designed as oval (or fan), crescent, or triangular (T) shapes.

6. Place additional mass or form flowers in a radiating pattern to fill in the desired outline.

7. Add filler flowers and additional foliage as needed to complete the shape, add softness, and cover the floral foam.

CASKET INSET PIECE

The family often orders a casket inset piece to coordinate with the colors and styles of the other family floral pieces. A ***casket inset piece*** is a small design displayed inside the casket lid. This design is traditionally sent from the younger family members—children or grandchildren. The casket inset piece may be designed like a corsage and placed on a satin pillow, heart, or cross. Some satin forms come with a floral foam mechanic attached to it. Other options are covering Styrofoam™ shapes (a cross or heart) with flowers by gluing or pinning. Another casket inset piece is a floral rosary, which may be used for the service of a devout Catholic. Rosary forms are available at the wholesale florist. The form has cone-shaped clamps to place around rose buds (or carnations). The floral rosary is draped and secured to the fabric in the lid of the casket by the funeral director.

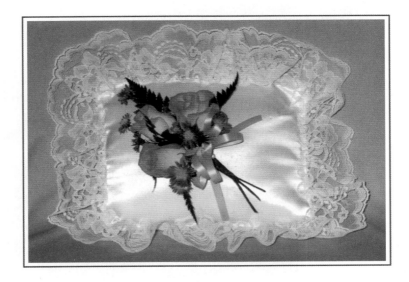

22-5. The casket inset piece is a small design sent by the younger family members and is pinned to the lid of the casket.

ARRANGEMENTS

Many sympathy tributes are arrangements designed in floral foam. The designs are typically oval, fan-shaped, or triangular. Symmetrical styles are the most common, but asymmetrical designs can also be tastefully created as a sympathy tribute.

The containers may be ceramic, plastic, papier-mâché, or baskets. Plastic containers with a handle are available and quite versatile. *Papier-mâché* containers come in various shapes and sizes and are made of a sturdy, molded, water-holding, paper-like material.

22-6. Sympathy tributes may be designed in a variety of containers and design styles. A triangular design in a rustic basket (top left). An oval shape in a basket with a handle (top right). A fan-shaped design in a ceramic container (bottom).

22-7. Papier-mâché containers come in various shapes and sizes.

Many types of baskets are available and can be designed with a variety of design styles. A *fireside basket* is a curved, open basket with a handle. A sympathy arrangement may be designed in this type of basket by wiring a small utility container (and foam) to the basket (like the cornucopia technique). The fireside basket may be designed in two ways, either as a centerpiece or a one-sided design. A centerpiece can be designed by placing the foam and container in the center of the basket. For a one-sided design, tip the basket forward and wire the utility container and foam to the front side of the basket near the handle. (see Figure 16-30) Fireside baskets are often placed on the floor under or near the casket.

A floral designer must take care to design a sympathy tribute with sturdy mechanics. Floral foam should be securely taped to the container. For papier-mâché containers, the tape should be stapled to the paper-like rim to secure it. Avoid filling containers with excess water or sending arrangements or easel sprays that are leaking water.

EASEL DESIGNS

An easel design is any design that is displayed on an *easel*, which is a tripod-like stand for holding floral designs. Easel designs are unique to sympathy tributes. Sprays, wreaths, and set pieces are examples of easel designs.

Easel Sprays

An *easel spray*, also called *standing spray*, is a one-sided flower arrangement placed on an easel. Easel sprays are designed as either symmetrical or

22-8. Easel sprays may be symmetrical or asymmetrical.

asymmetrical styles in a variety of shapes, including a radiating oval (called a double-end spray), vertical, triangular, or diamond-shaped. The easel spray for a funeral service and the candelabra design for a wedding service are designed with similar mechanics.

The mechanics for an easel spray include various types of spray bars or a plastic cage (to insert a brick of floral foam). The mechanic is securely wired with 22- or 24-gauge wire or a chenille stem to the easel. Easels may be wooden, heavy wire, or crafted from bamboo or branches. The wire easels may be covered with moss, ribbon, branches, or horsetail (*Equisaetum*)— split vertically and slid over the wire frame).

1. Attach the spray bar or cage with saturated floral foam to the easel.

2. Green up the design to form a framework in the desired shape.

3. Add line flowers (and linear filler) to the outline.

4. Place striking or fully opened flowers near the center of interest. If a bow is to be added, make one and position it near the center of interest.

5. Add additional mass flowers to fill in the shape. Repeat the center of interest flowers elsewhere in the design (being sure to balance them).

6. Cover any exposed floral foam with foliage and filler.

A *flat spray* is a triangular, one-sided spray that is regionally popular as a sympathy tribute. The flat spray may be hand-tied, that is, designed somewhat like a wedding arm bouquet, or arranged in Styrofoam™.

Set Pieces

Easel designs that are designed as special shapes, such as wreaths, crosses, hearts, pillows, or organizational emblems, are called *set pieces*. The set pieces may be fully covered with flowers or have just one or two areas of flowers.

Instead of covering the form entirely with flowers, any set piece frame may be partially wrapped with ribbon or bold leaves, such as ti, aspidistra, or dracaena leaves. The ribbon or leaves are secured on the underneath side with corsage pins or greening pins, respectively, to begin the wrapping. The ribbon is wrapped entirely around the wreath or heart frame with overlapping placements, except for the area where the floral cage will be attached. Leaves must be wrapped one at a time with overlapping placements, pinning each one securely with greening pins.

22-9. A set piece is a special shape, such as a cross, which is displayed on an easel.

22-10. This wreath was designed in a floral foam wreath ring. Allow ample time to drain before delivery.

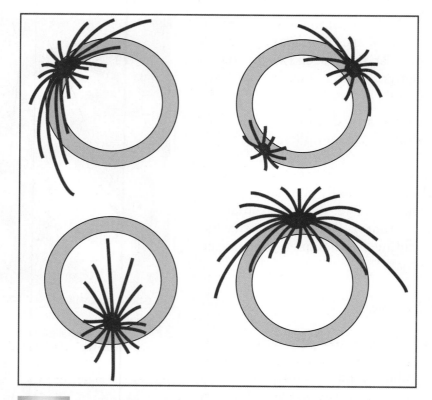

22-11. A wreath may be fully covered with flowers or have one (or two) area of floral emphasis.

Set pieces can be designed on floral foam frames, Styrofoam™ (also called hard foam) shapes, or vine or twig forms. Some mechanics are a combination of hard foam frame with a wettable floral foam area to add the fresh flowers. When using any floral foam base, the foliage and flowers are inserted directly into the foam to create the desired shape. Needless to say, sympathy flowers last longer in floral foam mechanics.

Clusters of flowers may be added to hard foam or twig bases by attaching a foam cage. Cages are easily attached to twig forms by wiring them on with chenille stems or enameled wire. To wire a cage onto a hard foam base, attach the wires to the cage and then insert the wires through the foam. Position wood picks or toothpicks on the underneath side of the hard foam and wire around them. The wood picks or toothpicks will keep the wire from cutting through the hard foam. This technique works for any set piece that needs a floral accent. Floral accents can also be added by attaching a foam cage (with a chenille stem) to one leg of the easel.

22-12. A heart set piece may be designed as an open heart, a solid heart, or a broken heart.

A heart may be designed as an open heart, a solid heart with or without floral accents, or a broken heart. An open heart is heart-shaped with the center removed; floral accents may be added to one side or centered at the bottom of the heart. A solid heart is the full heart shape that is completely covered with flowers, usually with a floral accent. A broken heart has a solid covering of white flowers with a zigzag line of red flowers.

Organizational symbols or emblems are designed on hard foam bases, which match the organization's insignia. These bases are available at the wholesale florist. The floral design should match the colors and placements

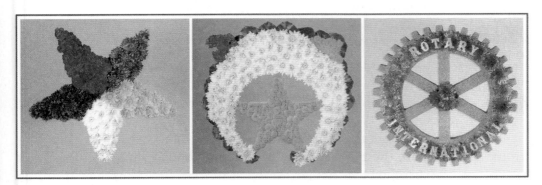

22-13. Organizational sympathy designs are unique set pieces that match the organization's symbol or emblem. (Left to right—Eastern Star, Shriner, and Rotary) (Courtesy, Teleflora)

as closely as possible for each organization. Flowers are designed to solidly cover the form, often with a foliage or ribbon outline.

Creating the Outline for Set Pieces

Sturdy leaves, such as salal, magnolia, or galax leaves, or pleated #40 ribbon are pinned to the underneath side of the base with greening pins or corsage pins, respectively, to create an outline for set pieces. The leaves should overlap each other. The leaves and the ribbon pleating should extend out from the base an inch or two.

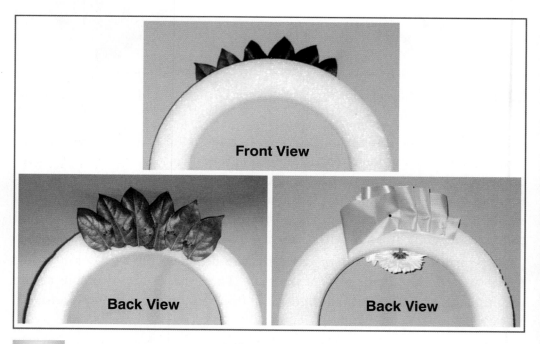

22-14. To outline a set piece form, pin leaves or ribbon in overlapping patterns to the underneath side of the base.

Attaching Flowers to Hard Foam Bases

Mass flowers, such as carnations or decorative or pompon chrysanthemums (pomps), are the most successful for completely filling in color for an area of a set piece. Flowers may be attached to hard foam bases by pinning, gluing, or attaching with toothpicks. The stem is removed from each flower. A corsage pin can be placed through the center of the flower into the hard

22-15. Flowers may be pinned, glued, or picked in a solid manner to completely cover areas of a set piece form.

foam; a generous amount of pan melt glue can be applied to the back of each flower before positioning on the form. Using toothpicks is the oldest method; attach one pointed end of the toothpick into the calyx and the other end of the toothpick into the hard foam. Sometimes for small flowers, it is easier to use only half of a toothpick with the cut end inserted into the foam.

The flowers should be attached to the frame in a consistent manner with all of the flowers facing the same direction. On the edges of the form, the flower facings are gently curved to cover the frame. The flowers are placed very close together as in the pavé technique. Foliage can be used to provide a green color and can be glued or pinned on with greening pins.

DELIVERY

Each sympathy design should have a card attached to it. The information included on the envelope would be the name of the deceased and the funeral home. The enclosure card should include the sender's name and a message, if desired. On the back of the card, the florist should print the sender's name and full address and a short description of the floral piece that was sent. Providing this information to the bereaved family is an essential service.

Once the sympathy tributes are completed, the designs are delivered to the appropriate location. Most florists will keep the obituary section of the newspaper handy to insure the delivery to the proper site and proper time. Timely delivery and proper mechanics will help to insure a good working relationship with the funeral director.

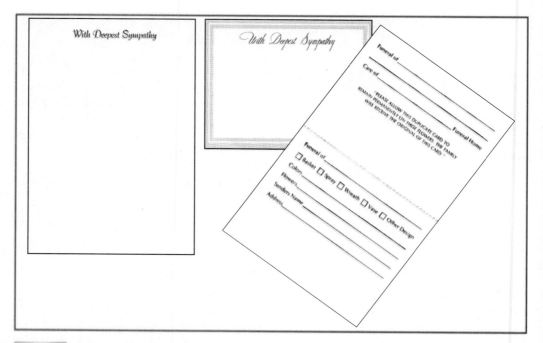

22-16. The sympathy card should include the sender's name and a message (if given) on the front and the sender's name, complete address, and a description of the sympathy tribute on the back. The envelope should include the name of the deceased and the funeral home.

REVIEWING

MAIN IDEAS

Sympathy flowers honor the deceased and give a comforting presence to the family of the deceased. Typical sympathy flowers include the family flowers, which are ordered by the immediate family. The family flowers include the casket spray, the casket inset piece, and a matching floral tribute. Other sympathy tributes include arrangements, basket designs, easel and flat sprays, set pieces, and plants.

A casket spray is a floral arrangement that is placed on the top of a casket during the visitation and funeral service. A full-couch casket spray is a large casket piece (4 or 5 feet) that is placed in the center of a closed full couch. A full-couch lid spray is a large casket piece that is placed in the center of the open lid of a full couch. A half-couch casket spray is a floral piece that is placed on the right side of a half couch and is 3 to 3.5 feet wide.

Casket sprays are designed using a casket saddle with floral foam. A casket saddle has a rounded base to fit the contour of a casket lid. Casket sprays may be oval (or fan), crescent, or triangular (or T).

A casket inset piece is a small design displayed inside the casket lid. This design is traditionally sent from the younger members of the family.

Typical sympathy arrangements are symmetrical and oval, triangular, or fan-shaped. Asymmetrical designs are also a suitable style. Appropriate and common containers for sympathy arrangements are ceramic, plastic (with a handle), papier-mâché, or baskets. Fireside baskets are open and curving baskets with a handle. These baskets can be designed as centerpieces or one-sided arrangements.

An easel spray or standing spray is a one-sided flower arrangement placed on an easel. Easel sprays may be symmetrical or asymmetrical and a variety of shapes, such as oval, vertical, triangular, or diamond-shaped. The mechanics for an easel spray include various types of spray bars or plastic floral foam cages.

A flat spray is a triangular, one-sided, hand-tied spray (or arranged in hard foam) that is regionally popular as a sympathy tribute.

Easel designs that are designed as special shapes, such as wreaths, pillows, hearts, crosses, and organizational emblems, are called set pieces. The set pieces may be solidly covered with flowers or have just one or two areas of flower. The rest of the frame may be covered with ribbon or leaves.

Each sympathy design should have a card attached to it, except for the family flowers. The enclosure card should include the sender's name and a message (if given); on the back of the card, the sender's complete address and a short description of the floral piece should be given. The envelope should include the name of the deceased and the funeral home.

Prompt and efficient delivery of the sympathy flowers is very important. Proper mechanics are also very important.

QUESTIONS

Answer the following questions. Use correct spelling and complete sentences.

1. Why are sympathy flowers important?
2. What are typical family flowers? What is the proper way to treat bereaved customers who are ordering the family flowers?
3. How is the size of a casket spray determined?
4. How is a casket spray different from a centerpiece?
5. What are some typical casket inset designs? Who sends these flowers?
6. What are set pieces? How are solid set pieces designed?
7. If a customer wants a set piece but cannot afford to have it fully covered with flowers, what can you suggest as an alternative? Give two suggestions and the design mechanics for creating these suggestions.
8. What is written on the enclosure card and envelope?

EVALUATING

Match the term with the correct definition. Write the letter by the term in the blank provided.

a. easel spray   e. dish garden   i. flat spray
b. casket inset piece   f. fireside basket   j. full couch
c. half-couch casket spray   g. casket saddle
d. set piece   h. standing spray

_____ 1. A triangular one-sided, hand-tied design.

_____ 2. A special shape, placed on an easel, that is fully covered with flowers or has one or two floral accent areas.

_____ 3. A casket with a one-piece lid.

_____ 4. A small design displayed inside the casket lid.

_____ 5. A selection of a variety of plants potted in the same container.

_____ 6. A container with a rounded base.

_____ 7. An open container with curved sides and a handle.

_____ 8. A one-sided flower arrangement placed on an easel.

_____ 9. A floral tribute that is placed on the right side of the casket.

_____ 10. A spray that stands in an easel.

EXPLORING

1. Purchase a hard foam and wettable foam wreath ring. Gather flowers and foliages to complete both wreaths. Choose two different design styles. Design each type using the proper mechanics and note the difference in lasting qualities of the flowers depending upon the design mechanic used.

2. Interview a funeral director in person or on the phone. Ask about both the good and bad points when working with sympathy flowers and florists. Make a list and use it as a reminder when designing sympathy flowers.

3. Create a fireside basket design, first as a centerpiece. Adapt the basket to design a one-sided arrangement.

23

Designing with Everlasting Flowers

Plant materials that can be successfully dried or preserved are called dried flowers or **everlasting plant materials**. Silk or other manufactured flowers are also everlasting materials. Everlasting flowers or "everlastings" are very long lasting, but do not really last forever. However, the term everlasting emphasizes the fact that these preserved or manufactured materials will continue to add color and texture to a setting for an extended time.

Dried or everlasting flowers bring the outdoors in with memories of the summer garden and its beauty and color. These plant materials have many of the same attractive qualities as their fresh counterparts and can be designed in many of the same ways. Everlastings have the added benefit of looking attractive while storing them in plain view.

23-1. Everlasting materials are long lasting and attractive, even in storage. These materials are hung from a grapevine at the back of the classroom.

567

OBJECTIVES

1   Describe when and how to harvest everlasting flowers

2   Explain the methods of preserving plant materials

3   Describe designing with everlasting plant materials (dried and silk)

TERMS

covering method
desiccant
drying agent
everlasting plant materials
fixative
freeze-drying method
glycerinizing
hanging method

pick machine
potpourri
pressing
shattering
silica gel
silica sand
wooden pick

PRESERVING PLANT MATERIALS

Few people take full advantage of the wealth of materials from the garden and nature that can brighten and enliven an interior. Many beautiful flowers, pods, leaves, and grasses may be gathered from the spring, summer, and fall gardens and roadsides to dry or preserve for enjoyment as wreaths or arrangements indoors. The methods of preserving plant materials range from very simple to more involved and are chosen according to the type of plant material.

WHEN AND HOW TO HARVEST

Flowers, pods, and grasses may be harvested in any season. For the best results and longest lasting qualities, flowers and other materials should be picked at the peak of color and shape. Look for the brightest colors for each type because some fading will occur.

The consequences of gathering plant materials after their peak is the condition known as **shattering**, which is a breaking apart or falling out of petals, seeds, or other plant parts. Grasses and cattails have very noticeable consequences if harvested too late. Ornamental grasses, including pampas grass and maiden grass, should be harvested just before peak or just before the grass plumes "fluff out." If picked when the grass plumes are already fuzzy looking, the grasses will totally "fuzz" a room when brought into a warm interior. Cattails should be harvested in summer when they have turned dark brown. The "old" cattail will shatter if harvested in fall.

The time of day for harvesting is also important. Plant materials should be picked when it is dry. Do not harvest when there is dew or any moisture on the plant. The middle of the day is an optimum time to avoid dew from

Spring	Summer	Fall
Daffodils	Black-eyed Susans	Bittersweet
Pansies	Blue Salvia	Chrysanthemums
Peonies	Cattails	Grasses (early fall)
Pussy willow	Gomphrena	Hydrangea
	Pods — honesty, poppy	Pods — iris, okra
	Wheat	
	Yarrow	

23-2. Flowers, pods, and grasses should be collected at their peak in any season for drying or preserving.

23-3. One person's weed is another creative person's bride. The materials used to create this bride were simply harvested from nature and dried by the hanging method. The bride is fashioned on a chicken wire frame with gray Spanish moss, yellow goldenrod, white asters and 'The Pearl' yarrow, brown dock, corn husk bows and face, and various pods and open flowers for the bouquet.

the morning and any collecting moisture at nightfall. Do not harvest when the plant is wilted.

Most plant materials can be harvested by cutting them with a knife, scissors, or florist shears. Cones can be picked from the tree or the ground.

Harvest flowers and leaves at different stages and sizes. Flowers can be chosen as buds, partially open flowers, and fully open flowers.

PRESERVING METHODS

Different methods of drying and preserving can be used depending upon the type of plant materials. Experience and trial and error testing will help determine promising drying methods for new materials. A floral designer should always dry or preserve more materials than actually needed to account for some losses.

Some plant materials require no extra care in drying, other than harvesting them at the proper time to avoid shattering. Examples include many types of pods (honesty or silver dollar plant, iris, poppy, okra, honey locust, milkweed), cones (spruce, pine, fir), seed heads (purple coneflower, teasel), and other materials, such as corn tassels and brown dock (a linear dark-brown roadside plant). A weed to one person may be a great dried flower to the next person.

Hanging Method

The **hanging method**, also called the hang dry method, is a method of collecting plant materials having a low moisture content and bunching them to hang upside down to dry. Some flowers and leaves dry with very little change in appearance; others will appear slightly wrinkled or puckered.

Annuals (last one season)	Perennials (last more that 3 years)
Accroclinium *(Helipterum)*	Artemisia, Silver King, Silver Queen
Baby's breath (annual type)	Baby's breath ('Perfecta', 'Bristol Fairy')
Bells of Ireland	Drumstick *(Craspedia)* — Zone 6
Blue salvia	German Statice
Celosia (feather wheat, plume, cockscomb)	Globe centaurea, globe thistle
Dusty Miller	Goldenrod
Globe amaranth	Grasses
Larkspur	Lady's mantle *(Alchemilla)*
Love-in-a-mist pods	Lamb's ear
Marigolds	Lavender
Statice	Roses
Strawflowers	Sea holly *(Eryngium)*
Wheat	Sea lavender *(Limonium latifolium)*
Winged everlasting *(Ammobium)*	Yarrow (yellow and white — 'The Pearl')

23-4. Many annuals and perennials that are easily dried with the hanging method can be grown in the garden.

Flowers with a higher moisture content can also be dried but may have a more puckered or wrinkled appearance.

This method works well for both annuals and perennials, such as baby's breath, blue salvia, plume or cockscomb celosia, goldenrod, clover-like globe amaranth or gomphrena, grasses, larkspur, lavender, love-in-a-mist pods, and strawflowers.

The hanging method is easy to do and requires only a few supplies, such as rubber bands, hooks or clothes hangers, and twist-ties to tie the bunches onto the hanger (if used). An airy, warm, dry area away from direct sunlight is an ideal place to help the drying process.

The steps for the hanging method are as follows:

1. Gather plant materials. Depending upon the nature of the leaves and the desired finished look, the foliage may be left on the stems. Optional: Remove all the unnecessary foliage to hasten the drying process.

2. Bunch the stems into small amounts (8 to 12 stems) and fasten with a rubber band. Large flowers can each be hung separately.

3. Hang the bunches upside down in an airy, warm, dry area away from direct sunlight. The bunches may be placed on a hook or tied to a clothes hanger. A clothes hanger is also a flexible and mobile way to store the dried flowers.

23-5. Flowers that have low moisture content can be gathered, bunched, and hung upside down to dry. This method is called the hanging method or hand dry method. (from left to right—carnations, roses, statice, globe amaranth)

4. When dry, store the bunched plant materials in dry place away from rodents. These bunches can be a decoration until used for an arrangement or wreath.

Hanging Method Variation

A variation of the hanging method is needed for plants with a daisy-like or larger flower heads. Placing the stems upside down causes the petals to droop

23-6. Flowers with daisy-like or large flower heads should not be hung upside down because the petals dry with an unnatural appearance. Place the stems through chicken wire with the flower heads up.

down rather than remain open and flat. For these types of flowers, hang the flowers through a chicken wire frame or a crate with the flower heads up. The flower head rests on the wire and dries with natural-looking petals.

Examples of flowers to dry this way are blanket flower or gaillardia, carnations, coreopsis or tickseed, peonies, purple coneflower, sunflowers, sunflower heliopsis, and zinnias.

Another variation of the flower heads up hanging method is to place the ends of the stem in a little water in vases below the chicken wire. When the water evaporates, do not replace it and allow the material to dry in the vase. Some flowers will even dry nicely in an arrangement designed in floral foam that has dried out.

A third variation is to place these flowers in their chicken wire frames in a cooler to dry slowly and retain color. A small amount of water for the stems can again be incorporated. Some flowers will dry better with a gradual process.

Covering Method

The **covering method** is a method that uses a drying agent to maintain the shape of the flower as it is drying. **Drying agents** or **desiccants**, such as silica sand, silica gel, fine-grain kitty litter, and borax and cornmeal, draw the

23-7. For the covering method, two-dimensional flowers can be dried face down in the drying agent; three-dimensional flowers should be dried face up in the drying agent.

2-Dimensional Flowers
FACE DOWN

3-Dimensional Flowers
FACE UP

moisture out of the flower or leaf. The desiccant holds the flower shape while the drying process takes place.

Silica sand is an inexpensive, white builder's sand that can be purchased at home builder supply stores. When the sand becomes too moist to be effective, the granules of sand will stay on your fingers. By heating the sand at a low-temperature for several hours, the moisture can be removed. **Silica gel** is available as white crystals or color-indicator crystals that change colors when the gel is too moist to use. Silica sand is lighter in weight than silica gel and generally dries flowers faster. Both silica sand and silica gel can be reused many times. Borax can be used alone or in combination with cornmeal. Fine-grain kitty litter, borax, and cornmeal are available at grocery stores. These desiccants have a one-time use.

The covering method is effective for flowers that wilt too drastically for the hanging method. These flowers may have fragile petals or high moisture content. The covering method works for these flowers because the sand or drying agent holds the petals in place as the moisture is removed. Examples of flowers that can be effectively dried with the covering method are black-eyed Susans, daffodils, dahlias, delphiniums, carnations, chrysanthemums, cymbidium orchids, dendrobium orchids, freesias, roses (both methods work for roses), and snapdragons. Experimentation is the best way to learn if this method will work for a particular flower. The results could be positive and surprising; it seems like uncovering buried treasure.

The supplies needed for this drying method are pans or boxes, a drying agent, a microwave (optional, but faster), a strainer (to remove flower petals or leaves after each use), a paint brush (to brush off small amounts of drying agent), and containers to store the dried flowers.

Flowers may be placed in the drying agent in two ways depending upon the flower shape. Two-dimensional flowers (such as daisies, daisy mums, and sunflowers) can be positioned face down onto the sand. Three-dimensional flowers (carnations, dahlias, orchids, and roses) would be smashed if positioned in the same way so these flowers must be positioned face up with the stem portion placed into the sand first. The sand is then poured carefully around (and within it, in some cases) the flower, maintaining its shape as much as possible.

An option for the covering method is the choice of air drying at room temperature or microwave drying. Air drying may take a week (longer for thicker flowers) and any type of pan or box can be used for drying the flowers. The length of time to air dry flowers will depend upon the thickness of the petals, the flower shape, and the humidity in the room. Microwave drying should be done only in microwave-safe dishes. The flowers are dried on high

	Air Drying	Microwave Drying
Containers	Any type	Only microwave safe
Length of Time — Thin petals	5–7 days	2 minutes on high/overnight
Medium	7–9 days	3 minutes on high/overnight
Thick	9–12 days	4 minutes on high/overnight
Stem Coverage	Optional	Completely covered
Stem Wiring	May be wired	Absolutely no wired stems

23-8. Comparison of air drying and microwave drying

for 2 to 4 minutes and then left in the drying agent overnight to cool. All plant parts must be covered before microwave drying or the area will smell like a burnt jungle.

A tip for the covering method is to completely fill each pan or container with the same type of flower to insure uniform drying of the entire pan. Different flowers will dry at different rates of time and should be kept separate. Once a flower has been removed from the drying agent, it is nearly impossible to cover it back up if it has not dried thoroughly.

The covering method steps are as follows:

1. Place an inch of drying agent in the bottom of the container. It should be microwave-safe if microwave drying.

2. Position the flowers (face down for 2-D, face up for 3-D) on the sand. Fill the entire container with like flowers.

3. Carefully cover the flowers with drying agent, work around the edges of each flower and build up the agent until the flower is completely covered. For air drying, the stems can be left uncovered; for microwave drying, the stems should be completely covered. Cover the flowers with approximately an inch of drying agent at the top of the container.

4. Dry the flowers with the 1) air drying technique or 2) microwave drying technique.

5. Uncover the flowers by carefully pouring off some of the drying agent on the top into another box or container. Brush away the drying agent in and around the petals and gently remove the flower. Use a brush to remove any excess desiccant from the petals.

6. Store the dried flowers carefully in containers in a dry area until used.

23-9. Beech leaves darken to a bronze color and are pliable and long lasting when treated with a glycerin solution.

Glycerinizing

A glycerin solution can be used to preserve foliages, such as fall-color leaves and eucalyptus, and some filler flowers, such as goldenrod, hydrangea, and sea lavender. *Glycerinizing* preserves foliages and fillers through the process of a glycerin solution being transported up the stem (xylem), which preserves the plant material and causes it to remain pliable and flexible.

Glycerinized plant materials are flexible and can be curved or shaped; plant materials dried by hanging or covering can be quite fragile and easily broken. The comparison of dried and glycerinized eucalyptus is very striking because the glycerinized eucalyptus bends and is very pliable; the dried eucalyptus cannot be curved without breaking into many pieces.

Some glycerinized plant materials have also been dyed in the same process. It is quite common to have a choice of glycerinized eucalyptus in green, brown, or other colors. Glycerin and glycerin dyes may be purchased at craft or hobby shops or chemical supply stores.

Keep plant materials in water until ready to treat it. For the best results, choose foliages such as beech, holly, forsythia, plum, and any with bronze or reddish leaves. Most foliage and fillers will darken in color after glycerinizing. The treated materials will have a smooth, satiny finish and will last indefinitely. Treated materials may be used in fresh arrangements as well as dried ones. Water does not affect glycerin-treated foliage.

To preserve foliages and fillers by glycerinizing, follow these steps:

1. Harvest foliage branches or fillers to be treated. Remove any damaged leaves. Wipe off any dust or debris with a damp cloth.

2. Mix 1 part glycerin with 2 parts warm water. Warm water is taken up the stem (xylem) more efficiently.

3. Place 4 to 5 inches of the glycerin solution in a narrow container. Maintain this level throughout the process.

4. Place the cut ends of the branches in the solution. Make a fresh cut before putting the stems in the solution. The top of the branches may be brushed with the glycerin solution to hasten the process.

5. Watch the plant materials for the desired color. Check the materials after one week. The foliage or filler is ready to be removed from the solution when oiliness is felt on the leaf surface.

6. Remove the plant materials from the solution. Hang them upside down in bunches until dry. Store away from direct sunlight.

Some foliage, such as English ivy, galax leaves, and leatherleaf, is more successfully preserved by completely immersing the stems in a 50:50 solution of glycerin and warm water.

Pressing

Pressing plant materials is a very old technique of carefully placing flowers and foliage between absorbent paper to flatten and preserve them in a

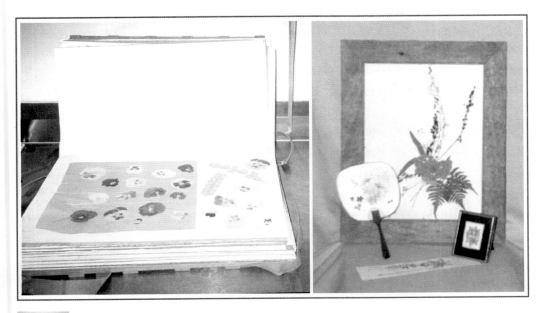

23-10. A plant press is an effective way to press many types of flowers and foliages, including pansies. Pressed flowers can be designed on pictures, fans, and bookmarks.

two-dimensional form. Many kinds of plant materials can be pressed for use in pictures, stationary, bookmarks, greeting and gift cards, business cards, jewelry, ornaments, pillows, and to cover vases. Nearly every type of flower or foliage can be pressed, including pansy, Queen Anne's lace, ferns, scented geranium leaves, larkspur, and pinks (*Dianthus*).

Flowers and leaves can be successfully pressed with a plant press, phone books, or a homemade plant press, made by gathering newspapers or phone books, and blotting paper or paper towels. Follow these simple steps:

1. Start the homemade plant press with a flat piece of plywood. Alternate layers of newspapers or corrugated cardboard, one piece of blotting paper, two paper towels, one piece of blotting paper, and more newspapers or cardboard. Or, use a phone book with paper towels between the pages. Or, use a plant press.

2. Collect fresh plant material at different stages of development. Do not allow the materials to wilt; begin pressing them at once.

3. Starting with the lowest layer, place the flowers and foliage between two paper towels. Carefully position each flower or leaf to lay flat and not touch another one.

4. Continue adding layers of paper and towels and pressing flowers and foliage between the two paper towels.

5. When the stack is 12 inches high, place a thin plywood board over the top and add weight, such as bricks, concrete blocks, or heavy books, distributing the weight evenly.

6. Dry the plant materials in a dry, warm, well-ventilated area.

7. Check the top layer after a week. Fresh towels may be substituted to prevent mold. Allow one to three weeks to dry. When the plant materials have completely dried, transfer them to boxes, folders, or an old phone book.

Potpourri

Potpourri is a scented mixture of dried petals, flowers, buds, leaves, spices, fragrance oils, and a fixative. A *fixative* is necessary to hold or to "fix" the scent for an extended period (up to a year or more). Fixatives, such as powdered orris root (the root of the Florentine iris) or fragrance crystals (a specially formulated form of salt with fragrance added), can be purchased at craft, herb, and health food stores.

23-11. Potpourri is a fragrant mixture of dried flowers, buds, petals, leaves, oils, and a fixative. Potpourri can add color and texture to vases.

Potpourri is a unique way to cover (by gluing) a topiary form, a round Styrofoam or sweet-gum ball ornament, or a clay pot or other vase. Another idea is to place a thin bud vase inside a wider clear vase and add potpourri between the two vases to give a lovely garden look with interesting texture and color (see Figure 23-11). For the vase technique, the dried plant materials do not need the fragrance added. Skip steps #3 and #4. A fresh or dried design can be created in the smaller vase.

The steps in making potpourri are very simple and easy to follow.

1. Dry the plant materials by placing in a single layer on paper towels, newspaper, or fine mesh screens.

2. Once the materials are thoroughly dried, store different colors separately. Mixtures can be made based upon color and texture. Choose red and green for a Christmas holiday theme or bright yellows and lime greens for a citrus fragrance.

3. Whole and powdered spices (no more than a teaspoon at a time) and a few drops of fragrance oil are added to provide a pleasant scent. Mix thoroughly.

4.   Add a fixative. Use a teaspoon for each quart of plant materials. Mix thoroughly.

5.   Cover tightly and place away from direct sunlight. Stir and mix the mixture every week or 10 days. Check at the end of a month for the desired fragrance. Additional drops of fragrance oil or spices, if necessary.

FREEZE-DRYING METHOD

Freeze drying is a commercial method of freezing the flowers first before drying them. Flowers are placed in large refrigerated vacuum chambers, which removes the moisture from the plant tissues. The flowers look very natural and hold their color. The cost of the chamber is prohibitive for most people.

DESIGNING WITH EVERLASTINGS (DRIED AND SILK)

Designers of dried or silk arrangements must employ the same principles and elements of design that are used with fresh flowers; however, some of the mechanics and specific techniques are slightly different. Designing with dried and silk flowers gives much flexibility to the designer. Stems can be lengthened or manipulated into various shapes. Materials may be glued, wired, and taped in a wide variety of ways that are not possible with fresh materials. A diverse range of containers can be used, including those that do not hold water. In many ways, designing with dried or silk flowers is much easier than with fresh flowers; because, wilting is no longer a concern. Designs will not need water added; wilted petals or leaves do not need to be removed. Care should be taken to avoid sunny or humid areas.

23-12. Designing with everlastings gives the designer much flexibility. Many styles and containers (including those that do not hold water) are possible with dried flowers.

Stem Techniques

Many flowers or leaves are dried without any stems at all. Both dried and silk flowers may need stems to be lengthened or strengthened. The methods used will depend upon the flower type and stem thickness. New or added stems should be taped with floral tape in the appropriate matching color before using them in a design.

To create a new stem, a heavy wire can be glued (with pan melt glue or glue from a glue gun) and secured to the flower. Another method is to use the daisy hook wiring method.

To lengthen or strengthen stems, several methods are available. 1) A *pick machine* attaches a metal pick or stem to single or clustered silk or dried flowers to add length and strength. 2) A *wooden pick*, a narrow, pointed piece of wood (available in several lengths) with a wire attached at the top, can add stem length. Stems can be lengthened or strengthened by wrapping the wire on the pick around both the stem and the wooden pick. 3) Stem length can be added for a short flower by placing it into a hollow stem, removed from another flower. Tape the flower to secure it. 4) A designer can tightly tape a short flower or leaf to a longer stem without wire or glue or hollow stem. This method is quick but the taping must be very secure to keep

23-13. Both dried and silk flowers can be lengthened and strengthened by using metal picks from a pick machine, wooden picks, and hollow stems.

23-14. Add several flowers or fillers to a design with one placement to increase quickness in designing.

the material from falling out. 5) Hot glue can attach a longer stem to a short flower or leaf.

To operate a pick machine, begin by loading the metal picks into the slot at the top of the machine. Next, the handle is pulled forward to feed the pick into the front of the machine. The stems of the dried materials are placed over the top part of the pick. The stems should be thick enough to allow the pick to grasp them; if too thin, the stems will slip out of the pick. Then, the handle is pushed downward with a firm, steady grip. The prongs on the pick close over the stems of the dried materials, clamping the stems tightly. The dried material is ready to use in a design.

To shorten designing time, several flowers, fillers, or leaves may be attached to one stem and placed into a design. Adding several small filler flowers on the same metal or wooden pick or hollow stem shortens the design time and gives a full look to the design. Larger flowers can be wired (at slightly differing heights) and taped to quickly add color, depth, and fullness to a design.

To secure silk flowers and leaves, some silks may need to be removed from their stem, hot glued, and reattached to the stem. Before designing with silks, determine if this step is necessary with a gentle tug on a silk flower or leaf. If the parts come off easily, gluing is essential to secure them.

To shape silk flowers, use the wired petals, leaves, and stems and position these parts in a natural way. Unfurl the petals and stage the flowers to look partially to fully open; position the leaves to appear growing and not wilted; the stems may be slightly curved to look "real."

Designing Tips

Floral foam created specifically for silk and dried flower arranging is available. The foam should be securely attached to the container or wreath frame by gluing or wiring. To keep the wire from cutting through the floral foam, moss can be added before wiring. Moss is also used to conceal the floral foam

23-15. Floral foam can be attached to containers by gluing or wiring. Moss will prevent the wire from cutting through the foam as well as camouflage the foam and other mechanics (wiring and gluing).

and other mechanics (wiring and gluing). Wooden picks can also be placed at the foam edges to keep the wire from cutting through the floral foam.

When designing, each stem may be glued (use pan melt glue and a quick dip) before placing it into the arrangement. Experienced designers (who will not change their mind about placement) can use this technique as they design; novices may want to glue the stems of the finished arrangement.

Designs with everlastings should not appear flat. Layering, the technique of placing some flowers deeper than others within an arrangement, will add fullness and avoid a flat look. Some flowers and fillers will appear quite "leggy" and layering avoids the see-through appearance.

23-16. Layering is a technique of placing flowers or fillers deeper in an arrangement to add depth and create fullness, avoiding a see-through, "leggy" appearance. Add layering materials near the beginning of the designing process.

Display finished designs away from direct sunlight and high humidity. Sunlight will fade the colors and humidity will "wilt" dried flowers.

Dried and silk materials are long lasting and low maintenance. These types of designs will need occasional cleaning by dusting with a lightweight feather duster, spraying with a commercial spray designed for cleaning dried and silk flowers, or a quick dusting with a hair blow dryer on a low setting.

REVIEWING

MAIN IDEAS

Everlasting plant materials may be dried, preserved, or manufactured (silk, paper) and are very long lasting. Flowers and plant materials may be harvested in any season when at their peak (or just before) color and shape. Gathering materials too late may cause shattering, the falling or breaking apart of petals, leaves, seeds, or other plant parts. Harvest materials at different stages and sizes during the middle of the day.

Methods to dry or preserve plant materials are the hanging method, covering method, treating with glycerin, pressing, making potpourri, and commercial freeze drying. The hanging method is ideal for plant materials with low moisture content. Flowers are bunched, fastened with a rubber band, and hung upside down to air dry. For daisy-type flowers, hang the flower heads through chicken wire for drying with a natural appearance. The covering method is a method that uses a drying agent to maintain the flower shape as it dries. Examples of drying agents include silica sand, silica gel, kitty litter, borax, and cornmeal. Flowers with high moisture content or fragile petals can be successfully dried with the covering method. Flower shape determines the manner in which flowers are placed in the drying agent, either face up for three-dimensional ones or face down for two-dimensional daisy-like ones. Another option is air drying at room temperature or microwave drying.

Stems of fillers or foliage can be treated with glycerin, called glycerinizing. The glycerin solution is transported up the stem through the xylem, preserving the plant material and making it pliable and long lasting.

Pressing plant materials preserves them in a two-dimensional form. A plant press, phone books, or homemade press can be used to press flowers. Potpourri is a scented mixture of dried petals and other plant parts, spices, fragrance oils, and a fixative. A fixative is an additive, such as orris root or fragrance crystals, for holding or "fixing" the fragrance. Pressed flowers and potpourri can be attached to pictures or vases for interesting textures and colors. Freeze drying is a commercial method of freezing the plant materials before drying them in vacuum chambers.

Designing with everlasting plant materials, both dried and silk, gives the floral designer much flexibility. Stems can be added, lengthened, and strengthened with wire, metal or wooden picks, hollow stems, taped stems, or hot glue. Several stems can be added as a cluster to the arrangement to shorten designing time. Silk flowers can be shaped to look as if they are alive.

Floral foam created specifically for silk and dried flower arranging is available. Use moss to conceal it and wire or glue it to the chosen container. Layering is a technique of placing some flowers deeper within an arrangement to add depth and fullness.

Display finished designs of everlasting plant materials away from direct sunlight and high humidity. These designs may need occasional cleaning with a feather duster, commercial spray for cleaning silk or dried materials, or a dusting with a hair blow dryer.

QUESTIONS

Answer the following questions. Use correct spelling and complete sentences.

1. What are four advantages of designing with everlasting plant materials compared to fresh materials?

2. Why do dried plant materials shatter? How is shattering avoided in ornamental grasses?

3. What is the best time of day and the best stage of development to harvest plant materials for drying?

4. What is the hanging method? What types of flowers are dried with the hanging method? What is a variation of that method? What flowers work well with that method?

5. Why are some flowers dried by the covering method instead of the simpler hanging method? How are flowers placed in the drying agent?

6. How is a glycerin solution used to preserve plant materials? What are examples of plant materials that are successfully treated with this method?

7. What are ways that pressed flowers can be used?

8. How can dried flowers with short stems be used in designing?

9. What are two tips when designing with silk materials?

10. What is the maintenance of everlasting floral designs?

EVALUATING

Match the term with the correct definition. Write the letter by the term in the blank provided.

a. potpourri   e. desiccant   i. pressing
b. shattering   f. layering   j. glycerinizing
c. silica gel   g. covering method
d. fixative   h. pick machine

_____ 1. A drying agent that draws moisture from a flower.

_____ 2. The method of preserving plant materials in a two-dimensional form between paper or towels.

_____ 3. A drying agent with color-indicator crystals.

_____ 4. A device to attach a metal stem to a single flower or cluster of flowers.

_____ 5. A powdered or crystal-like substance that holds the fragrance in potpourri.

_____ 6. A method in which a liquid substance replaces the water in the stem or xylem and preserves the plant material in a pliable manner.

_____ 7. A fragrant dried mixture made of petals, buds, leaves, spices, oils, and a fixative.

_____ 8. A technique of placing flowers or fillers deeper within a floral design.

_____ 9. The breaking apart of the plant parts or seeds.

_____ 10. A method of surrounding the flower with a drying agent to hold its shape and dry the flower in a natural-looking way.

EXPLORING

1. Choose three types of plant materials from the garden—a flower, a foliage, and a smaller flower or filler. Dry or preserve each one by the hanging, covering, glycerinizing, and pressing methods. Compare the results for each type and choose the preferred method(s) for each one.

2. Visit a garden center or florist that stocks a variety of silk flowers and foliages. Evaluate the flowers for a natural appearance and for wired petals, leaves, and stems. Buy three to five realistic-looking types, including both flowers and foliages, and create a design.

3. Select five kinds of flowers and leaves and press them with a homemade plant press. When the plant materials are completely dry, cover a clay pot or other vase with the pressed materials. The container can be completely covered or enhanced by a few carefully placed materials. Make a dried design for the new container.

24

Pricing Design Work

Pricing, along with proper buying practices, are very important responsibilities of the owner or manager of a retail florist shop. Beautiful and well-constructed designs must be appropriately priced to motivate customers to buy. The combination of effective buying and pricing will determine if a shop will be profitable or not.

Pricing and buying well does not have to be a mystery. A well-informed and conscientious person can unlock the mystery by following a few guidelines and determining which pricing method and other strategies fit their needs.

24-1. Retail flower shops sell to the public. (Courtesy, Jasper S. Lee)

OBJECTIVES

1 Explain the importance of effective buying

2 Explain how to determine the costs for floral arrangements

3 Describe typical pricing strategies

TERMS

broker
combined pricing
cost of goods
gross sales
hardgoods
labor
leader pricing
multiple price points
multiple unit pricing
nested basket
net profit
odd end pricing

operating expenses
percentage mark-up
pricing strategies
ratio mark-up
retail price
tie-in pricing
unit cost of goods
variable ratio mark-up
wholesale cost of goods or
    wholesale price
wholesale florist

IMPORTANCE OF BUYING

Buying can be a challenging part of the floral business. Finding the right plant materials at the right price at the right time is somewhat like fitting the pieces of a puzzle together. Knowledge, organization, and planning are a big part of being a good buyer. Flexibility and adaptability are also important because plant materials may not be available when ordered.

SOURCES OF GOODS

A retail florist may purchase flowers and foliages from wholesale florists, growers, a flower market, or a broker. A florist may use a combination of these sources.

Wholesale Florists

A *wholesale florist* is a purchasing link between the grower or broker and the retail florist. Some wholesale florists (also called wholesalers) may sell only fresh plant material. The wholesale florist that sells both fresh and nonperishable materials (vases, supplies) can provide one-stop shopping for the retail florist. An advantage of ordering from a wholesaler instead of a grower is the flexibility in ordering the desired number of bunches, instead of an entire box. In general, retail florists may have two or three favorite wholesalers due to varied delivery times and added availability of inventory from which to choose.

Growers

Growers, both foreign and domestic, will supply to a florist directly if the quantities ordered are large enough. Florists may order large quantities of roses at Valentine's Day and carnations and chrysanthemums during the rest of the year directly from the grower. Mixed boxes of specialty flowers and greens are also popular items to order directly from growers.

Flower Market

Some large cities have their own flower market. At the flower market, all of the local wholesalers are represented. The retail florist can compare and buy a wide variety of plant materials.

Brokers

A **broker** is an agent who purchases flowers, contacts customers (both wholesalers and retailers), and sells his or her inventory. A broker may purchase flowers directly from growers or from an auction. Often, a broker may never see or physically handle the plant materials, but will sell from inventory lists.

24-2. A broker purchases flowers, contacts customers, and sells inventory. (Courtesy, Kuhn Flowers, Jacksonville, FL)

BE A SUCCESSFUL BUYER

A successful buyer is informed about flower quality and price, effective in building a good working relationship with the suppliers, and knowledgeable about the manner and quantities in which flowers are sold.

Flower Quality and Price

An effective buyer is an informed buyer. Try to learn who sells the finest quality flowers, both at the grower and wholesale level. Keep notes about the quality of flowers received and request by name the growers with good quality. Learn about the handling practices of the wholesale florists. Ask questions, such as "Is floral preservative used?" "How fresh are these flowers?" "When were these flowers shipped?"

Expect quality from a supplier and always inspect each shipment for the desired quality and freshness. Remember, there will be a small amount of loss or damage in the normal handling and shipping of fresh flowers. Do not call the supplier for small claims of loss, but do inform them when an entire or part of a bunch is damaged, wilted, or very poor quality. Work to build an honest and cooperative relationship with your suppliers.

An effective buyer will be interested in both the price and the quality of plant materials. Sometimes, high-quality flowers and foliage deserve a higher price. Also, prices will often go higher for flowers that are in high demand during a specific holiday or season. Expect to pay more for roses and red flowers at Valentine's Day.

Building a Good Relationship with Suppliers

A successful buyer can build a good relationship with suppliers by being honest, trustworthy, and loyal. A florist should be honest about the quality expected and the amounts of flowers needed. Let a wholesalers know immediately if quantities change to avoid over-buying. Pay the bills on time to build trust. Although using only one wholesaler is not a wise idea, be a loyal and dependable buyer when purchasing from the two or more chosen suppliers.

Flower and Foliage Buying Tips

A buyer needs to know bunch sizes for typical flowers and foliages. Flowers may be bunched in 10s or 25s, or sold by the single stem. Review this material in Chapter 15 (Care and Handling of Fresh Flowers and Foliages). If the amount per bunch is in question, do not hesitate to ask the supplier.

In general, a better price will be given for materials that are purchased in greater quantities. For example, buying one to four cases of foam may cost $20.00; buying five to nine cases would cost $19.50. By planning ahead, an effective buyer will anticipate needs and purchase in larger amounts to save money in the long run.

DETERMINING UNIT COST OF GOODS

Since supplies and plant materials are sold in bunches, rolls, or cases, the price for a single unit or item should be calculated. The **unit cost of goods** is the price of a single item determined by dividing the overall bunch or case price by the number of items in the bunch or case. For fresh flowers, a physical count of the stems when the shipment arrives may be the best idea to insure the correct unit cost of goods.

This unit cost is also an important figure to add to the arrangement costs. The cost of each addition to a floral design should be recorded and included in the price. A designer should not give away supplies, but should charge a fair amount for each added item. For example, a poinsettia decorated with foil and a bow would be more expensive than one just chosen from the greenhouse with no decoration. To charge the same amount for both is to give away profit.

The unit cost of goods should be calculated for everything. Keep a separate list for supplies (or *hardgoods*) and for fresh flowers and foliages. Update these prices as needed. The prices of supplies will not change as quickly as fresh flower prices. The unit costs of flowers should be recalculated after each delivery.

Small design vase: $18.00 per case ÷ 36 (vases per case)   = $0.50

Tulips: $7.50 per bunch ÷ 10 (tulips per bunch)   = $0.75

24-3. To determine the unit cost of goods, divide the cost by the overall number of items in the case or bunch.

The unit cost of goods is a wholesale cost, not a retail price. The total of all unit costs of goods is the *wholesale cost of goods or wholesale price.* A *retail price* is the florist's selling price determined from the wholesale cost of goods (wholesale price) or other method as described in the next section.

Combined Pricing for Supplies

Combined pricing is a method of adding the total costs for typical supplies used for an arrangement. Combined pricing can be calculated for designs arranged in commonly used vases or containers. As a time-saver, each regularly used vase can have a combined price for the supplies posted near it. The typical supplies for that vase would be the costs of the vase, floral foam and tape (if appropriate), floral preservative, wire, card, envelope, cardette, wrapping materials (typical for the shop), and care tag. The combined price

COMBINED PRICES Supplies Needed and Costs			
6" PLANT	**Costs**	**9" BUD VASE**	**Costs**
Foil		Bud vase	
#9 ribbon		Floral preservative	
Card, envelop, cardette		Card, envelop, cardette	
Care tag		Care tag	
Wrapping supplies		Wrapping supplies	
Wax tissue		Wax tissue	
Cellophane		Cellophane	
Ribbon		Ribbon	
TOTALS	_____		_____

24-4. Combined pricing for typical supplies used to decorate a plant or design an arrangement in a specific vase can make pricing quick and more efficient.

of the supplies can be quickly added to the costs of the fresh flowers and foliages.

METHODS OF PRICING DESIGN WORK

Pricing design work may vary with each floral shop depending upon the type of shop and profit strategies. However, there are some general guidelines for determining price. The ratio mark-up and the percentage mark-up are two types of pricing methods.

RATIO MARK-UP

The *ratio mark-up* method of pricing relies on a predetermined increase (or mark-up) from the wholesale cost of goods. The selling price is called the retail price. Hardgoods (or supplies) typically have a 2:1 mark-up; perishables

Typical Ratio Mark-up		
Perishables	Carnations	10@$.30 = $3.00 × 3 = $9.00
	Leatherleaf	10@$.10 = $1.00 × 3 = $3.00
Hardgoods	Vase	1@$.90 = $0.90 × 2 = $1.80
	Floral Preservative	1@$.05 = $0.05 × 2 = $0.10
		TOTAL $13.90
Across-the-Board 3:1 Pricing Ratio		
Perishables	Carnations	10@$.30 = $3.00 × 3 = $9.00
	Leatherleaf	10@$.10 = $1.00 × 3 = $3.00
Hardgoods	Vase	1@$.90 = $0.90 × 3 = $2.70
	Floral Preservative	1@$.05 = $0.05 × 3 = $0.15
		TOTAL $14.85

24-5. An example of pricing the same vase arrangement with two different methods. A typical ratio mark-up would be 2:1 for hardgoods or non-perishables and 3:1 for perishables (flowers and foliages). Another florist might use an across-the-board 3:1 pricing ratio. (Note the price difference.)

(flowers and foliages) typically have a 3:1 mark-up. In other words, to determine the retail cost or the selling price, multiply the wholesale cost for supplies by 2 and the wholesale cost of flowers and foliages by 3.

These ratios may vary from florist to florist; some ratios may be a consistent 3:1 for both perishables and non-perishables. Others charge a 5:1 mark-up or more for labor-intensive design work, such as wedding work. (see variable ratio mark-up)

The weakness in this system is the failure to plan for net profit and to consider overhead costs and operating expenses. The ratio mark-up can make pricing guesswork because the designing time to complete the arrangement is not considered.

Adding Labor Charges

To account for the design time (or labor), a labor charge can be added to the ratio mark-up total. This charge may be based upon the hourly wage although the astute owner may want to add fringe benefits and other employee costs to the hourly wage. For example, let's pretend that a floral designer makes $7.00

24-6. Labor costs should be considered when pricing design work. (Courtesy, *Florist*, FTD)

per hour. By including health care or other costs to this hourly rate, the true hourly employee wage (or cost to the employer) may be $13.00 per hour.

Let's figure some design labor charges. First, think of the minutes spent in completing an arrangement as a fraction of an hour. For example, 45 minutes is ¾ of an hour or .75, 30 minutes is ½ hour or .5, 20 minutes is 1/3 of an hour or .33, and 15 minutes is ¼ of an hour or .25.

For a vase arrangement, requiring 15 minutes of design time, multiply $7.00 (hourly wage) times .25. $7.00 × .25 = $1.75. The labor charge for the design would be $1.75 using the hourly wage. The labor charge for the $13.00 per hour rate (employer's actual costs) is $3.25. $13.00 × .25 = $3.25. An employer would be paying for the extra $1.50 from profits if it is

---

Vase arrangement in Figure 24-5   Total $13.90

15 minutes to complete

$13.00 (employer's actual hourly labor costs) × .25 (1/4 hour) = $ 3.25

New total with labor = $17.15

24-7. Labor charges may be added with the ratio mark-up method.

not included in these labor charges. A florist may want to post a chart for standard labor charges for the design time.

Another method to calculate labor would be to add a 10 to 20 percent labor charge to the final price. A design costing $13.90 would have a $2.00 labor charge (15 percent) or a $2.75 (20 percent). Notice that these labor charges are less than the previous example based upon the employer's actual hourly labor costs.

Variable Ratio Mark-Up

Variable ratio mark-up has different mark-ups depending upon two factors—the type of design or the type of flower and the labor required to design with it. Labor-intensive designs or flowers would have a higher mark-up. Hardgoods would still have a 2:1 or 2.5:1 mark-up.

Type of Design	Mark-up
Basic arrangements, bud vases, boxed flowers, decorated plants	3:1
Creative designs, corsages	4:1
Wedding flowers, party flowers, special designs requiring time and attention	5:1 (or more)

24-8. Different mark-ups for different types of designs are called creative ratio mark-ups.

Type of Flower	Labor Required	Mark-up
Form flowers (orchids, lilies, tropicals, standard or Fuji mums)	low	2½:1
Average flowers (carnations, gladiolus, roses — need de-thorning)	medium	3½:1
Filler flowers (spray mums, daisies, statice, baby's breath, heather, foliage)	high	4:1

24-9. Some florists may use variable ratio mark-up for the different labor-requiring types of flowers.

		Ratio Mark-up	Variable Ratio Mark-up
Standard carnation	$0.24/stem	$0.72	$0.84
Orchid	$1.20/flower	$3.60	$3.00
Pompon spray mums	$0.60/stem	$1.80	$2.40 (5–7 placements)

24-10. Comparison of flower prices calculated with both ratio mark-up and variable ratio mark-up

The strength of the variable ratio mark-up is that the labor aspect of designing is included in the design. However, the planning for net profit is still a matter of guesswork. Another weakness may be the confusion of so many mark-ups. The owner can periodically post a retail price list with the varying mark-ups included (but not shown) without causing confusion to the employee.

PERCENTAGE MARK-UP

The **percentage mark-up** is a pricing method that plans for profit. The percentage mark-up method is the wholesale cost of goods divided by the cost of goods percentage as determined by the shop's financial statement. This pricing method requires the florist to analyze the business' financial records to determine the percentages of the four major aspects of gross sales (the total amount of sales for the year). At first, this analysis may be time-consuming, but once completed, the percentage mark-up is easy to calculate.

First, let's look at the four major parts of gross sales and some typical percentages based on averaged figures.

$$\text{Gross sales} = \text{Operating Expenses} + \text{Labor} + \text{Cost of Goods} + \text{Net Profit}$$
$$100\% = 35\% + 20\% + 30\% \ (30\text{–}33\%) + 15\% \ (12\text{–}15\%)$$

The four areas will vary somewhat from shop to shop. **Gross sales** are the total dollar amounts that the florist sells. **Operating expenses** include the costs of running the business, such as rent or costs of owning the building, salaries, selling costs (for wire services fees, advertising), delivery costs, and administrative costs. The operating expenses may be lower if the florist owns

24-11. Rent or the costs of owning the building are part of the operating expenses. (Courtesy, Kuhn Flowers, Jacksonville, FL)

the building, requiring no mortgage payment or rent. **Labor** is an operating expense that is calculated separately. Labor is the cost for the required time to design the specialized products that florists sell. **Cost of goods** is the cost of purchasing merchandise and materials that comprises the designs, plants, and giftware sold in a florist. **Net profit** is the return on the florist's investment, which can be reinvested or considered as the owner's income. The florist can plan for profit in a range of 10 to 15 percent. In the sample shown, if a 15 percent profit is planned, the cost of goods should be 30 percent; if 12 percent profit is projected, the cost of goods can be 33 percent.

Now, how do these figures relate to pricing? The cost of goods used in a design is calculated as 30 percent of the design price. For each arrangement, 30 percent of the price will be the actual wholesale cost of the flowers, foliages, and supplies.

Let's use the vase arrangement in Figure 24-5. The wholesale cost of goods is $4.95. To find the price, the cost of goods is divided by the cost of goods percentage. This method is also called the divisional percentage mark-up. Remember, the cost of goods is divided by the cost of goods percentage.

$4.95 ÷ 30% or $4.95 ÷ .3 = $16.50

The strength of the percentage mark-up is the planning for profit and knowing the specific percentages for each category, including cost of goods, for the individual floral shop. Although the preparation of this information may take some time, the effort will pay off with an efficient pricing system. A

Pricing Method	Price
Ratio mark-up (2:1 and 3:1)	$13.90
Ratio mark-up (3:1 for everything)	$14.85
Ratio mark-up plus labor	$17.15
Variable mark-up by flower type (carnations 3½:1)	$14.95
Variable mark-up by type of design (basic—3:1)	$13.90
Percentage mark-up (30% cost of goods)	$16.50

24-12. A comparison of the different pricing methods for the same carnation vase arrangement is an interesting exercise.

disadvantage is that the employee may not know wholesale prices of goods to make the calculations. However, the manager or owner could determine prices using this method for specials and for numerous commonly purchased designs, plants, and corsages. Planning for profit is profitable!

If the customer requests an arrangement for a specific amount, the price is multiplied by 30 percent to determine the cost of goods that can be used to make the arrangement. For example, a $20.00 arrangement should have $6.00 of wholesale costs in flowers, foliages, and supplies, including the vase.

$$\$20.00 \times 30\% = \$6.00 \text{ or } \$20.00 \times .3 = \$6.00$$

A florist must decide which pricing method fits the management style and the type of operation. The method chosen should provide the owner with enough profit without charging exorbitant prices.

PRICING STRATEGIES

Pricing strategies are well-planned methods and practices of pricing to attract customers to the floral shop and to motivate them to buy the products, perhaps more than originally planned. Using pricing strategies can help to increase sales volume and gross sales.

STRATEGIES TO ATTRACT CUSTOMERS

A good retailer is always thinking of ways to attract new customers to the floral shop. Advertising through window displays or print media can lure new buyers into the shop. Leader pricing, tie-in pricing, and advertised specials offering a good buy or a free item can bring new customers.

Leader Pricing

Leader pricing is a method of offering commonly purchased and recognizable items, such as carnations, daisies, roses, or special giftware, at a significantly reduced price compared to the competition. This strategy will attract new buyers and price-conscious customers and give the impression that all of the prices are more reasonable than the competition. The leader pricing method can be effectively used when good buys have been negotiated with trusted suppliers.

Multiple Unit Pricing

Multiple unit pricing is a strategy to encourage the customer to come to the shop and then buy more by offering price breaks for purchasing additional items. For example, one iris costs $1.75 and three irises cost $4.50 (a $.75 savings). The customer will feel that they are getting a lot for their money.

Advertised "end of the week" bouquet specials can encourage customers to stop by and pick up some flowers. Make (or purchase) cheerful mixes of flowers, give the bouquets a catchy title, and place the display in a prominent place to encourage the buyer. The single stems priced individually cost more than the mixture, which encourages the customer to buy the whole bunch.

A "buy one, get one free" special is another multiple unit pricing strategy. This method attracts customers to the shop because of the great bargains being advertised. Plan ahead for this method and work with the suppliers to find some good flower buys. Use this strategy carefully so the shop will not develop a "discount store" image.

STRATEGIES TO MOTIVATE MORE BUYING

Price Everything

Everything in the store should be priced to motivate a customer to buy. If a customer cannot figure out a price for something, she may just walk away and not buy it. Individual price tags can be tied on or pressed on like stickers. Signs or color-coded tags or stickers are another way to inform a customer about individual prices without placing a price tag on each one. The signs should be highly visible and informative to grab attention and encourage the buyer. For example, signs could be placed in each flower container informing the customer that these flowers are $1 each or 3 for $2.50. Every container would have its own pricing sign. Other decorative signs could price candles, ribbon, or vases. One-of-a-kind items should have an individual price tag to avoid confusion.

Rounding Prices

A common pricing strategy is to round up a price that comes out an odd number, such as $22.37 or $22.53. The price would be rounded up to the

24-13. Signs on in-store displays is one way to inform customers about individual prices. (Courtesy, Florists Transworld Delivery Association, Southfield, MI)

nearest 50 cents or dollar. The $22.37 price would be rounded up to $22.50 and $22.53 to $23.00. Do not round $22.53 to $22.50 because the loss of 3 cents will mean lost profits. For larger items, the price may be rounded from $122.53 to $125.00. All employees should be consistent and price by rounding in the same way.

Odd End Pricing

Some florists and other retailers prefer to price items with another rounding technique. *Odd end pricing* is rounding a product's price to $12.95 or $12.99, instead of a $13.00 price. The psychology is that the $12.95 price seems less expensive than $13.00 and will entice a customer to purchase something. If the odd end pricing method is adopted, the florist should choose the number to use—$.95 or $.99 and then consistently use it for all of the products and designs.

Multiple Price Points Strategy

Multiple price points is a method of pricing and displaying several related designs or products in varying sizes and varying prices to provide customer choice. The multiple price points will let the customer choose among various designs, such as vase arrangement 6, 9, or 12 flowers. Another offering to provide multiple price points would be to design in "nested" baskets. *Nested baskets* are baskets in three different sizes with one placed inside another. These three baskets could each have a unique style and mixture of flowers, each with a different price. The different price points or levels give the customer more choice and satisfaction when purchasing flowers.

Tie-In Pricing

Tie-in pricing is a method to encourage customers to buy related items by offering special discounted prices when the products are purchased at the same time. The florist can offer tie-in pricing for items that are a natural fit, such as a potted plant and watering can or a beautiful centerpiece and candles. Effective display of these items and eye-catching signs can motivate the shopper to purchase both products for a good price.

REVIEWING

M AIN IDEAS

A florist may purchase flowers, foliages, and other supplies from wholesale florists, growers, flower markets, and brokers. To be a successful buyer, the florist should be knowledgeable about flower quality, price, and helpful buying practices and should try to build a good relationship with suppliers.

The unit cost of goods is the price of a single item, calculated by dividing the overall bunch or case price by the number of items in the bunch or case. The unit cost of goods should be calculated for every item in an arrangement or item sold. Lists of up-to-date unit cost of goods should be calculated on a regular basis. Combined pricing is a method of determining the total costs of typical supplies used in an arrangement.

The methods of pricing design work are the ratio mark-up and its variations and the percentage mark-up.

The ratio mark-up method of pricing relies on a predetermined mark-up from the wholesale cost of goods. Hardgoods or supplies typically have a 2:1 mark-up; perishables (flowers and foliages) typically have a 3:1 mark-up.

The ratio mark-up has several variations. One variation is to add a labor charge. This labor fee can be calculated on the employee's hourly wage or the employer's actual cost of labor, which is the hourly wage plus fringe benefits and other employee costs. Another method to calculate labor would be to add a 10 to 20 percent labor charge to the final price.

The variable ratio mark-up is yet another type of ratio mark-up. Different mark-ups are figured depending upon either 1) the type of design or 2) the type of flower and the labor required to design with it. Basis designs and bud vases have the common 3:1 mark-up and the pricing would not change from the ratio mark-up method. Creative designs and corsages would have a 4:1 mark-up; wedding and party flowers would warrant a 5:1 mark-up because of the labor involved.

The weakness of the various ratio mark-up methods is the failure to provide for profit in a definitive way. Profit planning is a guessing game. Labor is also accounted for in some variations but not others.

The percentage mark-up is a pricing method that plans for profit. Net profit is one of four areas comprising gross sales. Net profit, the florist's return on the investment, should fall within a 10 to 15 percent range. A typical florist may have a 30 to 33 percent cost of goods percentage. If the florist chooses a 30 percent cost of goods percentage, 30 percent of a design's selling price should be the wholesale cost of goods. For a $20.00 arrangement, $6.00 is the wholesale cost of goods used to design the arrangement. $20.00 is multiplied by 30 percent to compute the wholesale cost of goods. To determine a price after designing, a design with $5.00 cost of supplies used will cost $16.66 or $16.70. The $5.00 is divided by 30 percent. This method is also called the divisional percentage mark-up because the wholesale cost is divided by the percentage.

Pricing strategies are well-planned methods and practices of pricing to attract customers to the floral shop and to motivate them to buy the products. Strategies to attract new customers include leader pricing and multiple unit pricing. Leader pricing is a method of offering commonly purchased and recognizable items, such as carnations and roses, at a significantly reduced price compared to the competition. Multiple unit pricing is a strategy to encourage a new customer to come to the store and then buy more by offering price breaks for purchasing additional items. Advertised specials can also encourage buying multiple items as well as a "buy one, get one free" campaign.

Strategies to motivate increased buying include pricing everything, rounding up prices to even or odd end amounts, having multiple price points, and using tie-in pricing. Pricing everything in the store makes it quick and convenient for the customer to know the price of an item and then buy it. Rounding prices up to easy numbers such as 50 cents or the dollar or rounding up to odd end amounts, such as $14.99, plays on the psychology of the numbers chosen in the minds of the customer. Even pricing is clear-cut and easy to remember; odd end pricing makes the product seem less expensive. Having multiple price points—differing sizes and prices of items—gives the customer choice and more satisfaction in flower selection. Tie-in pricing encourages an additional purchase of a related product with the purchase of certain item. For example, with each centerpiece purchase, candles may be purchased for 50 cents off the purchase price.

A florist must decide which pricing strategies to adopt and then use them in a consistent way.

QUESTIONS

Answer the following questions. Use correct spelling and complete sentences.

1. Where can a florist purchase flowers and supplies needed to conduct a retail business?

2. Why is buying an important responsibility for the florist?

3. What is a unit cost of goods? How is it calculated?

4. What is combined pricing? How can this method save time when pricing?

5. How are retail prices determined using the ratio mark-up method?

6. What are weaknesses of the ratio mark-up method of pricing?

7. What are two ways to charge for labor using the ratio mark-up method?

8. What are the four major parts of gross sales? What are some typical percentages for each part, as well as gross sales?

9. How is the percentage mark-up method calculated?

10. What are four effective pricing strategies for attracting and motivating customers to buy?

EVALUATING

Match the term with the correct definition. Write the letter by the term in the blank provided.

a. retail price
b. leader pricing
c. wholesale cost of goods
d. odd end pricing
e. multiple price points
f. broker
g. hardgoods
h. wholesale florist
i. pricing strategies
j. unit cost of goods
k. ratio mark-up
l. percentage mark-up

_____ 1. Rounding up to $9.99 or $9.95 so the design seems less expensive.

_____ 2. An agent who purchases and sells flower inventory.

_____ 3. The selling price.

_____ 4. The price of a single item in a case or bunch.

_____ 5. The pricing methods and practices to attract and motivate customers to buy.

_____ 6. Selling common items at significantly reduced prices.

_____ 7. A source of fresh and perishable materials linking the retail florist and the grower or broker.

_____ 8. Offering items of varying sizes and prices as a customer choice.

_____ 9. The total of all unit costs of goods, both perishable and non-perishable, in an arrangement.

_____ 10. Supplies or non-perishable items.

_____ 11. A pricing method that plans for profit.

_____ 12. A pricing method which relies on a predetermined increase from the cost of goods.

EXPLORING

1. Price a vase arrangement of 15 mixed flowers and 10 stems of foliage. Use the following wholesale prices: $.50 for 5 flowers, $.75 for 5 flowers, and $1.00 for the last 5 flowers, foliage at $.25 per stem, vase at $1.00, floral preservative at $.05. The design time was 15 minutes. Price this arrangement using 1) ratio mark-up, 2) ratio mark-up plus labor, 3) percentage mark-up. Choose a rounding up strategy, and list the three prices. Compare the three prices; rank them from most expensive to least expensive. Which method would you use and why?

2. Use the variable ratio mark-up to figure the price of another design using the 15 flowers in a $3.00 vase with $1.00 foam. All costs listed are wholesale. For this method, the five $.50 flowers are filler flowers (high labor), the five $.75 flowers are average labor-requiring ones, and the five $1.00 flowers are form flowers with low labor requirements. Compare this price to the first three.

3. Visit a florist, and list how many pricing strategies are being featured. Note your own reaction to the strategies. Which type or types do you think are the most tempting for a buyer? Why?

25

The Retail Flower Shop

The retail flower shop business is so much more than designing with flowers. A good floral designer should ask, "What other qualifications should I have to become a successful florist?" The astute florist should be aware and knowledgeable about the niche that their business fills in their location. Marketing, advertising, and effective selling, packaging, and delivery are each important facets of the florist business.

25-1. A successful florist has a strong base of knowledge about both designing and selling flowers.

OBJECTIVES

1   Describe the qualifications to be a florist

2   Know the types of flower shops

3   Learn the basics about good location and starting a floral shop

4   Describe the importance of marketing and promotion

5   Explain the importance of effective sales skills

6   Learn about effective packaging and delivery

7   Explain key aspects of an effective flower shop floor plan

TERMS

bucket shop
business plan
carriage trade shop
clearinghouse
demographic study
display
empty nest couples
fictitious name statement
filling florist
franchise
gray market

marketing
marketing mix
promotion
resale permit
satellite shop
sending florist
stem shop
tax number
up-selling
visual merchandising

QUALIFICATIONS TO BE A FLORIST

What does it take to be a successful florist? A successful florist needs floral knowledge, business understanding and know-how, and highly developed personal qualities.

FLORAL KNOWLEDGE

Most people enter the florist trade because of their love of flowers and plants. A floral designer wanting to open his or her own shop should also have training and knowledge of cut flower and foliage care and handling, elementary and advanced floral design training, and knowledge of effective display techniques. Creative flair and the ability to spot or keep up with trends can give any florist an edge.

Beginning designers can learn floral skills by working at a flower shop and by taking courses at the high school, community college, and university levels. Floral design schools at various locations throughout the country and the world also offer intensive training of three- or four-week duration. Gaining experience by working at several types of shops is great training to someday own and operate a floral shop.

BUSINESS KNOWLEDGE

The business side of being a florist is very important. For example, a knowledgeable florist will want to develop business skills in advertising and marketing, buying and inventory control, effective pricing strategies, computer skills, bookkeeping and accounting, and training a sales force.

Since it is difficult to be proficient in every area, be sure to hire competent, trustworthy people in the areas in which you are weak. Some florist businesses are partnerships to allow the combining of strengths. For example, one partner may be a great businessperson while the other partner is a creative and artistic floral designer who does not care about the daily ends and outs of the business.

Involvement in the Chamber of Commerce and other community activities can be a smart business practice. Community involvement lets the florist be knowledgeable about local business issues and builds name recognition and possibly a greater customer base.

Floral Knowledge	Business Skills	Personal Attributes
Flowers	Advertising	Honest
Care/handling	Marketing	Trustworthy
Design	Personnel management	Consistent
Display techniques	Buying and inventory management	Self starter
Creativity	Pricing knowledge	Motivated
Trend watcher	Computer skills	Energetic
	Bookeeping/accountancy skills	Patient
	Salesmanship skills	Tactful, compassionate
	Good communicator	Ethical
	Delegator	Friendly, polite
		Goal oriented

25-2. Qualifications of a successful florist.

PERSONAL ATTRIBUTES

Personal skills are equally important for a successful florist. Personal qualities, such as honesty, trustworthiness, drive and energy, patience, tact, compassion, consistency, and integrity, are valuable attributes for the ethical businessperson. A florist who is a "people person" and a good communicator is a win-win combination for employees and customers alike. A florist who is dependable and pays creditors on time is a valuable member of the community.

TYPES OF FLOWER SHOPS

Retail flower shops are as varied as the people operating them. However, florist shops do fit into some broad categories. Florist shops can be full-service shops, large-volume shops, carriage trade businesses, specialty shops, or stem shops. Flower shops can be satellite operations or franchises.

FULL-SERVICE

A full-service neighborhood flower shop is the traditional type of retail florist. This type of shop offers a wide range of services and products. A full-service neighborhood shop is a member of a wire service, does wedding and sympathy work, and all types of design work.

The person who owns and operates a full-service neighborhood shop should have good business and design knowledge and be versatile in many areas, such as waiting on customers, ordering and picking up flowers, doing some book work, setting up window displays, and arranging flowers. This florist is good at many duties and enjoys both flowers and a variety of activities, rather than organizing and motivating others.

LARGE-VOLUME FLORIST

A large-volume florist sells a large quantity of design work because of an excellent, well-executed marketing plan. This type of shop has identified the floral needs of its market area. Eye catching, profitable, often mass-produced designs, and effective marketing and advertising are the key aspects of a large-volume shop. A large-volume shop can be mostly full service but with restricted, but profitable product lines and design services. Much time is spent on planning, budgeting, financing, and training.

The person who runs a large-volume florist is a businessperson who understands what customers want and is effective in creating marketing ideas and strategies to excite the customer to buy the product. This florist is an organizer, a planner, and a motivator of employees.

PARTY/WEDDING FLORIST

The party/wedding florist shop is a specialty shop that has restricted its design services to event planning, that is party work and wedding work. The specialty shop should be located in a market area that can support this type of design specialization. Sometimes, the party/wedding flower shop will work cooperatively with other related businesses, such as bridal gown shops, caterers, wedding rental places, and printing places, specializing in wedding and party invitations.

The person who is a party and wedding florist should be extremely creative and resourceful in carrying out the ideas. It is important to be creative and dramatic as well as a good communicator who can sell these ideas to the client. A party/wedding florist likes the challenge of making a striking statement with each new event and likes to work on a flexible, varied schedule.

CARRIAGE TRADE SHOP

A **carriage trade shop** provides extensive personal service to a limited, elite clientele. This type of shop may offer the same services as a full-service shop but in a lavish, upscale manner to a limited customer base. Corporate accounts and wealthy clientele make up the customer base.

A person who operates a carriage trade shop must first develop name and reputation recognition with the desired customers. A designer should be very creative to consistently design new and striking floral designs. It is also essential to understand and to effectively communicate with these types of customers.

25-3. A carriage trade florist provides lavish, personal, full service to a limited elite customer base.

STEM SHOP OR BUCKET SHOP

A **stem shop** is a cash and carry operation that offers a wide variety of flowers and foliages by the single stem or as bunches. Another name for a stem shop is a **bucket shop** because the flowers are sold out of containers or buckets directly to the public. A stem shop does not offer arrangements or delivery. The product line is fresh flowers and possibly a few vases. A high-traffic area is essential for the success of a stem shop.

An operator of a bucket shop should enjoy fresh flowers and foliages but not be interested in the artistic design aspect of the florist business. This type of owner should be conscious of customers' preferences and be an effective buyer of the needed product. A stem shop fits a person with a low-key management style and good mathematical skills. Generally, just a few employees are needed to run this type of shop.

25-4. A stem shop sells flowers, rather than arrangements and services.

SATELLITE SHOP

A **satellite shop** is a second business location operated by a large, full-service flower shop. Some full-service shops open a second location in a shopping mall or strip mall. The mall location is primarily for merchandising and selling, not for designing because of the expense of the space. Other satellite locations may be in a hospital gift shop or office building.

The owner who decides to add a satellite shop should be well versed in the business aspects of a multi-shop operation. Planning, organization, and training of sales personnel for the second location are valuable skills needed to make the satellite shop financially viable.

FRANCHISES

A **franchise** is a flower shop that is purchased from and operated according to the parent company's operating specifications. The owner pays a percentage of the gross sales to the parent company. There are not many franchise retail flower businesses, but the advantage of a franchise business is name recognition and proven business techniques and products. The initial cost of purchasing the franchise can be quite high.

A person interested in purchasing a franchise should have strong business skills. Since the franchise determines the designs and product line, a strong floral design background is not a requirement. A proven business and advertising track record appeals to some florists who are not interested in building a business, but running one.

In summary, a prospective florist should match his or her interests and skills to the requirements of a particular type of flower shop. The type of floral shop should also fit the location, geographical area, and desired target market.

LOCATION, LOCATION, LOCATION

A floral expert was once asked what were the three most important components of a successful flower shop. He replied, "Location, location, location!" Location must be important!

A prospective florist should research the state, the city, and then the neighborhood before selecting an established business or a new site. Look at the number of competing businesses in the city or neighborhood. As a general rule, 15,000 people can support one flower shop. Determine the size and then the population of the prospective area to be served. Divide the population by the current number of flower shops to see if the market is already saturated with florists in that area. Also, look at traffic flow, parking accessibility, site visibility, and availability of wholesale florists. Look at the population trends. A site in a growing area has much potential.

Besides the geographical research, both economic and demographic information should be gathered before making a decision about location. This information can be obtained from the county regional planning commission, the chamber of commerce, or the library. Look at the economic factors of a location, such as employment and income of the customer base, the per capita retail sales, and the health of the local business economy.

A *demographic study* is the reporting of the size and distribution of population in a specific area. Demographics can reveal the population age and education level. The age of the population can be important to the florist because of age-specific buying habits. For example, singles and couples from ages 25 to 45 usually have higher discretionary income and have great potential as good flower buyers because of their entertaining habits and spontaneous purchases. Couples or single parents with children at home (any age) are more children-oriented and spend less on flowers except for holidays, such as Mother's Day or Christmas. The *empty nest couples* (younger than 65, still

Geographic Factors	Economic Factors	Demographic Factors
State, city, neighborhood	Employment	Population age
Population	Income	Education
Population trends	Per capita retail sales	
Number of competing businesses	Health of the local businesses	
Traffic flow		
Parking		
Site visibility		
Availability of wholesale florists		

25-5. Is this location a good one? Factors to consider...

employed, children no longer at home) have great potential as good flower buyers because of higher discretionary income and entertaining needs. The *gray market* (over 65, generally retired) spends money on traditional flower needs, such as holidays or birthdays, and usually have more controlled spending due to a fixed income.

A BUSINESS PLAN

A *business plan* is an organizational business tool to state the business' purpose and goals and estimate the financing needed to fund the new florist. A description of the proposed business is an integral part of the business plan. The business plan is an essential document to present to a banker when seeking financing.

A business plan may include (but is not limited to) the following sections:

Introductory Material

Title Page — Logo
           Company name and address
           Owners' names and telephone numbers
Table of Contents
Statement of Purpose — 1) Business goals
               2) Purpose of this document
                    *Application for financing
                    *Give summary of specific capital needs

Business Data

Market and Competition Analysis

Description of the Business — Type of flower shop
Business niche
Products and services

Business Operation — A description of operation from product procurement to manufacturing, sales, and delivery

Location — Give a description of the site
Give building specifications (floor plan)
List traffic-flow count
For a new location, identify at least two location options

Marketing Plan — The marketing plan will describe the initial promotion and advertising strategies as well as the long range plans for advertising and promotion

Future Change Strategies —List the long-range plans for growth and expansion

Management Team

Operating Personnel

Venture Development Schedule — For a new business, show a 12-month time frame of the business from its conception to its opening

Proposed Use of Requested Capital

Critical Risks and Problems — List the difficulties and problems that may occur after the business is open and the plans to overcome them

Summary

Financial Data

(The prospective owner will need to submit a personal financial statement.)

Capital Needs and Sources — List the source of all capital, including the owner's funding and other loans and investments.

Capital Equipment List — List all equipment needs, including a cooler, computer system, delivery vehicle, display tables, wrapping tables, design tables, office furniture, and non-inventory items.

Balance Sheet at the Start of the Business

Break-even Analysis

Income Forecast

Cash-Flow Analysis

Balance Sheet — Three year summary and three yearly forecasts

Loan Proposal

A prospective owner should consult with a certified public accountant to prepare portions of the business plan. Other information can be included in the appendix, such as the floor plan and shop front illustration, biographical information about the owner(s), and an equipment list for a similar operation.

BUSINESS LICENSES AND REQUIREMENTS

Business licenses are a required part of operating legally as a florist. The required permits and licenses are regulated at the federal, state, county, and local levels. Since state, county, and local regulations vary widely, a florist should thoroughly check with state, county, and local officials to determine proper compliance.

Five important licenses or requirements are new business, employer, resale, professional, and special use. The first three areas are the most critical for the business aspects of starting a new flower shop.

NEW BUSINESS LICENSES

New business licenses include a fictitious name statement, any operating licenses required by the state, county, or local governments, and any local building permits. A *fictitious name statement* is a document that must be filed with the county to register the business name and prevent another business from using that name in the county. The florist is required to pay a filing fee and publish the fictitious name statement in two publications in the county. For information on zoning laws, occupancy permits, and fire code compliance, check with the county clerk's office and the local city hall.

EMPLOYER REQUIREMENTS

Any florist who has employees must have a Federal Employer Identification Number (FEIN). Some states also require a State Employer Identification Number. Both the Internal Revenue Service and the Social Security Administration use the FEIN to identify the florist's business. If a florist is a sole proprietorship with no employees, the florist's social security number is used instead of a FEIN to identify the business. Contact the Internal Revenue Service to apply for a FEIN and to request federal tax forms required of a new business. A floral business must complete quarterly and year-end payroll tax returns.

A florist with one or more employees must comply with Occupational Safety and Health administration (OSHA) requirements. The latest regulations are available from the Department of Labor in Washington, D.C.

25-6. A florist must have a resale license by sell flowers, collect tax, and buy goods from a wholesaler.

RESALE LICENSES

Every business must have a *resale license* or permit (also called a *tax number* or seller's permit) to register the business as a seller, to collect sales tax, and to buy goods for resale from a wholesaler without paying tax. (This license does not apply to states that do not collect tax.) A tax number or resale license is applied for with the state's Department of Revenue. Once the permit or number is received and used, the florist must remit sales tax to the state on a monthly, quarterly, or yearly basis, depending on the state. Check with the local county clerk's office or city hall to determine if municipal or county resale licenses are required.

PROFESSIONAL LICENSES

Professional licensing for florists is not mandatory in most states. The regulations should however be researched with the state Department of Agriculture before proceeding with financing and a new business. Many wire services and state florists' associations are providing certification programs to increase the educational and professional level of the florist industry.

SPECIAL USE LICENSES

Special use licenses include a liquor license and a pesticide applicator's license. Check with local and state agencies for the details. The pesticide applicator's license is administered through the state Department of Agriculture. The use of helium is regulated with required helium tank inspections and possible additional regulation in the future.

IMPORTANT AFFILIATIONS AND SUBSCRIPTIONS

Affiliation with a wire service is an integral part of providing good service for customers. The wire services (in the order of their establishment) include Florists' Transworld Delivery Association (FTD), Teleflora, Florafax, American Floral Services, and Carik. A florist who sells a wire service order is called a *sending florist*. The sending florist sends the order by phone, computer, or fax to a florist in the city and zip code of the person who will receive the flowers. The florist who fills or designs the order and delivers it is called the *filling florist*. Each month, the *clearinghouse*, the wire service's main office, settles the accounts for each florist and sends a bill or a check to the florist. The sending florist receives a small percentage of each order sent.

Membership in state florists' associations, allied (regional) florists' associations, and other professional floral design organizations can help the florist by providing continuing education and networking opportunities. The Society of American Florists (SAF) is a national trade association, which lobbies for and represents the needs of all facets of the industry. Any qualified floriculture-related business or individual may apply.

Several organizations are joined by invitation only or by meeting specific requirements. These organizations include AIFD (American Institute of Floral Designers), AAF (American Academy of Floriculture), and PFCI (Professional Floral Commentators). For continuing wire service membership, florists pay 1 percent of outgoing wire orders as their dues.

Subscription to floral industry publications is also an important education source. A complete list is given.

American Academy of Floriculture
c/o Society of American Florists
1601 Duke Street
Alexandria, VA 22314
(800) 336-4743

American Institute of Floral Designers
720 Light Street
Baltimore, MD 21230
(301) 752-3320

American Floral Marketing Council
c/o Society of American Florists
1601 Duke Street
Alexandria, VA 22314
(800) 336-4743 or (703) 836-8700

Professional Floral Commentators—International
c/o Society of American Florists
1601 Duke Street
Alexandria, VA 22314
(800) 336-4743

Society of American Florists
1601 Duke Street
Alexandria, VA 22314
(800) 336-4743

25-7. Trade organizations.

Floral Management (monthly by SAF)
Society of American Florists
1601 Duke Street
Alexandria, VA 22314-3406
(800) 336-4743
(703) 836-8700

Floral Nursery Times
629 Green Bay Road
Wilmette, IL 60091
(708) 256-8777

Floral Finance (monthly by AFS)
Floral Finance, Inc.
8001 S. Yale, Suite 400
Tulsa, OK 74137
(800) 722-9934
(918) 491-9933

Florists' Review (13 times a year)
Florists' Review Enterprises, Inc.
P.O. Box 4368
Topeka, KS 66611
(913) 266-0888

Flowers & (monthly by Teleflora)
Teleflora Plaza
Suite 260
12233 W. Olympic Blvd.
Los Angeles, CA 90064
(213) 826-5253

Holland Flower (quarterly by the Flower Council of Holland)
Flower Council of Holland
250 West 57th Street
New York, NY 10019
(212) 307-1818

Florist (monthly by FTD)
29200 Northwestern Highway
P.O. Box 2227
Southfield, MI 48037
(313) 355-9300

Flower News (weekly)
549 W. Randolph Street
Chicago, IL 60606
(800) 732-4581

PFD (Professional Floral Designer)
American Floral Services, Inc.
P.O. Box 12309
Oklahoma City, OK 73157-2309
(800) 456-7890

Floral Mass Marketing (bimonthly)
Cenflo, Inc.
549 W. Randolph Street
Chicago, IL 60606
(312) 236-8648

Supermarket Floral (monthly)
Vance Publishing
7950 College Blvd.
Overland Park, KS 66210
(913) 451-2200

SAF: Business News for the Floral Industry
Society of American Florists
1601 Duke Street
Alexandria, VA 22314
(800) 336-4743

The Retail Florist (monthly by American Services, Inc.)
The Retail Florist
Attn: Promotional Services
American Floral Services, Inc.
P.O. Box 12309
Oklahoma City, OK 73157-2309
(800) 456-7890

25-8. Floral industry publications.

MARKETING AND PROMOTION

EFFECTIVE MARKETING

Effective marketing is an essential aspect of the successful florist. *Marketing* is the process of selling products and providing services that the customer wants or needs. The goal of marketing is to determine the most effective marketing mix and marketing strategies for the targeted customers.

A *marketing mix* is a combination of activities and shop characteristics, such as advertising, shop layout, window display, writing educational articles for the newspaper, pricing strategy, and selling techniques, which a florist implements to attract and retain his or her targeted customers. A shop's marketing mix will vary depending upon the target market (targeted customers).

Every florist should follow the five guidelines or steps for effective marketing:

1. Define the specialties or strengths of this floral business.

2. Define the targeted customers or target market.

3. Determine the products the customers want to buy.

4. Determine how to communicate the message.

5. Decide the specific products and services to offer the target market.

This case study will follow the five steps of effective marketing:

- Step 1—A florist who defines his shop's specialties or strengths realizes that creating and selling flowers for non-holidays is an important emphasis and strength.

- Step 2—The targeted market would traditionally be the gray market and empty nesters; however, this florist wants to bring in more customers in the singles and couples groups.

- Step 3—The gray and empty nest groups want traditional, high-quality arrangements. The singles and couples want more contemporary styles and more casual, loose arrangements.

- Step 4—To reach the new targeted group, the florist tries three activities. He runs a radio spot on a station with a large group of 25- to 45-year-old listeners, gives an arranging demonstration for the local young women's group in town, and changes the shop layout and window display to emphasize both types of design styles.

■ Step 5—The florist determines that he will offer the following products based on the targeted customers.

For the **gray market and empty nesters**, he will continue to offer traditional centerpieces and one-sided designs.

To attract new **singles and couples** customers, two up-scale designs, a vase arrangement of unique flowers for $20 and a high-style design for $30, will be promoted.

Promotion and Advertising

Promotion encompasses a variety of activities that lead to public name recognition. These activities—the tools of promotion—are advertising, community involvement, contests, coupons, demonstrations, direct mail, educational articles or a newspaper column, logo and image development including the packaging and delivery vehicle, effective selling techniques, public relations, publicity, signage, and window display.

As a part of the marketing mix, advertising can effectively communicate products and services that the floral shop can provide. The most common type of advertising for a flower shop is yellow pages advertising. It is a necessary (and expensive) type of advertising because so many floral customers conduct their business over the telephone. Other types of advertising for the florist include web sites, radio spots, newspaper ads, direct mail pieces, and school or community publications. Coupons or punch cards have been used successfully by many florists to not only promote flower use but also to advertise floral services.

Smart Selling

Hiring and training excellent sales staff is a highly effective means of promotion. An effective salesperson is invaluable to the retail florist. What makes someone a good salesperson?

Qualities of a Good Salesperson

A good salesperson is a positive, motivated person who likes to work with people and is knowledgeable about flowers. Hiring someone with a friendly, personable, positive manner is important to the image of the flower shop.

The person can then be trained in shop procedures and in flower care and information. Other qualities to look for in a good salesperson are good communication skills and the ability to think quickly and work under pressure. Enthusiasm about flowers and a high energy level are very helpful attributes of a top-notch salesperson.

A good salesperson should be a good listener and a thorough note-taker. When making telephone sales, the phone should be answered promptly with a greeting, the shop's name and person's name. Smile while talking on the phone because the positive attitude will come across to the listener.

Whether taking telephone orders or in-store orders, the effective salesperson asks appropriate questions and learns all of the vital information, such as occasion, desired design style and colors, price range, message on the card, complete delivery information and

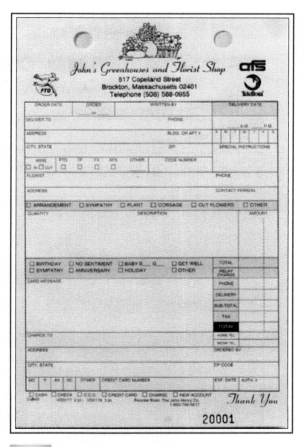

25-9. An effective salesperson will learn all of the vital information needed to make the sale.

phone number (street address, not a box number), and the payment method. The successful salesperson directs the conversation without being pushy. When describing flowers, use descriptive terms, such as velvety red or soft and fine-textured, to help the customer to visualize the product. In the store, a good sales staff uses the selection guides to help the customer decide the appropriate arrangement to purchase.

Other techniques of good personal selling are to match the customer's mood, voice rate, and volume and to practice up-selling. **Up-selling** is the sales practice of persuading a customer to make a larger purchase than originally planned by suggesting several ranges of price, not just the least expensive, and offering related products.

EFFECTIVE PACKAGING
AND DELIVERY

PACKAGING

Packaging can serve two purposes—to protect the design from the weather and to promote the shop's image. The effective packaging of flowers

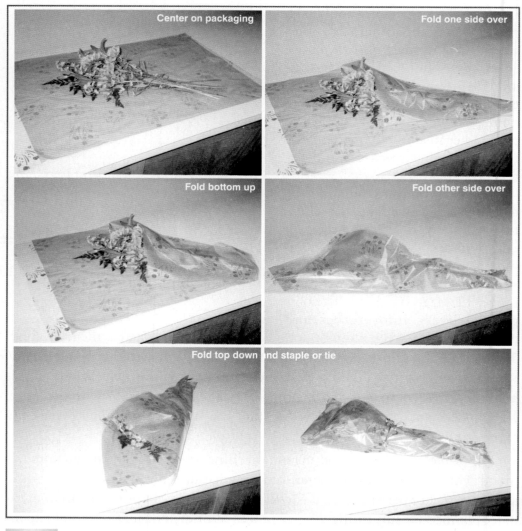

25-10. Attractive packaging can protect the flowers from the weather and promote the shop's image.

is necessary to protect the arrangement from extreme cold (below the freezing point) and high winds. For very cold days, the delivery vehicle should be running and warmed up and the arrangement should be double packaged with tissue and cellophane, plastic or paper. An attractive, image-announcing style and type of packaging should be planned and consistently carried out.

Simple bud vase and loose flowers can be covered with sleeves. Larger bunches can be packaged with cellophane, tissue, paper, or a combination of two. The bunch is centered diagonally on a square piece of packaging material. One side is loosely folded over the flowers; the lower edge is brought up; the other side is folded over the flowers. Neatly fold the edges. Staple the bunch at the bottom and the side or attach with the shop's packaging sticker. In cold weather, bring the top portion down to cover the flowers and staple again. Some shops prefer to roll the loose flowers in the paper and staple, seal with a sticker, or tie with a length of ribbon. Be sure to attach the card.

Arrangements or bridal bouquets can be protected with plastic delivery bags. Place the arrangement in the bag, blow a cushion of air into the bag, and tie with a matching or signature color of ribbon.

25-11. A centerpiece can be protected with a plastic delivery bag.

DELIVERY

Delivery is an essential part of the florist business. The delivery person is an important link between the designing process and the customer. A delivery person is responsible for general upkeep of the delivery vehicle (cleaning exterior and interior, checking gas and oil), efficient scheduling and routing of the deliveries, efficient loading of the floral products, safe and timely delivery of floral products, and occasionally performing other duties as assigned. Efficient scheduling and routing means to group orders by their proximity in the delivery area and delivery them in an organized manner. Some shops have morning and afternoon deliveries, others deliver to certain areas in the morning, such as north and east and the south and west areas in the afternoon.

Efficient loading of the delivery vehicle starts with placing the last-to-be-delivered items in the vehicle first with the closest and easiest-to-reach products comprising the first deliveries. Tall items should be placed along the sides. Every item should be securely anchored or supported with sandbags, bricks, or placed in boxes of newspapers or compartmentalized carriers.

Since the delivery person may be the only contact a customer has with the floral shop, the delivery person should have a neat appearance, polite and friendly manner, knowledge of the area, good driving ability, conscientious attitude toward delivering the product, and good speaking, reading, writing, and spelling skills. For part-time help at the holidays, off-duty police and fire personnel are an excellent source because they know the area so well.

Deliveries fall into several categories. Each shop owner or manager needs to determine what distances and locations the different categories cover and also the delivery charges for each category. The most common category is the normal or regular delivery, which is located within the predetermined everyday delivery area for the shop. The next category would be the out-of-area deliveries, which would have a larger delivery charge. A timed delivery occurs when a customer requests a special delivery time for a special anniversary or birthday. Special or last minute deliveries occur when the customer has forgotten or did not know about a floral need until the last minute. Holiday deliveries comprise the last category.

THE FLOOR PLAN

The components of a flower shop floor plan are the sales area, the design area, the wedding consultation area, and an office.

SALES AREA

The sales area starts at the outside window display and the front door. The sales area should be an inviting area with display units, tables, and shelves, the cooler, the sales counter and computer and cash register, window display, and a plant area (optional). This area should have adequate lighting, durable and attractive flooring and wall coverings, and possibly, suspended display ceilings, such as lattice or vines. Movable and changeable display units lend versatility in display possibilities.

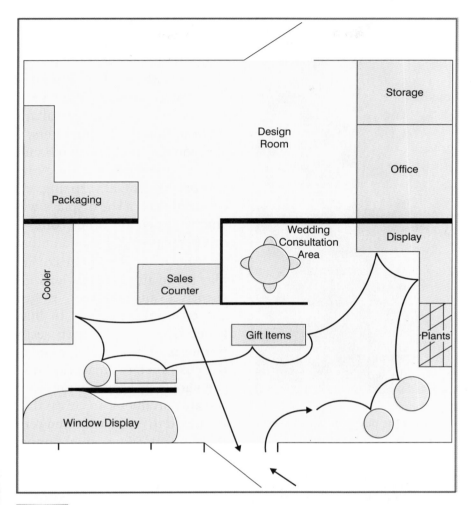

25-12. This floor plan has moveable display units, a wedding consultation area, a highly visible sales counter and cooler, and an open traffic flow that allows easy and comfortable movement through the entire sales area.

The traffic flow should encourage the customer to look at all of the merchandise. The sales counter should be easily visible from the front door for the customer and from the office or design area for the floral staff.

Effective Display in the Sales Area

The shop's signage and exterior, the colorful window display, and the interesting vignettes or settings inside the shop are all types of visual merchan-

25-13. One of the purposes of effective display is to attract attention.

dising. *Visual merchandising* is a coordinated effort and plan to attract customers to the flower shop and to motivate those customers to buy flowers and related products. *Display*, the pleasing visual arrangement of flowers and products, is one component of visual merchandising. Planning, coordinated buying, inventory control, advertising, and the coordination of the displays with the shop's image are other components of effective visual merchandising.

The primary purposes of any display are to attract attention, creating surprises and interest, motivating the customer to want to buy, and generating sales. Other secondary purposes of a display are to educate the customer, to create and reinforce the shop's image, to showcase flowers and products, to unify the sales area, and to emphasize and reinforce the current advertising campaign.

25-14. Vignettes or display settings that are carried throughout the floral shop in various ways can unify the sales area.

25-15. Educating the customer is one of the purposes of attractive displays.

DESIGN AREA

The design room or work room should include design benches, easily accessible storage for containers and supplies, a receiving and delivery area for incoming wholesale orders, as well as outgoing finished arrangements, an of-

25-16. The design room should have ample storage and a place to organize flower orders.

fice, a storage cooler, a supply and props storage area, and a potting area (if needed). The design area needs good lighting, easily accessible water source (faucets with hoses or overhead water sources at the design benches), drains to accommodate water spillage, ample shelving, and an area to organize the flower orders, both daily and weekly.

WEDDING CONSULTATION AREA

The wedding consultation area should located where the conversation will be undisturbed by telephones or other people. A table and enough chairs to accommodate three or four people should be provided.

OFFICE

For convenience and supervision, the office should be located near the sales area and the design room. It should be adequately equipped with modern office equipment, such as a computer with Internet access, a fax machine, a copy machine, and a telephone with as many lines as necessary to handle calls efficiently.

REVIEWING

MAIN IDEAS

The love of flowers may not be enough of a qualification for running a successful flower shop. A florist should have floral knowledge, business skills, and important personal attributes. A floral shop owner should have extensive knowledge of flowers and plants, their care and handling, and floral design expertise. Display knowledge, trend watching, and creativity are other floral skills. Needed business skills include knowledge of advertising, marketing, delegating, buying and inventory, pricing, bookkeeping and accountancy, as well as knowing when to hire a professional in an area, communication skills, and computer skills.

The types of floral shops are a full-service shop, large-volume florist, carriage trade shop, party/wedding florist, stem shop, satellite operations, and franchises. Location is very important to the success of a retail florist. Research the geographic area – state, city, and neighborhood. Look at the number of competing businesses, the population and trends, the size of the trading area, and the traffic flow, parking, and availability of wholesale florists. Research economic and demographic information, such as employment, income, prosperity of community as well as the demographics of the distribution of age within the population.

A business plan is an organizational business tool to state the business' purpose and goals and estimate the financing needed to fund a new flower shop. The business plan includes introductory material, business data and research findings and projections, and financial data.

The business licenses and permits needed for being in a retail floral business are a fictitious name statement, a Federal Employer Identification Number, a resale license, and any professional or special use licenses. Affiliation with a wire service is an integral part of providing good customer service. The wire services are FTD, Teleflora, Florafax, American Floral Services, and Carik. Membership in trade associations and professional groups is a good source of continuing education and networking.

Marketing is the process of selling products and providing services that the customer wants or needs. The astute florist should seek an effective marketing mix. A marketing mix is a combination of activities and shop characteristics, which a florist implements to attract and retain his or her targeted customers. A florist needs to define the shop's strengths and the targeted customers, determine the products the customers want to buy and how to communicate the message, and decide the specific products and services to best suit the customer's needs.

Promotion is a variety of activities that lead to public name recognition. Advertising is just one part of promotion.

A good salesperson is a positive, motivated person who likes to work with people and plants. Good communication skills, enthusiasm, and the ability to think quickly and work under pressure are other good qualities in a super salesperson.

Packaging protects the design from the weather and promotes the shop's image. Protective packaging and secure positioning in the delivery vehicle help to guarantee that the design will arrive in the condition in which it was arranged.

The floor plan of a flower shop has a sales area and a design area. The traffic flow in the sales area should be open and encourage the customer to browse through all parts of the store.

Visual merchandising is a coordinated effort and plan to attract customers to the flower shop and then motivate them to buy something. Display is one component of visual merchandising along with advertising and coordinated planning and buying.

QUESTIONS

Answer the following questions. Use correct spelling and complete sentences.

1. What type of flower shop would you like to own? Define the type you chose. Tell why you chose that type.
2. What are important aspects of location to research before choosing a site. Be thorough.
3. What is a business plan and why is it important?
4. What are the important business licenses required before opening a flower shop?

5. How do wire services work?
6. What are the components of a marketing mix for a florist?
7. How are promotion and advertising different?
8. What are qualities of an effective salesperson?
9. What are the important parts in a flower shop floor plan?
10. Why is packaging important?

EVALUATING

Match the term with the correct definition. Write the letter by the term in the blank provided.

a. marketing
b. gray market
c. bucket shop
d. filling florist

e. carriage trade shop
f. clearinghouse
g. tax number
h. demographics

i. satellite shop
j. empty nesters

_____ 1. A shop providing lavish, personal service to an elite clientele.
_____ 2. The license to register the business as a seller and to permit the collection of sales tax and buying wholesale.
_____ 3. Couples who are younger than 65, still employed, and their children are no longer at home.
_____ 4. A shop that sells flowers and foliage by the stem.
_____ 5. The florist who designs the wire service order and delivers it.
_____ 6. A second business location operated by a full-service shop.
_____ 7. The study of the size and distribution of population in a specific area.
_____ 8. The wire service's main office.
_____ 9. The process of selling products that customers want to buy.
_____ 10. People who are older than 65 and generally retired.

EXPLORING

1. Write a marketing plan for selling something at school. Interview prospective customers to help determine the products to sell.

2. Draw a floral shop floor plan for your dream florist, using the dimensions of your classroom.

3. In a floral design class, become a salesperson. With a classmate as the buyer, guide the buyer through his or her flower purchase.

Glossary

Abscisic acid—A growth-inhibiting hormone largely responsible for seed dormancy and contributes to senescence along with ethylene.

Acclimatization—The process in which a plant becomes accustomed to a new environment.

Acidic—Refers to a pH or relative concentration of hydrogen ions in a solution of 1 through 6.

Acrylic structured sheets—Glazing material manufactured with twin walls in the same fashion as polycarbonate sheets. They have a high light transmission of 86%, second only to glass. They are less flexible than polycarbonates and they are more prone to hail damage.

Advancing colors—Warm hues which look larger and seem to advance or move toward the viewer.

Adventitious roots—Roots that begin growth from the stem or a leaf.

Aeration—The exchange of gases in the media.

Aerosol—Atomized spray or smoke particles distributed through the air.

African violet—Potted flowering plant native to areas south of the equator on the African continent. Flower colors fall in the white-pink-purple range. They are produced for Valentine's Day, Easter, and Mother's Day.

Aisle runner—Fabric or cloth-like paper covering for the center aisle for the bride to walk on during the wedding ceremony.

Aisle runner tape—Double-sided tape to secure an aisle runner.

Alkaline—A pH of 8 through 14.

Alstroemeria—Known as the Peruvian lily or Inca lily, it is everblooming, produces high yields, and it is easy to grow under cool temperatures. Flowers of the *Alstroemeria* have a long vase life, two weeks or more, and come in many colors including yellow, orange, red, pink, purple, lavender, white, and bicolor.

Altar arrangements—Floral designs placed near the altar of the church to provide a beautiful frame for the bride and groom during the wedding ceremony.

Amaryllis—Tropical or sub-tropical bulb found growing naturally in South America. Varieties of amaryllis have been improved through hybridization, providing a wide range of large, colorful flowers.

American Colonial period—A simple style of floral design in the Colonies (pre-United States) that combined fresh and dried materials in arrangements.

Analog controls—Environmental controls that use proportioning thermostats or electronic sensors to run amplifiers and electronic circuitry. They integrate the operations of heating and cooling equipment.

Analogous—A color scheme incorporating colors of two or three adjacent hues on the color wheel and their tints, shades, and tones.

Anchor pin—A plastic, four-pronged design mechanic that is attached to a container and holds floral foam securely.

Annuals—Herbaceous plants that grow from seed to flower in one season before dying.

Anther—The part of the stamen that produces and holds the pollen.

Anthocynin—A plant pigment responsible for many of the blue, purple, and red colors.

Aphids—Pear-shaped, soft-bodied, usually wingless insects, green or yellowish in color, and have the ability to reproduce very rapidly.

Apical dominance—The term to describe the apical bud's dominance over the lateral buds.

Apical meristem—The primary growing point of the stem.

Arm bouquet—A grouping of flowers and foliages that is tied together and cradled in the bride's left arm.

Asexual propagation—Plant reproduction using vegetative parts of a plant.

Asiatic lilies—Bulb crop native to the Asian Continent. They come in a wide range of colors, including yellow, white, red, and orange. They are forced throughout the year.

Asymmetrical balance—Differing weights and placements of plant materials on either side of the vertical axis that appear to be visually balanced.

Automated seeders—Automated system that permits the sowing of hundreds of flats of bedding plant seeds.

Automated transplanters—Automated system in which small plants are removed from seed flats and planted into pots for finishing.

Auxins—A group of compounds that stimulate certain plant responses. The major plant response influenced by auxins is cell elongation. Auxins are produced in the apical meristem of a plant's stem and migrate down the stem.

Available water—The water that can be absorbed by the plant's roots.

Balance—Physical or visual stability of a floral design.

Bark—Organic growing media component that improves the moisture holding ability and aeration of a mix. Bark ground into fine pieces is the most useful because of its uniform qualities.

Basal plate—A hardened portion of stem tissue to which bulb scales are attached. Roots develop along the outside edge of the basal plate.

Basal rooters—Plants whose roots form at the base of the stem cutting.

Bedding plants—Bedding plants are herbaceous, annual flowers and vegetables that lack the ability to survive freezing temperatures. Bedding plants include impatiens, petunias, marigolds, tomatoes, and many other plants.

Bench—A structure that holds crops off the ground.

Bent neck—A rose that wilts and bends over just under the flower or bud.

Binding—The technique of physically tying stems together for physical support and beauty.

Biological control—The use of living organisms to control pests.

Botanical insecticides—Natural materials obtained from plants that are toxic to the insect pest.

Botrytis **blight**—A fungus disease that can attack nearly all greenhouse crops and is a common problem with cut flower storage. It causes a brown rotting and develops fuzzy, gray mold as it produces spores.

Bract—Modified leaves that take on a petal-like appearance.

Breaks—Refers to the development of lateral branches that contribute to a bushy appearance.

Brick—The typical size of floral foam, approximately the size of a fireplace brick.

Broker—An agent who purchases flowers from growers and sells the materials to both wholesale and retail florists.

Bucket shop—Another name for a stem shop.

Bud scale—Cover and protect undeveloped leaves, stem, or flowers during dormancy.

Budding—A form of grafting in which the scion consists of a bud.

Buds—Structures that contain undeveloped leaves, stem, or flowers.

Bulb—Short, flattened stems that bear fleshy food storage leaves. Examples of bulbs include tulip and Narcissus.

Bulbets—Tiny bulbs produced below the ground.

Bulbils—Tiny above ground bulbs produced in the axils of leaves.

Bulk density—The ratio of the mass of dry solids in a media to the volume of the media.

Business plan—An organizational business tool to state the business' purpose and goals and estimate the finances needed to fund a new flower shop.

Buyer—Person who locates sources of products and places bids or offers for purchase.

Calcined clay—Growing media component in which clay aggregates are heated to form hard, stable particles. Calcined clay improves water drainage and aeration in a media, has a high bulk density, and also has some cation exchange capacity.

Callous—A group of cells with no particular function.

Calyx—The collection of the sepals of a flower.

Cambium—A layer of cells where cell division takes place. These dividing cells become either xylem or phloem cells depending on which side of the cambium they are located.

Candelabra design—An arrangement of flowers attached to a candelabra for decoration during a wedding ceremony.

Candleholders—A plastic support for candles with a round fitted top for the candle and a pronged base to insert into the floral foam.

Capillary mats—Porous mats laid on a bench and wetted. The media in the pots absorb the water by capillary action.

Carotene—A pigment that produces orange-yellow colors. It plays a much smaller role in photosynthesis than chlorophyll. Carrots have a high carotene content.

Carriage trade shop—A retail florist that offers lavish full service to a limited customer base.

Cascade bouquet—A bouquet with a full rounded central area and a trailing (cascading) line of flowers and foliages.

Case cooled by forcer— Cooling method in which the bulbs are cooled in their packing cases by the forcer.

Case cooled by supplier—Cooling method in which the bulbs are cooled in their packing cases by the supplier before they are shipped to the customer. The forcer pots the bulbs upon arrival and begins the forcing process.

Casket inset piece—A small design displayed inside the casket lid.

Casket saddle—A container with a specially rounded base to fit the curving contours of a casket lid.

Casket spray—A floral tribute placed on the top of a casket during a funeral service.

Cation exchange capacity—The measure of a media's capacity to hold nutrients.

Catkin—A spike, raceme, or cyme composed of unisexual flowers without petals and falling as a unit.

Cell packs—Molded plastic containers divided into two, three, four, or six separate growing compartments used for bedding plants.

Cellular respiration—The process in which sugars made in photosynthesis are broken down into simpler molecules. The energy is applied towards growth and development of the plant.

Cellulose—Huge molecules used in cell walls for strength and rigidity that result from the bonding of thousands of glucose molecules. Once sugars are converted to cellulose, they are not reclaimed for other purposes.

Center bud removal—Method of disbudding which involves the pinching off of the most terminal flower bud.

Centering—Placing dominant plant materials along the central vertical axis.

Center of interest—An area that ties or visually pulls an arrangement together, located in the lower half of the design.

Chaplet—A garland or a wreath worn on a person's head.

Chemical control—The use of chemicals to control pests and diseases.

Chenille stem—A wire covered with soft, fuzzy chenille fibers, also known as a pipe cleaner.

Chlorophyll—A green pigment that absorbs light and is a key component of the photosynthetic process.

Chloroplasts—Specialized organelles within the individual plant cells that harness light energy. They contain chlorophyll, carotene, and xanthophyll pigments.

Chrysanthemum—Potted flowering plant originating in China, Japan, and Europe. These short-day plants come in many colors and the flower forms differ.

Chuppah—A canopy under which a Jewish bride and groom stand to be married.

Cineraria—A cool season potted flowering crop with daisy form flowers held in a cluster above the foliage. They come in blues, pinks, reds, and white.

Clearinghouse—The wire service's main office.

Clone—Offspring that are the genetic duplicates of the parent plant.

Coir—Growing media component that is a waste product of the coconut industry and a renewable resource. Its characteristics are similar to those of peat moss.

Colonial bouquet—A round bouquet.

Color wheel—A circular representation of the primary, secondary, and tertiary and their relationship to each other.

Combination method—A wiring technique that employs two methods of wiring to secure a flower or leaf within a corsage or boutonniere.

Combined pricing—A method of adding the total costs of typical supplies used for a specific arrangement in a particular vase or container.

Complementary—A color scheme of direct opposites on the color wheel and their tints, shades, and tones.

Complete flowers—Flowers that have sepals, petals, stamens, and a pistil.

Compound leaves—A petiole and two or more leaf blades called leaflets.

Computer controls—Environmental controls that utilize microprocessors. The microprocessors make complex judgements based on information from a number of sensors. Those sensors might gather information on temperature, relative humidity, and sunlight.

Computerized environmental management—Expensive environmental control systems that are accurate and offer the greatest range of uses. All pieces of automated equipment can be controlled together. For instance, vents may be open or closed at the same time curtains are open or closed. Computerized environmental management systems also can be programmed to provide different zones in the greenhouse different climate conditions.

Conditioning—Preparation of plant materials before arranging them by allowing for uptake of water or preservative solution to extend the life of the flowers.

Conical centerpiece—A cone-shaped or three-dimensional isosceles triangle centerpiece, often designed as a tabletop Christmas tree.

Conservatory—A greenhouse designed for the display of plants.

Contemporary design—An arrangement designed using the latest styles and trends in floral design.

Contour—The three-dimensional radiation of an arrangement from the vertical to the horizontal, as viewed from a side.

Contrast—Objects or plant materials with striking differences in color, texture, shape, or size.

Controlled temperature forcing (CTF)—Method of cooling whereby bulbs are received by the forcer and potted immediately.

Cool hues—Blue (and sometimes violet) and its tints, shades, and tones.

Cormels—Miniature corms that can be separated and planted.

Corm—A short, swollen, underground stem. Crocus and gladiolas are corms.

Cornucopia—A horn-shaped container typical of the Thanksgiving season, also called a horn of plenty.

Corolla—The collection of petals on a flower.

Corymb—A more or less flat-topped inflorescence having a main vertical axis and pedicels or branches of unequal length.

Cost of goods—The total wholesale cost or prices of materials that comprise the designs, plants, and giftware sold in a retail flower shop.

Cotyledon—Seed leaves. Embryos of monocot plants have one cotyledon, while those of dicot plants have two cotyledons. Monocot plants store the bulk of their energy in the endosperm. Dicots store their food in the two cotyledons.

Counterbalancing—Balancing plant materials with visually equal ones on both sides of the central axis.

Covering method—A drying technique that employs a drying agent to maintain the shape of the flower as it is drying.

Crescent—A geometric design resembling a C shape.

Crescent bouquet—A variation of the cascade bouquet that is designed in a C shape.

Crocus—Bulb crop that is actually a corm and is native to Central and Western Europe. Crocus varieties offer flowers of bright purple, yellow, and white colors.

Cross-pollination—When the pollen of a plant pollinates the flower of another plant.

Cultural/physical control—Methods that physically prevent activities of pests.

Cultural practices—The control or management of light, temperature, air, and water to promote healthy growth.

Cut flowers—Flowers grown in a greenhouse or field, cut when they reach a certain maturity, and sold to a wholesaler. Roses, carnations, chrysanthemums, and orchids are a few common cut flowers.

Cut foliage—Leaves harvested for floral design work, often referred to as "greens." Leatherleaf, lemonleaf pittosporum, podocarpus, asparagus fern, and huckleberry are common foliage materials used in floral work.

Cuticle—The waxy coating on epidermis cells that serve to prevent excessive water loss from the leaf tissues.

Cuttings—One of the most common and simplest methods of asexual propagation in which portions of stems, leaves, or roots are used.

Cyclamen—Potted flowering plant native to the Mediterranean. The unusual shaped flowers come in white, pink, carmine, and red. Cyclamen are considered a cool crop.

Cyme—Usually a flat-topped inflorescence.

Cytokinins—Hormones responsible for cell division and differentiation. They are produced in the roots and play a role in apical dominance of intact plants. While auxins inhibit the growth of lateral shoots, cytokinins promote lateral shoots. In roots the situation is reversed. Auxins promote the branching of roots, and cytokinins inhibit branching.

Daisy hook method—A wiring technique for daisies or asters for use in corsages or boutonnieres.

Damping off—A term used to describe the early death of seedlings that have germinated. A number of fungi can be the cause.

Day-neutral plants—Plants unaffected by day length.

Deionizer—Used to remove the minerals in water.

Demographic study—A report of the size and distribution of population for a specific area.

Depth—The third dimension within a design.

Desiccant—A drying agent.

Design elements—Physical characteristics of plant materials.

Design mechanics—Techniques and devises that hold a corsage or arrangement together in a secure way.

Determinate—Term used when the first flower of a inflorescence to open is at the apex of the stem and the progression of flowering is downward or outward.

Dicot—One of two main types of plants. Dicotyledon plants or dicot plants have xylem and phloem in a ring within the stem. Examples of dicots are hydrangea, florist azalea, African violet, and chrysanthemum.

DIF—The mathematical difference between the day temperature and the night temperature.

Dip—Plants submerged in a pesticide that has been mixed with water.

Dip dyes—Semi-transparent paints that change flower color by directly dipping the flower head in the solution.

Diploid—The nuclei of normal cells that contain a double set of chromosomes.

Disbudding—The removal of flower buds to improve the overall quality of the plants.

Disease—A disturbance to the normal, healthy growth and development of a plant.

Dish garden—Differing types of potted plants in the same container.

Display—The pleasing visual arrangement of flowers and products.

Division—Asexual propagation in which the plant roots or the entire plant may be cut into sections to make two or more plants from the original plant.

Dominance—The prominence or prevalence of one element or characteristic with other characteristics being subordinate

Double fertilization—Process in flowering plants whereby both sperm nuclei in the pollen grain are involved in fertilization.

Drench—Pesticide application in which material, mixed with water, is simply poured into the pots.

Drip irrigation—Drip irrigation is similar to spaghetti tubing except the tube provides a slow steady drip with little run-off.

Drying agent—Holds the shape of the flower and draws the moisture from the flower as it dries.

Dutch Flemish period—A style of floral design that featured large, flamboyant arrangements and accessories.

Dwarf iris—Dwarf iris is a bulb crop native to the Caucasus region. They are purple in color.

Easel—A tripod-like stand for holding sympathy flowers.

Easel spray—A one-sided sympathy flower arrangement placed on an easel.

Easter lily—Bulbs grown in the United States and Canada as a potted flowering crop for the Easter season. They produce a single stem and 1 to 20 large, fragrant, white trumpet-shaped flowers.

Ebb and flood—Watering method in which water is pumped into the system at regular intervals, filling the bench. The pots sit in the water while the media in the pots slowly absorbs water. After a certain period, the water drains from the bench.

Egyptian period—An early style of decorative flower use, valuing simplicity.

Electromagnetic spectrum—Radiant energy given off by the Sun has wavelengths that are measured in nanometers, and based on the measurements have been placed on a scale or spectrum.

Embryo—An immature plant.

Empty nest couples—Couples who are generally younger than 65 and still employed with no children living at home.

Endosperm—Tissue in which food is stored for the embryo.

Energy curtains—Automated systems utilizing fabrics that insulate the greenhouse at night and shade the crops during the day.

English tradition—A style of floral design that featured fragrant bouquets and both formal and casual arrangements.

Enzymes—Chemical activators with specific jobs. With split-second timing they break down sugars and recombine them with nitrogen and other minerals to produce many complex molecules are produced.

Epidermis—The protective layer of cells on leaves.

Equilateral triangle—A triangle with three equal sides.

Erwinia—A bacterial disease that causes rotting of plant tissues. The bacteria enter the plant through wounds. It is a common problem on *Dieffenbachia, Philodendron,* chrysanthemum, and cyclamen.

Ethylene—A colorless gas produced in the nodes of stems, ripening fruits, and dying leaves. It causes the thickening of stems and speeds the aging of plant parts, particularly fruit.

Ethylene inhibitors—Treatments or chemicals that block or tie up the ethylene within the flower and reduce its impact.

Etiolation—Term used to describe a severe case of stretching of plants grown in low light or darkness.

Even-span greenhouse—Greenhouse structure that has a roof with an even pitch and an even width. It is a single house.

Everlasting plant materials—Plant materials that can be dried or preserved successfully, also called dried flowers.

Explant—Small pieces of plant material.

Fan and pad cooling system—Cooling system based on the evaporation of water. This system involves a wall of cellulose or aspen pads on one end of the greenhouse. The pads are kept wet by a system of pumps and gutters that recirculate the water. On the other end of the greenhouse there are a series of fans. The fans pull air through the pads and across the greenhouse. As the air passes through the pads, the water evaporates.

Fan-jet tubes—Polyethylene tubes that run the length of the greenhouse, and they have holes along the side of the tube. The fan-jet tubes are attached to fans associated with unit heaters. When the fans are operating, the tubes inflate. Air is blown through the holes in the tube. Fan-jet tubes promote an even circulation of air in the greenhouse.

Far-red light—A wavelength that plays an important role in plant growth and development as it triggers a shade avoidance response in plants when levels of blue or red light are low.

Feathering—A wiring technique for making smaller flowers from a larger carnation.

Fertigation—The practice of fertilizing while irrigating.

Fertilization—The fusion of a sperm with an egg.

Fertilizer—Any material added to growing media that provides nutrients for plants.

Fertilizer injector system—Standard equipment in today's greenhouses. A concentrate of water-soluble fertilizer is mixed in a tank in exact proportions before irrigating plants. With fertilizer injectors growers can provide exact levels of nutrients.

Fiberglass—Glazing material widely used in the 1960s and 1970s. Light transmission on new sheets is good, but it discolors after 7 to 10 years. Hail can cause some damage. Fiberglass is highly flammable.

Fictitious name statement—A document that must be filed with the county to register a business name and prevent another business from using that name.

Filament—The stalk of the stamen that holds the anther.

Filler flowers—Small flowers that are used to fill space and provide texture, color, and depth within a design, also called fillers.

Filling florist—The florist who fills or designs a wire service and delivers it.

Finished—Grown to saleable size.

Finishing dips or sprays—Treatments applied to a finished corsage to minimize water loss and keep the corsage fresh for a longer period of time.

Fireside basket—A curved, open basket with handle.

Fixative—An additive to potpourri to hold or "fix" the scent or fragrances for an extended period of time.

Flat spray—A triangular, one-sided sympathy spray.

Flavonol—A pigment that produces yellow and cream colors.

Floral arranger—People with the training required to make and copy floral designs.

Floral design—The art of organizing the design elements inherent in plant materials, container, and accessories according to the principles of design to attain a composition with the objectives of beauty, simplicity, harmony, suitability, and expression.

Floral designer—Person considered to be more skilled than an arranger in that he or she has the ability to create and design unique floral art.

Floral foam—A porous material that holds water and provides stability for flower stems.

Floral foam holder—A wedding mechanic with floral foam encased in a plastic cage with a handle.

Floral production—The growing of flowering or foliage crops to sale size or maturity.

Floral sprays—Opaque paints that will completely change any flower color.

Floral tints—Translucent paints that allow some of the flower color to show.

Floriculture—Literally defined as the "culture of flowers," floriculture is an international, multi-billion dollar industry based on flowering and foliage (leafy) plants.

Florist—Person who works with cut flowers and foliage.

Florist azalea—Two species of *Rhododendron* are grown as florist azaleas. Different varieties are grown for Christmas, Easter, and Mother's Day.

Florist hydrangea—Florist hydrangeas are native to Japan. They are grown primarily for Easter and Mother's Day. The color of their long-lasting flowers (blue, pink, white or red) is influenced by pH.

Florist shears—A cutting tool with short, serrated blades.

Flowers—The reproductive organs of plants.

Focal area—A center of interest.

Focal point—A center of interest.

Fog system—Cooling system that involves an atomizer that produces water vapor. The water vapor cools the house by flash evaporation. Fog systems increase the humidity within the house while they cool.

Foliage grid—The overlapping and interlocking of leaves within a vase arrangement to give support to the flower placements.

Foliage plants—Tropical and subtropical plants grown for their leaves rather than for their flowers and selected for their ability to be grown indoors. They are also called houseplants.

Foot candle—A measure of light intensity based on the amount of light distributed by a single candle one foot away.

Forcing—A term used to describe practices that get bulbs to grow and produce flowers.

Form—The three-dimensional shape of a design.

Form flowers—Flowers with special forms or shapes that provide interest within a design and can create an effective center of interest.

Franchise—A flower shop that is purchased from and operated according to the parent company's operating specifications.

Free form—A style that allows the floral designer to convey creativity and individual expression by bending or breaking the rules of floral design.

Freesia—A cut flower with very fragrant lily-like flowers, borne on a horizontal spike. They come in bright colors including yellow, red, white, blue, and pink.

Free, variable rhythm—Irregular, unpredictable use of plant materials to add surprise and interesting lines and forms with a floral design.

Freeze drying—A commercial method of freezing the flowers and then drying them.

French period or the Grand era—A refined and elegant style of floral design during the Louis IV period.

Full couch—A casket with a one-piece lid, which may be closed or open.

Full-couch casket lid spray—A large casket spray placed in the center of the open lid of a full couch.

Full-couch casket spray—A large casket piece that is placed in the center of a closed full couch.

Fumigant—Poisonous gases that are distributed through the air to all parts of the greenhouse.

Fungicide—Pesticide used to control fungus.

Fungus gnats—Long-legged, winged, gray-black insects less than an eighth of an inch long. The larva of fungus gnats feed on root hairs and tunnel into plant stems.

Garland—Flowers and foliages woven or fashioned into a strand or a rope (roping).

Gauge—The thickness or thinness of florist wire.

Genetic engineering—Selecting and moving genetic material from one plant to another.

Geometric form—Designs which mirror the shapes of geometry such as the circle and triangle.

Georgian era—An English style of floral design that developed the first centerpieces and miniatures.

Germination—The beginning of growth from a seed.

Germination rate—The percentage of seeds capable of germinating.

Gibberellins—Hormones that induce stem cell elongation and cell division. Gibberellins play a key role in stimulating the development of flowers. They also have an important role in the production of enzymes during seed germination.

Gladiolus—Cut flower valued for their large showy floral spikes. Cultivars are available in nearly every color. As cut flowers, they are long lasting.

Glamellia—A composite flower of gladiola florets made to resemble a camellia.

Glass—Considered to be the best glazing material for plant production. It provides the highest light transmission of any glazing material at 88% to 89%. The initial cost of glass is expensive, but it is very long lasting, provided it doesn't break.

Glazing—The covering of a greenhouse.

Gloxinia—Potted flowering plant native to Brazil with large, trumpet-shaped flowers that come in red, pink, purple, white, and two-tones. Gloxinias are propagated from their tubers or by seed.

Glycerinizing—A preserving technique that replaces the moisture of a plant with a glycerin solution, preserving the plant material and causing it to remain pliable and flexible.

Golden mean—The Greek proportion of 1 to 1.6.

Grades—Flowers grouped according to size or quality.

Grafting—The process in which the stem of one plant is made to grow on the roots of another plant.

Granular—Pelleted form of pesticide that is carefully measured and applied on the surface of the growing medium.

Grape-hyacinth—Bulb crop native to Asia Minor. Grape-hyacinths have clusters of blue or white flowers. The blues can sometimes appear iridescent.

Gravitropism—A plant's response to the force of gravity.

Gray market—People who are older than 65 and usually retired.

Greek and Roman period—A style of flower use which includes the use of strewed or scattered flowers and garlands, wreaths, and chaplets.

Greenhouse—A structure enclosed by glass or plastic that allows light transmission for plant growth.

Greening pins—S-shaped hairpins for securing moss or foliage in a design.

Greenhouse sanitation—The efforts made to keep a greenhouse clean.

Green rose—A rose at a premature stage with the greens sepals prominently enclosing the bud.

Grid—A framework of materials at the top of a vase to provide support for flowers in a vase arrangement.

Gross sales—The total dollar amounts that the retail florist sells in a year.

Grouping—Placing flowers or foliages in sections or areas of just one type to repeat their growth in nature.

Grower—The person in charge of the crop production.

Growing media—The material in which plants are grown.

Growth retardants—Chemicals that inhibit the action of gibberellins on stem elongation.

Guard cells—The stomata are opened and closed by a pair of guard cells. When water is plentiful and light is shining, the guard cells are pumped full of water. This causes the cells to push apart, creating an opening to allow an exchange of gases.

Hairpin method—A wiring technique for ferns or other compound leaves and for multi-flowered stems.

Half couch—A casket with a two-piece lid with the left side open during the visitation services.

Hand-tied bouquet—A three-dimensional grouping of flowers and foliages that are tied together with the natural stems showing.

Hanging method—A drying technique of bunching and hanging plant materials upside down to dry.

Haploid—Reproductive cells, sperm and egg, that have a single set of chromosomes.

Hard baskets—Hanging baskets that contain plants that are propagated by cuttings, such as fuchsia, geraniums, and New Guinea impatiens.

Harden—To condition or prepare flowers for use in arranging.

Hardgoods—Nonperishable supplies, such as vases, wire, or ribbon, used in floral designs.

Hard pinch—The removal of everything but 3 or 4 leaves by pinching.

Hard water—Water that contains high amounts of minerals.

Head—A rounded or flat-topped cluster of sessile flowers.

Headhouse—A structure attached to the greenhouse. It serves as a storage area for growing media, containers, fertilizers, and other materials. It is a work area.

Heat delay—A delay of flowering by several days to weeks because of high temperatures.

Herbicide—Pesticide used to control weeds.

High-intensity discharge (hid) lighting system—New efficient and effective light sources.

Highly buffered—Resistant to a change in pH.

High-visibility colors—Warm hues, light values (tints), and bright intensities which are very noticeable from a distance.

Hogarth curve—A geometric shape resembling a slim S.

Holiday cactus—Potted flowering plant with three types available—Thanksgiving, Christmas, and Easter. The natural photoperiodic response of these plants brings them to flower around the holiday for which they are named.

Hook cut—The removal of a portion of the old wood with a flower when roses are harvested.

Hoop-house—Even-span greenhouse that has an arching pipe framework.

Hormones—Natural chemicals produced by plants to regulate growth.

Horticultural oils—Material sprayed on the insects to clog the breathing pores of the insect, causing suffocation.

Hot water system—Heating system that uses water heated in boilers and pumped through pipes in the greenhouse. The pipes are most often placed under the benches or in the floor. Hot water systems have relatively low maintenance.

Hue—The name of a color.

Hyacinth stake—A long, green wooden stick used for extending height and supporting flowers and accessories within a floral design.

Hyacinth—Bulb crop native to Greece and Asia Minor. They produce a fragrant flower that may be purple, white, pink, or multi-colored. Most hyacinths are produced in Holland.

Hybrid—The offspring of two plants of the same or related species that differ genetically.

Hybridization—The process in which plant breeders select plants for outstanding characteristics, collect pollen from one plant and transfer it to the flower of another in the hope of having the outstanding characteristics expressed in the offspring.

Hybrid tea rose—A large, usually solitary flower. The majority of the hybrid tea roses produced are red. Other popular colors include pink, yellow, and white.

Ikebana—Japanese flower arranging.

Imperfect flowers—Flowers that lack one of the two sex structures.

Incomplete flowers—Flowers that lacks any one of the following; sepals, petals, stamens, and pistil.

Indeterminate—Term used when the last flower of an inflorescence to open is terminal on the main axis and the progression of flowering in inward or upward.

Indoleacetic acid (IAA)—The primary auxin.

Indolebutyric acid (IBA)—Widely used synthetic root-promoting material.

Infectious disease—A disease that can be spread to other plants.

Inflorescence—Flower clusters, formed by the branching system of the stem.

Infrared heat system—Heating system in which infrared wavelengths are absorbed by the plants, media, and benches. The heat then transfers to the air space around them. Therefore, infrared heat does not heat the air directly.

Insect growth regulators—Materials that disrupt the growth and development of the insects.

Insecticidal soaps—Materials that dissolve the protective membranes of insects, bringing on death.

Insecticide—Pesticide used to control insects.

Integrated pest management (IPM)—Use of a wide range of strategies to control pests and diseases.

Intensity—The relative brightness or dullness of a hue.

Interior plantscaping—The use of plant materials to improve the appearance of the indoor environment.

Intermittent mist system—Watering method used to deliver water in tiny droplets for the purpose of keeping plant material moist. Intermittent mist systems are used for plant propagation.

Inverted T—A variation of the isosceles triangle that incorporates more space and fewer flowers.

Irrigation—Furnishing plants with water by flooding or sprinkling.

Irrigation booms—Watering method involving booms with nozzles that sweep across greenhouse benches delivering overhead water.

Isosceles triangle—A triangle having two equal sides and a narrower width than the equilateral triangle.

Italian Renaissance period—An early style of flower arranging that is considered the beginning of flower arranging in vases.

Japanese influence—A style of floral design emphasizing space and significant placement of each type of plant material.

Joining point—The place where the wired and taped stems of a bouquet converge and are eventually taped together.

Kalanchoe—Succulent short-day plants native to Africa and Asia. Their flowers range in color from bright yellow to orange to hot pink.

Kneeling bench—A bench provided and decorated for a wedding ceremony in which the bride and groom kneel as a part of the wedding ceremony.

Labor—An operating expense, a cost of manufacturing (designing) an arrangement.

Language of flowers—The tradition of assigning meanings to flowers to convey messages which was initiated and became popular during the Victorian era.

Lateral bud—Buds located along the sides of a stem.

Layering—A method of asexual reproduction whereby roots form on a stem while the stem is still attached to the parent plant.

Leaching—The process in which soluble salts are washed from a growing medium as water flows through the growing media.

Leader pricing—A pricing strategy of offering commonly purchased items at a significantly reduced price compared to the competition.

Leaf blade—The large broad part of a leaf.

Leaf-bud cutting—Cuttings composed of the leaf blade, the petiole, a bud at the base of the petiole, and a portion of the stem.

Leaf counting—Practice used to monitor the progress of an Easter lily crop and to determine whether growth needs to be speeded or slowed.

Leaf cutting—Entire leaves or portions of a leaf are removed from the parent plant for use as cuttings.

Leaf margin—The edge of the leaf blade. The margins can be one of many forms including wavy, toothed, lobed, and entire or smooth.

Leaf miners—Small stocky flies whose larva feed on the interior of the leaf, making tunnels as it moves along.

Leaf-petiole cutting—The leaf blade and the petiole are taken from the parent plant for use as a cutting.

Lean-to greenhouse—A greenhouse structure that is attached to a building, with the building providing support for the roof.

Leaves—Plant organs responsible for the production of food (sugars) for the plant.

Line—The visual movement between two points within a design.

Line arrangement—A design that is based upon the Japanese ikebana designs and emphasizes space, rhythm, and line.

Line mass—An American design style that combines the line and space of the Japanese influence with the colorful mass style of the Europeans.

Line materials—Flowers or foliage that are very tall or long compared to their width that are useful in creating the outline of a design.

Liners—Small-branched plants are sold as 4", 6", or 8" diameter in azalea production.

Lines of opposition—A design with a high contrast use of two different design lines or forms, sharing a center of interest.

Long-day plants—Plants that flower as days lengthen in the summer.

Low-visibility colors—Cool hues, dark values (shades), and dull intensities which do not seem to show up very well from a distance.

Macronutrient—Six of the 17 essential elements that are required in greater quantity than the others including nitrogen (N), phosphorus (P), potassium (K), calcium (Ca), magnesium (Mg), and sulfur (S).

Marketing mix—A combination of activities and shop characteristics which a florist implements to attract and retain targeted customers.

Marketing—The process of selling products and providing services that the customer wants or needs.

Mass arrangement—A design of many flowers, usually in a geometric shape that is based upon the lavish European flower arrangements of the 17th and 18th century.

Mass flowers—Round or solid flowers that are useful in filling out the shape of the design.

Mealybugs—Slow moving, oval-shaped, whitish insects that have a waxy finish and produce small cottony masses.

Mesophyll—Photosynthetic tissue sandwiched between the epidermal. The bulk of photosynthetic activity for a plant takes place in the mesophyll cells.

Metabolism—Term used to describe all of the chemical reactions in a plant.

Micronutrient—Sometimes they are called trace elements because they are needed in small amounts. They are boron (B), copper (Cu), chlorine (Cl), iron (Fe), manganese (Mn), molybdenum (Mo), sodium (Na), nickel (Ni), and zinc (Zn).

Mineral soil—Growing media component obtained from nature and is the result of weathered rock. It has become more difficult for growers to find uniform mineral soil with a favorable pH and good structure and texture.

Mini carnation—One of three types of carnations. Mini carnations are ½ to ⅓ the size of standard carnation flowers.

Mites—Tiny eight legged bugs related to spiders. Mites pierce plant leaf tissues and suck juice.

Miticide—Pesticide used to control mites.

Monochromatic—A color scheme including only one hue and its tints, shades, and tones.

Monocot—One of two main types of plants. Monocotyledons or monocot plants have xylem and phloem scattered throughout the stem and tend to have narrow leaves. Easter lilies, iris, spider plants, and dracaenas are examples of monocotyledons.

Mottled foliage—Leaves with flecks of a differing color throughout the entire leaf.

Multiple price points—A pricing strategy of displaying and pricing several related designs or products in varying sizes and prices to provide the customer a choice.

Multiple unit pricing—A pricing strategy offering the customer price advantages for purchasing additional items.

Naphthaleneacetic acid (NAA)—Widely used synthetic root-promoting material.

Narcissus—Also known as daffodils. This bulb produces brilliant yellow flowers, with some varieties available in white, two-tone colors, and peach.

Natural cooling—Method of cooling whereby bulbs are potted as soon as they arrive. They are placed outdoors or may be kept in a poly house if temperatures drop below freezing.

Naturalistic form—Designs repeating and suggesting nature, often using groupings of plant materials.

Needlepoint holder—A design mechanic with a heavy metal base and sharp, closely spaced pins for holding flower stems.

Nested baskets—Containers which are three different sizes with each one placed inside another.

Nestled boutonniere—A boutonniere with a smaller flower placed within the center of a larger carnation.

Net profit—The income at the end of the year after expenses, the return on the florist's investment.

Non-infectious disease—Diseases caused by environmental imbalances and cannot be spread to other plants.

Non-precooled—Bulbs that are not given cold treatment by the supplier.

Non-tunicate bulbs—Bulbs that lack a tunic and the protection a dry, papery covering would provide.

Nosegays—Fragrant handheld bouquets of flowers, herbs, and foliages.

Novelty design—A whimsical, imaginative arrangement of flowers designed to resemble animals, birthday cakes, or clowns.

Nutrient deficiency—If a plant fails to receive the needed amount of nutrients, it will show signs of an unhealthy plant appearance. Symptoms vary with the nutrient that is in short supply.

Odd end pricing—A pricing strategy of rounding a product's price to a set price just below a whole dollar amount, for example $9.99 or $9.95 instead of $10.00.

Operating expenses—The costs of running a retail flower shop.

Organic matter—Decayed or partially decayed remains of plants and animals found in the media.

Oriental lilies—Bulb crop native to the Asian Continent. They come in a wide range of colors, including yellow, white, red, and orange. They are forced throughout the year.

Ornamental horticulture—The practice of growing and using plants for decorative purposes.

Ovary—The part of the pistil that contains one or more ovules.

Overhead sprinklers—Sprinkler nozzles in a fixed position above the crops deliver overhead water.

Ovule—The part of the flower in which the eggs are produced and seeds develop.

Paddle wire—A continuous length of wire wound onto a piece of wood (paddle).

Palisade layer—A stacked layer of mesophyll cells found just below the upper epidermis.

Panicle—A more or less elongated inflorescence with a central axis along which there are branches that are themselves branched.

Papier-mache—Sturdy, molded, paper-like material which holds water and is used to fashion a container used for sympathy flowers.

Parts per million—A measure of nutrients in solution.

Pathogens—Disease-causing organisms such as bacteria, fungi, or viruses.

Pattern—The coloration of plant materials and arrangement of the plant parts.

Pavé—The technique of placing plant materials very close together in rows or sections to completely cover the foam and fill in the design.

Peat moss—Widely used organic growing media component dug from peat bogs. Peat moss has light bulk density, good moisture holding ability, good air space qualities for the exchange of gases, adequate cation exchange capacity, and a stable pH that is usually between 3.5 and 4.5.

Pedicel—The stem of a flower.

Peduncle—The main stem of an inflorescence.

Percentage mark-up—A pricing method of dividing the wholesale cost of goods by the cost of goods percentage, based on the retail shop's financial statement.

Perfect flowers—Flowers that have both the male and female parts.

Perianth—Term used to describe the sepals and petals together.

Perlite—Lightweight, white growing media component originating from volcanic rock. Perlite is stable, sterile, has little cation exchange capacity, has a pH of 7.5, and provides good water drainage and aeration. Perlite contains fluorides that cause leaf damage to some monocotyledon plants.

Persian violet—Persian violet is from the Island of Socotra off the tip of Somalia. It has pretty violet-blue flowers that cover the whole plant.

Pest—A living organism that can cause injury or loss to a plant.

Pesticide—Chemical used to control pests and diseases.

Petals—Structures located just inside the sepals. Petals appear leaf-like and are often very colorful to attract pollinators.

Petiole—The leaf stalk that connects the leaf blade to the stem.

Pew decorations—Bows, flowers, or floral designs attached to the ends of the pews in the aisle where the bridal party walks

Phloem—Conductive tissue of the stem in which food made in the leaves is transported to the rest of the plant.

Photoperiodism—A plant's response to light duration.

Photosynthesis—The process of a plant making sugars (food) from water and carbon dioxide. Photosynthesis takes place in the leaves. Growth and development of greenhouse crops is determined by the rate of photosynthesis.

Phototropism—The ability of a plant to bend towards a light source.

Physical balance—The secure, stable placement of plant materials within the container.

Phytophthora—A fungal disease similar to *Pythium*. It causes crown and stem rots in cool, wet conditions.

Pick machine—A flower design tool that attaches a metal stem to a dried or silk stem to add length or strength.

Pierce method—A wiring technique for corsages or boutonnieres that requires inserting a wire horizontally through the thickened calyx of a flower, such as roses or carnations.

Pillowing—The technique of placing flowers close together and very low in a design, forming undulating peaks and valleys.

Pinching—Removal of the apical meristem. Pinching is a common practice used to produce bushy, well-branched crops.

Pistil—The female part of the flower.

Plant growth regulators (PGR)—Natural occurring or synthetic chemicals that regulate all growth and development of plants.

Plant health—Refers to plants that are free of pests and disease.

Plantlet—Shoots that develop from buds in tissue culture.

Plant nutrition—The absorption of nutrients available in the growing media for plant growth. Current fertilizer practices allow growers to adjust and deliver nutrients to maintain desired plant growth.

Plant propagation—The reproduction of plants by seed or by a portion of a plant.

Plugs—Small plants grown in a small amount of media in divided trays.

Plush animals—Stuffed animals that are suitable for accessories within an arrangement.

Pocketbook plant—Native from Mexico to Chile, the flowers this cool-season potted flowering crop resemble a woman's purse. The flowers are very colorful yellows, oranges, and reds.

Poinsettia—Plant native to Mexico associated with Christmas and sold as a potted plant only during that time of the year.

Pollen—Produced by the anther, contains the male sex cells.

Pollination—The transfer of pollen to the female part of a flower.

Polycarbonate structured sheets—The most widely used structured sheet, commonly manufactured with a "twin wall" held together by ribs. Polycarbonates have a good 80% light transmission. They resist hail damage.

Polychromatic—A color scheme the incorporates a wide range of colors, both warm and cool.

Polyethylene—Flexible plastic sheets, usually 6-mil in thickness, used as a glazing material by stretching it over the greenhouse framework.

Poly foil—A foil with a thin plastic covering on the silver side.

Polyploid—Plants that have more than the normal double set of chromosomes.

Porosity—The percentage of pores or spaces between the solid particles of a growing media.

Pot fillers—Automated greenhouse systems that helps workers fill pots or flats with growing media.

Potpourri—A scented mixture of dried petals, flowers, leaves, buds, fragrances, and a fixative.

Potted flowering plants—Plants grown in pots for their showy flowers. Some popular potted flowering plants are poinsettias, chrysanthemums, cyclamen, and African violets.

Powdery mildew—A fungal disease. Characteristic symptoms include a white dusty coating to leaves and flowers. Infected plants can become stunted.

Precooled—The process of providing cold treatment to bulbs for early forcing, or quickly cooling flowers after harvesting and packaging and prior to shipping.

Pressing—A drying technique that preserves plant materials in a two-dimensional form.

Pricing strategies—Well planned methods and practices of pricing to attract customers and motivate them to buy something.

Primary colors—The foundation colors of red, yellow, and blue, which cannot be created by mixing any other colors.

Primary root—A single, main root.

Primrose—Six species of this cool-season potted flowering crop are used in greenhouse production. All of these originated in the northern temperate regions of the world. Primroses are available in a wide range of bright, colorful, and fragrant flowers.

Principles of design—The rules and guidelines to follow in creating pleasing floral designs.

Promotion—Activities that lead to public name recognition of the flower shop.

Proportion—The pleasing relationship in size and shape among objects or parts of objects.

Pruning shears—A cutting tool with sharp cutting blades that will cut thick or woody plant material without pinching.

Pythium—A fungal disease that attacks greenhouse plants under cool, wet conditions.

Raceme—An elongated inflorescence with a central axis along which are simple pedicels of more or less equal length.

Radiation—The appearance of flower stems emerging from one point.

Raffia—The fiber of a palm tree used to tie objects together or to add a decorative flair in packaging.

Ratio mark-up—A method of pricing which relies on a predetermined increase from the wholesale cost of goods.

Receding colors—Colors such as blue and violet which are not highly visible from a distance and seem to become smaller or disappear (recede) because of their color.

Receptacle—The tip of the stem that holds the flower parts.

Regular, repeated rhythm—Repetitive, predictable placements of plant materials to create a bold, strong visual pathway through a design.

Repetition—Repeating one or more of the design elements throughout a floral design.

Resale license—A permit registering the business and allowing the business to collect sales tax and purchase for resale from a wholesale business without paying tax.

Respiration—The process of the plant using its stored food.

Retail floral manager—Person who has the responsibility of coordinating the operations of the business. Tasks associated with this position include managing personnel, working with budgets, and maintaining the store's inventory.

Retail florist—Provides floral design services, cut flowers and other floriculture crops. Retail florists have typically been small independent businesses.

Retail price—The florist's selling price based on the wholesale cost and predetermined pricing methods and strategies.

Retractable-roof greenhouse—Greenhouse structures with roofs that can be opened and closed. They allow the grower to open the house to the elements when weather is favorable for plant growth and close the roof when the crops need protection.

Rhizoctonia—A fungal disease prevalent under wet and warm conditions.

Rhizome—An underground horizontal stem. Iris and calla lilies are rhizomes.

Rhythm—The related, orderly organization of the design elements to create a dominant visual pathway through a floral design.

Ridge-and-furrow greenhouse—Greenhouse structures that consist of a number of greenhouses connected together along the length of the houses. Shared side walls are eliminated, creating a large interior space.

Right triangle—An L-shaped asymmetrical triangle.

Rock wool—A human-made growing media component made from an igneous rock, basalt. It consists of fibers similar in appearance to cotton candy. Rock wool is used extensively in hydroponic operations. Rock wool has good water holding capacity and good aeration. It is slightly alkaline and has a low cation exchange capacity.

Rolling bench—Benches rest on pipes allowing each bench to be rolled from side to side. With this system only enough space needs to be kept for one aisle.

Roll out pinch—The removal of just the meristematic tip of the stem.

Root cap—A mass of cells on the root tip that protects the root from coarse soil.

Root hairs—Tiny hairs found near the growing tip of the root. Root hairs greatly increase the surface area of the root allowing more water and minerals to be absorbed into the plant.

Rooting room A—Involves bulb production for early flowering, before February 14.

Rooting room B—Involves bulb production for later flowering, after February 14.

Rootstock—The lower portion of the graft that includes the root system.

Root system—Term used when the roots are discussed collectively.

Root tuber—An enlarged food-storage root with adventitious shoots.

Rosettes—Foliage placement technique of placing all of the stems emerging from one point to mimic the growth of ferns.

Salesperson—Person who has direct and usually frequent contact with the retail florist. The salesperson takes orders and arranges delivery of the products.

Salinity—Salt content.

Sand—Natural growing media component that is a result of the wearing of rock. Sand is heavy and has a high bulk density that provides solid support for larger plants. It improves water drainage and aeration when used with soil. The pH of sand is between 7.5 and 8.5.

Satellite shop—A second business location that is operated by a large, full-service flower shop.

Saucers—Saucers are used with overhead irrigation systems in a manner similar to capillary mats. As water is applied, it is collected in the saucer and drawn up into the growing media by capillary action.

Scale—Insects with flat, oval, often brown bodies. They may or may not be covered with an armored shell. Scale insects pierce plant leaves and stems and suck juices. Also, the relative size among objects or parts of objects.

Scalene triangle—An asymmetrical triangle with three sides of differing lengths.

Scales—Fleshy modified leaves of a bulb.

Scalettes—Small bulbs that grow on bulb scales that were removed from a bulb and planted.

Scarification—Dormancy mechanism that requires the breaking down of the seed coat for germination to occur.

Scion—The portion of the graft that is to become the stem.

Scooping—The removal of the basal plate of the bulb and the base of all of the bulb scales.

Scoring—Similar to scooping, however, the basal plate is not removed. Two cuts that cross the basal plate are made about a 1/4 inch deep.

Secondary colors—Colors creating by mixing the adjacent primary colors, orange, green, and violet.

Secondary root—A smaller root that branches off the primary root.

Seed—Structures that have an embryo and a source of stored food contained within a seed coat.

Seed coat—A protective shell that protects the embryo and the endosperm from drying and from physical injury.

Self-pollination—When the pollen of a plant pollinates a flower on the same plant.

Sending florist—The florist who sells a wire service order and then sends the order by phone, computer, or fax to the florist in the city and zip code of the person who is receiving the flowers.

Senescence—The aging of plants.

Sepals—Green, leaf-like structures on the exterior of the flower. The sepals fold back as the flower opens.

Separation—Vegetative plant structures that are removed intact from the parent plant.

Set pieces—Sympathy designs in special shapes, such as wreaths, crosses, hearts, or organizational symbols, that are displayed on easels.

Sexual propagation—Reproduction that involves flowers and seeds. In sexual propagation, flowers are pollinated and eggs fertilized. The resulting offspring is genetically different from the parent plants.

Shade—A dark value of a hue, the hue with black added.

Shape—The two-dimensional term for form, the outline of a design.

Shattering—The breaking apart or the falling out of petals.

Shelf life—Refers to the time the plant maintains its health while on display for sale.

Short-day curtains—Curtains that block light from reaching the crops. When closed for 12 to 13 hours a night, they produce a short-day (actually a long-night) effect.

Short-day plants—Plants that will begin to flower naturally in the fall when the day lengths get shorter.

Silica gel—A type of drying agent available as white crystals or color-indicator crystals that change colors when the desiccant is too moist to effectively use.

Silica sand—A type of drying agent, white builder's sand.

Simple leaves—A single leaf blade and a petiole.

Single flowering carnation—One of three types of carnations. Produce a flower without the need of disbudding.

Slow-release fertilizers—Fertilizers that continually discharge a small amount of nutrients over a period of time.

Snapdragon—Cut flower with an elongated floral inflorescence that comes in a variety of bright colors. White, pink, and yellow are very popular. Other colors available include red, bronze, and purple.

Soft baskets—Hanging baskets that contain plants that are propagated from seed.

Softened water—Water that has been treated with salts to remove minerals.

Soft pinch—The removal of ½" to ¾" of the stem.

Soil-less mix—Growing media that lack any mineral soil.

Soil pH—The measure of acidity or alkalinity of the media.

Solitary flower—Flowers borne one to a stem. Examples include tulip, narcissus, and rose.

Soluble salts—Dissolved mineral salts that can be harmful to plants. Nutrients in solution along with mineral salts from the water and media contribute to the soluble salt content in the growing media.

Sow—Planting of seed.

Spadix—A spike with a thickened, fleshy axis, usually enveloped by a showy bract called a spathe.

Spaghetti tubing—A watering method involving small tubes connected to a main line. The end of each tube is placed in an individual pot. When operating, water dribbles through the tubes, watering all the pots on a bench simultaneously.

Spike—An elongated inflorescence with a central axis along which are sessile flowers.

Split complementary—A color scheme which combines one hue with the two hues that are on each side of its direct complement.

Splitting—A condition associated with hyacinths where the flower stalk separates from the basal plate.

Splitting of the calyx—The biggest problem with harvested carnations. This condition, when the calyx splits, petals spill out and the flower appears misshapen, is caused by fluctuations of temperatures and is more common with some cultivars than others.

Spongy layer—A loosely arranged layer of mesophyll cells underneath the palisade layer.

Spray—Pesticides applied by small droplets of the spray that cover the surface of the plant.

Staging the bow—Arranging the bow loops so the bow appears balanced and full or rounded.

Stamens—Male reproductive parts of a flower.

Standard carnation—One of three types of carnations. A large, solitary flower that has been disbudded.

Standing spray—Another term for an easel spray.

Starch—Huge molecules in which food is stored for plants resulting from the bonding of thousands of glucose molecules.

Steam heat—Heating system involving large boilers that bring water to a boil to produce steam. The steam then flows through pipes in the greenhouse. Steam heat is not as uniform as hot water heat. Nor is it as easy to adjust the temperature.

Stem blockage—An obstruction of the xylem due to air, bacteria, or other microorganisms, salts, undissolved particles, or other debris such as sand or soil.

Stem cuttings—Method of cutting in which stems are taken 2 to 5 inches in length.

Stem dyes—Color solutions that are transported through the xylem of a plant to change the flower color.

Stem shop—A cash and carry operation the offers a variety of flowers and foliages by the single stem or as bunches.

Stem tuber—Swollen tips of a rhizome. The Irish potato is a stem tuber.

Sticking cuttings—The practice of placing cuttings in rooting cubes or directly into a media.

Stigma—Found at the end of the pistil and it has a sticky surface on which pollen can be caught.

Stitch method—A foliage wiring technique.

Stock plant—Plants from which cuttings are removed.

Stolon—A stem that grows horizontally above the ground and may produce roots at its tip or at nodes. Airplane or spider plants and strawberry begonia are two foliage plants that produce stolons.

Stomata—The pores or openings in the epidermis that allow the exchange of oxygen, carbon dioxide, and water vapor.

Stratification—The process whereby a seed must go through a period of cold temperatures before it will germinate.

Strewing—The scattering of flowers and loose petals on the ground.

Style—The neck of the pistil.

Styrofoam—Growing media component made of synthetic polystyrene material. It is very lightweight and stable. While it provides good drainage and aeration, it lacks cation exchange capacity, water holding abilities, and has a neutral pH.

Sweetheart (floribunda) rose—A smaller rose that grows as a spray and is often disbudded. Sweetheart roses are used extensively in wedding work, corsages, and centerpieces. Yellow and pink make up a large percentage of those produced. New cultivars also offer many pastel colors.

Symmetrical balance—Similar weight and appearance of plant materials on either side of the vertical axis within a floral design.

Sympathy flowers—Flowers that are sent to a funeral home or funeral service to honor the deceased and to comfort the bereaved.

Synthetic growth regulators—Chemical compounds that regulate growth but are not produced by plants.

Tape grid—The placement of waterproof tape across the opening of a vase at 90-degree angles to form a support grid.

Tax number—Another term for resale license or permit.

Tepal—Term used when a clear distinction between petals and sepals cannot be made.

Terminal bud—The large bud at the tip of a stem.

Terracing—The technique of placing plant materials in differing levels, one above another.

Tertiary colors—A mixture of a primary and a secondary color.

Tetraploid—Plants with four sets of chromosomes.

Texture—The visual and tactile qualities of plant materials.

Thermoperiodism—Term used to describe a temperature requirement that produces a plant response.

Thermostats—Low cost and easy to install environmental controls. There are two types, on-off and proportioning thermostats. On-off thermostats control fans, heaters, vents with a change of temperature. Proportioning thermostats provide continuous control of systems with changes in temperature.

Thielaviopsis—A fungus that causes root and stem rots.

Tie-in pricing—A pricing strategy to encourage customers to buy related items by offering special discounted prices when the items are purchased at the same time.

Tint—A light value of a hue, the hue with white added.

Tip spraying—A special spray technique that applies color to the edges only of the petals.

Tissue culture—A very technical method of asexual propagation that involves the culture or growing of small pieces of plant tissue.

Tone—A full spectrum hue with gray added.

Toning—A term used to describe procedures used to prepare plants for a post-production environment.

Topiary—A formal pruned tree or shrub fashioned into shapes; also a two-tiered floral design.

Toss bouquet—A small, wired and taped bouquet that is thrown by the bride to unmarried friends during a traditional part of the wedding reception activities.

Total dissolved salts (TDS)—The salt content of the water.

Transition—Smooth, gradual change from one thing to another.

Transpiration—The movement of water vapor through stomata.

Transplanted—The process of moving plants from one container to another or from a container to the ground.

Tray mechanization—Also known as Dutch trays or palletized benches, this system consists of benches that hold 100 or more pots. The trays are rolled on a series of rails from one area of the greenhouse operation to another.

Triad—A color scheme combining three equally spaced hues on the color wheel, such as the primary colors or the secondary colors.

Triploid—Plants that have three sets of chromosomes.

Tulip—Bulb plant from southwestern Europe and the Near East. They are available in practically all colors with the exception of a true blue, and are grown for cut flowers or as potted flowering plants.

Tulle—Florist netting, available in many colors and finishes.

Tunic—A dry, papery covering.

Tunicate bulb—A bulb with a dry, papery covering.

Turgid—Tissues full of water.

Turgidity—Water pressure in the plant cells.

Tussie-mussie (tuzzy-muzzy)—Another name for a nosegay.

Umbel—An inflorescence having several branches arising from a common point.

Unavailable water—The thin film of water that binds so tightly on media particles that it can not be used by plants.

Uneven-span greenhouse—A greenhouse structure that has a roof with an unequal pitch and width. Use of the uneven span structure is limited to hillsides.

Unit cost of goods—The wholesale price of a single item.

Unit heaters—Heating system with which air is heated within a unit and then blown by fans throughout greenhouse. Unit heaters are less expensive to install than hot water systems.

Unity candle arrangement—A centerpiece featuring a candle which the bridal couple light during a wedding ceremony.

Up-selling—The sales practice of persuading a customer to make a larger purchase than originally planned by suggesting a range of prices and offering related products.

Value—The lightness or darkness of a hue.

Variable mark-up—A pricing method with differing increases based upon the type of design or the type of flower and the labor required to design with it.

Variegated foliage—Leaves with lines, stripes, or areas of a differing color along the leaf edge or center.

Variegation—The different color patterns of leaves caused by pigments.

Variety—A diverse mixture or differing components.

Vase life—The length of time cut flowers and foliage live after they have been cut.

Vents—Panels that open and allow air exchange with the outside.

Vermiculite—Common growing media component made from the mineral, mica, that has a good cation exchange capacity and a neutral to slightly alkaline pH (6.3-7.8).

Vernalization—A physiological process whereby a period of cold temperature is required for flowering.

Viability—The ability of seeds to germinate under optimum conditions.

Victorian era—The period during the reign of Queen Victoria of England known for establishing floral design as an art form and the language of flowers.

Vigor—The ability of seeds to germinate under different conditions and still produce healthy seedlings.

Virus—Symptoms of infection include discoloration of plant tissues, stunting of growth, and deformed growth. Tobacco mosaic and Aster yellows are two common viral disease associated with greenhouse crops.

Visual balance—The perception of an arrangement looking stable.

Visual merchandising—The coordinated effort and plan to attract customers to the flower shop to motivate those customers buy flowers and related products.

Visual weight—Perceived lightness or heaviness of plant material based upon its combined characteristics of color, shape, pattern, size, texture, and spatial arrangement.

Votive candles—Short, stocky candles placed in holders to give a soft light and festive effect.

Warm hues—Red, orange, and yellow and the tints, shades, and tones of these hues.

Water-soluble fertilizers—Fertilizers that dissolve completely in water and stay in solution.

Water tubes—Small, rubber-capped, plastic tubes which hold water and a single flower or cluster of small flowers.

Western flower thrips—Small insects with two pairs of fringed wings. They are dark brown in color.

Whitefly—Small white insects that camp out on the undersides of leaves where they pierce the tissues and suck juices. Their flat, scale-like larva feed on the undersides of the leaves.

Wholesale cost of goods—The price of all materials in a floral arrangement, determined from the prices paid at the wholesale florist or from a broker.

Wholesale floral manager—Person who oversees the operations of the business by supervising the staff, estimating retail demands for products, and preparing long-range plans.

Wholesale florist—A business that buys from growers or brokers and sells to retail florists at wholesale prices.

Wholesale price—Another term for wholesale cost of goods; the amount or cost of materials based upon their purchase price from a wholesale florist.

Wilting—A drooping condition and a lack of firmness to the plant tissues caused by inadequate water.

Wooden pick—A narrow, pointed piece of wood with a wire attached at the top to attach to dried or silk stems to add length or strength.

Worms—Larva of various moth species. They damage greenhouse crops by eating the plants.

Wrap around method—A wiring technique for securing small bunches of foliages or filler flowers.

Wreath—Flowers and foliages woven or fashioned into a circular shape.

Wrist corsage—A lightweight corsage designed to be attached to a wristband for wearing on the wrist.

Xanthophyll—A pigment with colors that range from yellow to nearly no color at all.

Xylem—The conductive tissue in the stem that transports water and minerals from the roots to the leaves.

Yellow sticky traps—Brightly colored traps on which insects land on, get stuck, and die. They are effective in monitoring pest populations.

Zygote—A fertilized egg.

Bibliography

A Manual for Flower Judging. Prepared by Pi Alpha Xi National Floriculture and Ornamental Horticulture Honor Society, Edited by the Department of Horticulture, University of Maryland, San Luis Obispo, CA: Printed by Department of Ornamental Horticulture, California Polytechnic State University.

Armitage, Allan M. *Bedding Plants: Prolonging Shelf Performance*. Batavia, IL: Ball Publishing, 1993.

Ball Redbook, 16th ed., edited by Vic Ball. Batavia, IL: Ball Publishing, 1998.

Blessington, Thomas A. and Pamela C. Collins. *Foliage Plants, Prolonging Quality*. Batavia, IL: Ball Publishing, 1993.

Capon, Brian. *Botany for Gardeners*. Portland, OR: Timber Press, 1990.

Floriculture and Environmental Horticulture Situation and Outlook Report. United States Department of Agriculture, Economic Research Service. October, 1997.

Floriculture Crops: 1997 Summary. United States Department of Agriculture, National Agriculture Statistics Service, 1998.

Flowers by Design. Lansing, Michigan: The John Henry Company, 1998.

Greenhouse Business. Park Ridge, IL: McCormick Communications Group Ltd.

Greenhouse Product News. Des Plaines, IL: Scranton Gillette Communications.

Grey, Don. "Equipping Your Retractable-roof Greenhouse," *Grower Talks Magazine*. January, 1997.

Grower Talks on Plugs II, 2nd ed., edited by Debbie Hamrick. Batavia, IL: Ball Publishing, 1996.

GrowerTalks on Crop Culture. Geneva, IL: George J. Ball Publishing, 1991.

Hartman, Hudson T. and Dale E. Kester. *Plant Propagation: Principles and Practices*. Englewood Cliffs, NJ: Prentice Hall, Inc.

Hunter, Norah T. *The Art of Floral Design*. Albany, New York: Delmar Publishers Inc., 1994.

Lectures by and discussions with Dr. Marvin Carbonneau, Professor Emeritus, Ornamental Horticulture, University of Illinois.

McMahon, Robert W. *An Introduction to Greenhouse Production*. Columbus, OH: Ohio Agricultural Education Curriculum Materials Service, 1992.

Noland, Dianne A. and Ken McPheeters. *The Principles of Floral Design*. Urbana, Illinois: Vocational Agriculture Service, 1983.

Powell, Charles C. and Richard K. Lindquist. *Ball Pest & Disease Manual*. Geneva, IL: Ball Publishing, 1992.

Professional Floral Design Manual. Oklahoma City, OK: American Floral Services, 1989.

Redbook Florist Services Educational Advisory Committee. *Basic Floral Design*. Leachville, Arkansas: Printers and Publishers, Inc., 1993.

Redbook Florist Services Educational Advisory Committee. *Selling and Designing Sympathy Flowers*. Leachville, Arkansas: Printers and Publishers, Inc., 1994.

Redbook Florist Services Educational Advisory Committee. *Advanced Floral Design*. Leachville, Arkansas: Printers and Publishers, Inc., 1992.

Redbook Florist Services Educational Advisory Committee. *Purchasing and Handling Fresh Flowers and Foliage*. Leachville, Arkansas: Printers and Publishers, Inc., 1991.

Redbook Florist Services Educational Advisory Committee. *Visual Merchandising for the Retail Florist*. Leachville, Arkansas: Printers and Publishers, Inc., 1994.

Redbook Florist Services Educational Advisory Committee. *Marketing and Promoting Floral Products*. Leachville, Arkansas: Printers and Publishers, Inc., 1994.

Royer, Ken. "Buy Like A Professional," *Florists' Review* (March 1987). Topeka, KS: Florists' Review Enterprises, Inc.

Royer, Kenneth R. "What Kind of Florist Are You?" *Florists' Review* (October 1998). Topeka, Kansas: Florists' Review Enterprises, Inc.

Rutt, Anna Hong. *The Art of Flower and Foliage Arrangement*. New York: The MacMillan Company, 1958.

Schroeder, Charles B., Eddie Dean Seagle, Lorie M. Felton, John M. Ruter, William Terry Kelley, and Gerard Krewer. *Introduction to Horticulture*, 3rd ed. Danville, IL: Interstate Publishers, Inc., 2000.

Soloman, Eldra Pearl, Linda R. Berg, Diana W. Martin, and Claude Villee. *Biology*. Saunders College Publishing, 1993.

Water, Media, and Nutrition for Greenhouse Crops, edited by David Wm. Reed. Batavia, IL: Ball Publishing, 1996.

Index